GALEN

ON ANATOMICAL PROCEDURES

GALEN
ON ANATOMICAL PROCEDURES

Περι Ανατομικων Εγχειρησεων

De Anatomicis Administrationibus

TRANSLATION OF THE SURVIVING BOOKS
WITH INTRODUCTION AND NOTES

BY

CHARLES SINGER

OXFORD UNIVERSITY PRESS

OXFORD
UNIVERSITY PRESS

Great Clarendon Street, Oxford OX2 6DP

Oxford University Press is a department of the University of Oxford.
It furthers the University's objective of excellence in research, scholarship,
and education by publishing worldwide in

Oxford New York

Athens Auckland Bangkok Bogotá Buenos Aires Calcutta
Cape Town Chennai Dar es Salaam Delhi Florence Hong Kong Istanbul
Karachi Kuala Lumpur Madrid Melbourne Mexico City Mumbai
Nairobi Paris São Paulo Singapore Taipei Tokyo Toronto Warsaw

with associated companies in Berlin Ibadan

Oxford is a registered trade mark of Oxford University Press
in the UK and in certain other countries

Published in the United States
by Oxford University Press Inc., New York

Special edition for Sandpiper Books Ltd., 1999

British Library Cataloguing in Publication Data
Data available

ISBN 0-19-924016-7

1 3 5 7 9 10 8 6 4 2

Printed in Great Britain
on acid-free paper by
Bookcraft (Bath) Ltd,
Midsomer Norton

ACKNOWLEDGEMENTS

I OFFER my grateful thanks to the Wellcome Trustees who have made this research possible for me. I am grateful also to the Wellcome Historical Medical Museum for publishing this work, and to the Wellcome Foundation for defraying the printing and publishing costs. Dr. E. Ashworth Underwood, Director of the Museum, has taken great interest in the work throughout and has made innumerable useful suggestions. I am very much obliged to Professor W. E. Le Gros Clark of Oxford for many hints. He has provided me with bodies of Rhesus monkeys, as have both Professor S. Zuckerman of Birmingham and the Zoological Society of London. My former pupil, Mr. Richard West of Clare College, Cambridge, has made many dissections for me which have been of the greatest use and have saved me much time. The editors and publishers of Professors Hartman and Straus's *Anatomy of the Rhesus Monkey* have graciously given me permission to use a large number of figures from that work. My debt to Mr. J. F. Crace and Professor Benjamin Farrington is acknowledged on p. xxv of the Introduction. To Professor A. J. E. Cave of St. Bartholomew's Hospital Medical College I am particularly indebted. He has read the proofs, and has acted as my mentor on anatomical matters. He has saved me from many errors, but those which will, in due course, be discovered by my critics are, I am quite sure, not of his but of my own making. I am very much obliged to Mr. C. A. Earnshaw for the immense amount of care which he has devoted to the preparation of the very full index.

C. S.

TABLE OF CONTENTS

BOOK I

On Dissection in General and on Muscles and Ligaments of Upper Limb in particular

BOOK II

On Muscles and Ligaments of Lower Limb

BOOK III

Nerves, Veins, and Arteries of Hand and Foot

BOOK IV

Muscles of Face, Head, Neck, and Shoulders

BOOK V

Muscles of Thorax, Abdomen, Loins, and Spine

BOOK VI

On the Alimentary Organs

BOOK VII

Heart, Lungs, and Arteries

BOOK VIII

The Remaining Thoracic Organs

BOOK IX

On the Brain

ILLUSTRATIONS

(See note on p. 255)

(*All the figures refer to the Rhesus monkey, except where otherwise stated*)

INTRODUCTION

THE reader has before him a translation of lectures, accompanying demonstrations on anatomy and physiology, delivered in the Greek language at Rome in the year A.D. 177. I believe that the text was taken down in shorthand and that it repeats substantially the actual words of Galen. There is no comparable work in ancient literature. The experiments recorded are among those that determined a physiological standpoint which was not improved upon for 1450 years, that is until Harvey published his results in 1628. Moreover, this book by Galen has a special place in the modern revival of anatomy, since it was study of the Latin translation of it, published by Guenther of Andernach in 1531, that started Vesalius on his triumphant career. This, culminating in his *Fabrica* of 1543, ushered in modern anatomy and did much to determine the line of development of the biological sciences.

It is not necessary to tell here the life of Galen. For that the reader may turn to the scholarly contribution of Professor Mewald in a supplementary volume of Pauly-Wissowa's great classical encyclopaedia, or to the pleasant series by the late Dr. Joseph Walsh in the *Annals of Medical History* (1934–9), or to Professor George Sarton's *Galen of Pergamon* (1954). These provide ample bibliographies. But a chronological list of events may be useful.

A.D. 129–30. Galen was born at Pergamum, an important centre of Hellenistic culture in Asia Minor, 46 miles due north of Smyrna. His father was a distinguished architect. *Galenos* means 'calm' and was a given name. No other name for him is known: that of 'Claudius' is fictitious.

144. Began study of philosophy at Pergamum.

147. Began study of medicine at Pergamum, learning anatomy from Satyrus.

150. Father died. He seems to have left Galen ample means.

151. Visited Smyrna to study anatomy under the Dogmatist Pelops. In this year he wrote his earliest work that has survived. The original Greek is lost but it has come down to us in an Arabic version which has been translated into English by Dr. R. Walzer, as *Galen on Medical Experience*, Oxford, 1944.

152. Went to Corinth to study anatomy under Numisianus who, he found, had moved to Alexandria. Thither Galen followed him and remained for some years.

157. Returned from Alexandria to Pergamum, possibly owing to his mother's death and to attend to his estate. Was appointed physician to the gladiators.

c. 159. Discovered action of recurrent laryngeal nerves and respiratory action of thoracic muscles.

161. The Emperor Antoninus Pius died and Marcus Aurelius succeeded him.

162. Left Pergamum. After visiting Greece, reached Rome and settled in practice.

164. Became acquainted with Flavius Boëthus and Sergius Paulus, and made anatomical demonstrations for them. Proved that arteries contain blood, not air.

165. Boëthus appointed Governor of Palestine.

166. Visited various parts of Greece and settled again in Pergamum. During his stay there he visited Palestine and Cyprus.

168. Recalled by Emperor Marcus Aurelius to Aquileia in Venetia to deal with plague in the army.

169. Marcus Aurelius and Galen return to Rome. Galen appointed physician to Commodus, son of Marcus. Sergius Paulus became Prefect of Rome and thus gave Galen another friend at court.

169–75. Spent these years supervising the health of Commodus at the Emperor's palace at Laurium, 12 miles north of Rome, at Lanuvium in the Alban hills, 20 miles south of Rome, and at Ostia at the mouth of the Tiber. This period was his most fruitful for scientific writing. He produced *On the Natural Faculties*, *On Respiration*, and his great treatise *On the uses of the parts of the body*, as well as other works.

175. Commodus joined his father in the East and both returned to Rome, where Galen had again settled in practice.

176–7. Became physician to the Emperor. Began to give public lectures on anatomy in Rome. The present work is probably expanded from a shorthand record of a series of these.

178. Marcus Aurelius died.

179. Visited Athens and Pergamum and returned to Rome with his library.

180. Commodus became Emperor.

192. Commodus assassinated. Pertinax Emperor.

193. Pertinax assassinated. Septimus Severus Emperor.

197. Finished his last major work, *Methodus medendi*.

198. Compiled the catalogue of his own works.

199? 200? 201? Died.

It may be handy for the reader to have here some information concerning the so-called 'Schools' or 'Sects' of medicine. These bulk largely in older histories of the subject and they certainly did form a feature in the medical world of Imperial Rome. Nevertheless, the separateness of these 'attitudes toward practice'—for that is all that they were—has been much over-emphasized in text-books and dictionaries. This tendency was encouraged by the view, which must now be abandoned, that these Schools arose as heresies from a pure and primitive 'Hippocratic' original. Modern critical scholarship, in disposing of this pristine orthodoxy as a myth, thus necessarily softens the distinctions between the later heresies. Nevertheless, in Galen's time there were fairly apparent four ways of thinking about medicine which may be taken as representing the somewhat over-written Schools.

The *Pneumatic School* was the most philosophical and its views accorded with those of Stoic thought. It flourished as early as the beginning of the first century A.D., and traces of it are possibly discernible in both Philo and the fourth Gospel. The representative medical Pneumatist was Archigenes of Apamea in Syria, who practised in Rome in the time of the Emperor Trajan (A.D. 98–117). Some of his works survive, translated into a 'Hippocratic' dialect by Aretaeus of Cappadocia during the lifetime of Galen. The Stoics in general, and Galen and the Pneumatists in particular, believed in a general *world-pneuma* which all living beings share, as is manifested by their breathing. The physiology of Galen, based on this view, I have set out in my translation of *Vesalius on the Human Brain* (London, O.U.P., 1952).

The *Methodist School* had, as traditional founder, Asclepiades of Bythinia (*c.* 110–*c.* 40 B.C.) who practised in Rome and, like Lucretius, was an adherent of the Epicurean or atomistic philosophy. He thus held that the body consisted of 'atoms'. These, he considered, move in 'pores' which penetrate all parts of the body. Disease results from relaxation or constriction of these pores and treatment should be directed at counteracting this looseness or tension. The typical Methodist physician was Soranus who practised in Rome under Hadrian (A.D. 98–138). The greatest work of Soranus survives in a Latin version of the fourth to fifth century bearing the name of Caelius Aurelianus.

Dogmatist is a term, perhaps introduced by Galen himself, to describe a certain medical group which emphasized theoretic principles. While accepting anatomical knowledge as necessary, it laid a stress on unseen entities and causes. DOGMA means only 'doctrine' and the word 'dogmatic' had not then acquired any pejorative meaning. Applied to a school of medical thinkers it might perhaps be translated as 'ratiocinative', 'given to theoretical reasoning'. Their best representative is held to be Celsus. The Dogmatists considered medicine under five heads: Physiology, Aetiology, Hygiene, Semiotics, and Therapeutics. They might be described as men of the 'middle way' between Pneumatists and Methodists. The putative father of Dogmatism is Diocles of Carystos (fourth century B.C.).

The *Empirics* formed a group of non-thinkers, rather than a school of thought. Rejecting theory, or disliking the effort of understanding it, they relied solely on personal experience. They distrusted anatomy of the dead body and were content to acquire anatomical knowledge in the course of their surgical practice. In the work of Galen which follows, the reader will frequently encounter the Empirics whom he roundly dislikes.

The number of Schools might be multiplied by adding *Sceptics*, who doubted the conclusions of one School, or another, or all, and *Eclectics*. who chose doctrines from several Schools. Again it is possible to distinguish intermediate Schools as those between the Empiric and Dogmatic. Such distinctions would lead to no further understanding of ancient medicine since they would always lead back to Galen's own judgements. For in truth Galen's works are of such overwhelming mass that we are almost forced to look at the medicine of his age through his eyes. We might fairly describe him as a member of the Pneumatist School with leanings toward the Dogmatic.

Forgetting the classical jargon about Schools, the history of Greek medicine may be sketched as having taken a much simpler and more natural course than has been generally suggested. The 'Hippocratic' physicians before Alexandrian times based their knowledge of disease directly on observation of the sick. When concerned with the theoretical causes of disease they were mostly content with the ancient views of elements, of humours, and of the 'epidemic constitution' of the seasons. Their ignorance of anatomy, both human and animal, was fairly comprehensive, though they had some knowledge of the structure of the parts concerned in the commoner dislocations.

With the establishment of Alexandria as a medical teaching centre by the Ptolemies, about 300 B.C., there was a real change. The best medical outlook began now to be based on anatomy. The distinction from one another of the so-called Schools or Sects depended basically on their attitude to anatomical knowledge. For the next 500 years—from Herophilus and Erasistratus to Galen (and for that matter on to the present day)—the great majority of practical medical men, their training once over, relied for their judgement of disease and for their choice of treatment on tradition fortified or occasionally modified by personal experience. The rare few, among whom were Herophilus, Erasistratus, and Galen, influenced the medical traditions of their day in the same sense that physiologists, pathologists, and epidemiologists influence ours. Schools differed from each other in the degree to which they were able to absorb this new science, that is, in effect, on their understanding and acceptance of the results of practical anatomy and experimental physiology. Of those two disciplines the work before the reader is one of the most important survivors from antiquity.

I must say a little on the difficulties, other than linguistic, that have confronted me in the work of translation. Of these I would treat three in descending order of gravity. They are (*a*) lack of technical vocabulary; (*b*) false physiological concepts; (*c*) ascription to man of anatomical features of other animals.

(*a*) *Lack of technical vocabulary*. The Greeks, unlike ourselves, had no classical language from which to draw scientific terms. These they made either by combinations of words, or by giving ordinary words a special meaning, or by using short descriptive clauses. Taking examples from our text, one illustrative of the first method is PERIKRANION, 'around the cranium'; of the second is KŌNARION, 'cone-shaped thing', pineal gland; of the third is O TOU BRACHIONOS PROSTHIOS MYS, the anterior muscle of the arm', biceps. Manifestly these terms were far less distinctive for Greek speakers than are their equivalents for English speakers. It is especially for the description of muscles, vessels, and nerves that the text presents difficulties to the translator. The obstacles to understanding for those ancient readers who did not dissect and had no anatomical figures were insuperable. Until modern times, and until the revival of the practice of dissection and the introduction of representational art, the anatomical works of Galen were almost incomprehensible.

(*b*) *False physiological concepts*. Certain of Galen's theoretical concepts present the translator with special obstacles. Examples of three may suffice.

1. The veins are described as arising from the liver and pro-

ceeding peripherally, that is the reverse way to that adopted by a modern anatomist. Incidentally the pulmonary artery is, for Galen, the 'arterial vein' and the pulmonary vein the 'venous artery'. The trachea is a special kind of artery.

2. Even greater difficulty arises from his theory of the nature of nerves. Galen saw that a nerve, NEURON, passes into each muscle and that it then divides. Knowing that many muscles end in a whitish tendon, he thought that the branches of the nerves had reunited within the muscle to form this tendon, which he naturally also called NEURON.

3. Again, Galen ascribed various fictitious activities to parts of the brain, notably to the infundibulum and the pineal gland. Fortunately, or rather unfortunately, this particular difficulty seldom arises for our text, since most of the section that deals with the brain is missing.

(*c*) *Ascription to man of anatomical features of animals.* Galen had perhaps some slight direct knowledge of human anatomy, certainly of the bones. This text is, in general however, a description of the soft parts of the ape imposed on the skeleton of man. For the gluteal region and the pelvis the misfit is of a gross order. For the hand and arm, to which the modern anatomist will think Galen gives quite undue attention, the difference is less, though there are many divergent details. The hand of the Barbary ape happens to differ from that both of man and of the Rhesus monkey in that the fourth finger instead of the third is the longest and most powerful. This is a very obvious difference. That Galen does not refer to it in this text itself suggests to the translator that he was working mainly on Rhesus. This is the more remarkable in that Galen is, as we might say, almost a 'specialist' on the hand. He uses that member to illustrate his teleological views and the early part of his *De usu partium* might be described as a long hymn to the Divine Wisdom in fitting the hand for its functions.

The translation which follows needs little commentary. Galen's great text-book of Physiology and Anatomy is his *De usu partium* which was completed by A.D. 175. It is a comprehensive theoretical treatise and is being translated into English by Mrs. May of Cornell University. The *De anatomicis administrationibus*, which is presented here, is a practical work. It describes the actual procedure of dissection and of physiological experiment. I believe that it is a shorthand record of actual lectures, though doubtless lightly revised by its author. If so, it is unique as the record of the actual words used in the lectures of a teacher in antiquity.

The text is in a tolerable state, despite long neglect and the absence of any effective editing since 1541. My translation is based on the edition of Kühn as being by far the most convenient. The relevant section (vol. ii, pp. 215–731) of his *Opera omnia* of Galen dates from 1821 and there is no later edition. Despite the many aspersions on Kühn's text, I have found very few misprints and no large number of passages either grammatically or anatomically unintelligible. This, however, is no merit of Kühn, for both his Greek version and its accompanying Latin rendering are taken bodily from vol. IV of the immense production of René Chartier (1572–1654), which contains all the works ascribed to both Hippocrates and Galen and was issued at Paris in thirteen folio volumes between 1639 and 1679. Nor must great credit be given to Chartier for the state of this work. The Greek text in Chartier's edition was taken direct from that of the *Opera omnia Galeni*, which Andreas Cratander issued in five folio volumes at Basel in 1538. The Cratander Greek text was prepared for the press by Johan Kammermeister (Camerarius, 1500–74), Leonhard Fuchs (1501–66), and Jerome Geschmauss (Gemusaeus, 1505–43), all scholars of high standing. The Latin version of Galen *On anatomical procedures* of Chartier is taken from that of the Giunta edition of Galen's works. It is that of Johannes Guenther of Andernach (1487–1574), published originally at Paris in 1531, revised by Vesalius, and edited by Agostino Gadaldino for the Giunta (Venice) edition of 1541 and for the verbally identical Froeben (Basel) edition of 1542.

Thus in the early sixteenth century this Greek text and its Latin translation occupied several men of great and exact learning. It is doubtful whether there are any important manuscripts of it that were not accessible to them. For what modern scientific scholarship can do for it, we must wait until Greek specialists see fit to turn from their other activities, often over-exercised on familiar grounds, to topics in more urgent need of attention. But as regards the Greek of this particular work, to me it seems remarkable that it should have emerged in relatively so good a state. Between Galen's death and the issue of the first (Cratander) printing of the Greek text in 1538 there was no dissection in the Greek-speaking East, and therefore no one could have understood it. To the scribes who wrote the manuscripts it was certainly quite unintelligible. The publication of Guenther's Latin translation in 1531 and the revival of dissection in Italy and France in the sixteenth century gave it, at last, some real meaning.

Galen based this work chiefly on the anatomy of apes. He evidently had no difficulty in getting large numbers of them and he knew many different kinds. He advised the use of 'those most like man' and, attaching importance to the absence of a tail, preferred the Barbary ape.* This creature was, however, never as common or as widespread as the Rhesus monkey (Fig. 1), which is smaller and is much easier to handle. For this and for other reasons I think that Galen must often have used Rhesus monkeys. Thus his very extensive descriptions of the hand accord better with that of the Rhesus than that of the larger animal (p. xix). I have dissected the Rhesus which is much more accessible, and here use illustrations of its parts. Galen dissected many other animals also. In this book he mentions pigs, especially for experiments on the breathing and vocal apparatus and on the spinal cord, other ungulates for the brain, and one elephant.

Had Galen any knowledge by dissection of the structure of

* It should be understood that he knew nothing of the anthropoids.

the human body? I have thought much on this topic and have several times changed my views but now think that he had such knowledge. The matter requires some consideration.

Objection to dissection is neither of philosophical origin nor perhaps is it based on 'religion', as that word is understood in our society. Even the least reflective must be aware that after death the body is dissolved into its elements. The objection is not of rational origin at all. The fear and disgust aroused by a dead body are linked to age-old chains of awareness and of feelings that go far beyond and are far deeper than any formal belief or reason. Medical men know too well that the processes of post-mortem examination have to be hidden and can hardly be spoken of beyond the professional circle. We cannot suppose that it would have been otherwise in the days of Galen. What he may have said about human dissection he would not have wished or allowed to pass into 'publication', even in the limited sense in which that word can be used of his age. Can we then anywhere read between the lines of Galen's text? Does he ever betray that he has a knowledge of points in human anatomy reached by direct contact with the object? I now think the answer should be 'Yes'.

There is no evidence that Galen or any other of the ancients appreciated the value of graphic methods in anatomy. He never indicates that he used figures in our sense of the word and he very seldom employed even diagrams. In two cases in this book he does refer to diagrams which can be reconstructed (pp. 28, 105) but, except for them, he avoids graphic methods here, though it would seem to us that figures are demanded. In their absence the three-dimensional impression created by viewing and handling the dissected part is the only way in which the relations of organs, tissues, and vessels to one another can be memorized or even grasped. Galen repeatedly urges dissection and the handling of dissected parts and suggests from time to time that they should be human.

There are a number of passages in this book which, read together, yield the impression that Galen knew more about human anatomy than he cared to have written down. The reader should study in succession the following passages:

Page 3, paragaph 2, to page 7, end of paragraph 1.
Page 31, paragraph 1, to page 36, end of paragraph 2.
Page 39, paragraph 3, to page 40, end of paragraph 1.
Page 51, paragraph 3, to page 52, end of paragraph 1.
Page 163, paragraph 2, to end of paragraph 5.
And others given in Index under 'Galen, human anatomy'.

It may be that there are many comparable passages in other works of Galen. Mrs. Frederic May of Cornell University draws my attention to one in the *De usu partium* (vi. 4; K. iii. 423). Here Galen had been discussing the varying number of lobes of the lungs in different animals, and he says: 'If death come not to me too soon, I shall some day explain construction in animals too, dissecting them in detail, just as I have done for man.'

Galen's anatomical and physiological lectures—for such they are—reveal a vivid and understandable personality. He is an enthusiast for his subject, of great industry, ardent for the experimental method, and full of anger against those who do not appreciate it. On the other hand, he is arrogant, self-centred, contentious, and a wearisome word-splitter, once his argumentative tendencies are roused. One would naturally think that, with his manipulative skill and his desire to impart both his knowledge and his method, he could not fail to have many pupils. Several times he refers to these and to his way of instructing them. It would be quite understandable if he had had successors and followers. Yet it was not so. When he died experimental science too fell dead. Galen was heir to 500 years of physiological research. How was it that all this hoarded physiological wisdom of antiquity came to this sudden dramatic end? This question may perhaps one day be profitably discussed but hardly until the main writings of Galen himself are presented in a form that can be easily studied.

Galen presents at times—though at times only—a very

modern attitude to research. But it would mislead the reader grossly if this Introduction were to leave him with the impression that this attitude was quite typical of the man. He showed himself not seldom to be gullible and superstitious, and sometimes, as it must seem to us nowadays, merely foolishly empirical. He mixed moral judgements and personal animosities with his science in a way which would now be thought scientifically indecent. His methods of controversy are detestable. His experiments, though often very well designed, were not accompanied by controls—a procedure almost unknown in antiquity.

The very bulk of Galen's writings cuts us off from adequate historical judgement of his predecessors. His surviving medical works are more voluminous than those of all earlier physicians. He is obviously the heir to a long line of experimental research and it is possible that some of his predecessors were as good or better men of science than he. He is far from generous in his acknowledgements. At any rate, if we would form a true picture of Galen, we must remember that he was a contentious, verbose, acrimonious fellow and that his science was but one side of him. His best thought-out and scientifically most complete work is his *De usu partium*. His *Anatomical Procedures*, here presented, has less literary and philosophic merit but has the unique distinction of preserving the very words of an ancient teacher.

It is necessary to explain how this translation has been evolved. It has occupied a part of my time, on and off, for fifteen years. At first I prepared a quite literal translation, with the help of the late Miss Margaret Meldrum, of Somerville College, Oxford. I worked on this at intervals for some years while I was studying the anatomy of the Rhesus monkey and improving my knowledge of medical Greek. Gradually nearly every sentence in the book began to take rational form and to assume anatomical intelligibility. This naturally involved endless adjustment of the English against the Greek. The passages that remain untranslatable are almost certainly corrupt. Some unintelligible passages proved, on long examination, to be merely displaced.

When I had at last got the English text into a generally intelligible form, I invoked the aid of my friend and neighbour, Mr. J. F. Crace, late of King's College, Cambridge, and Eton College. Together we revised the translation, sentence by sentence. I am most grateful for his help. I have also received much kind assistance, especially for Books VIII and IX, from Professor Benjamin Farrington of University College, Swansea.

A few words on the text as here presented. The arrangement of the Books is less haphazard than it seems, if the standpoint of Galen be kept in mind. Book I, after four introductory chapters, launches into Galen's favourite theme of the muscular construction of the hand and forearm, as a specially favourable demonstration of the Divine plan, which is fundamental for his philosophy. Book II is devoted to the structures of the leg and foot which afford parallels to those of hand and forearm. In Book III the vessels and nerves of both arm and leg substantially complete the treatment of the limbs. In Book IV the muscles in the head, shoulder, and neck, and in Book V those in the torso are treated. Books VI, VII, and VIII deal with the organs which illustrate Galen's physiological scheme and the evidence on which that scheme is based. Of Book IX, devoted to the brain, only a fragment of the original Greek remains.

An Arabic translation of the whole work survives. This is important for Books X to XV, which are wanting in the Greek. These six missing Books, together with Book IX, have been rendered into German from the Arabic, with valuable introductory matter, by Max Simon, *Sieben Bücher Anatomie des Galen,* Leipzig, 1906. They were also translated into French by G. Dugat about 1850. Dugat's version is unpublished but exists in a very legible manuscript now in the library of the Royal College of Physicians of London. I have not included these 'lost' Books in my version because, being unknown to scholars till the nineteenth century, they had no influence on the history of anatomy or physiology. The Arabic version of the first nine Books, however, might well throw light on difficult or corrupt passages in the Greek text and would be worth investigation for that reason. I have published a note on Dugat's manuscript in the *Journal of the History of Medicine*, vol. vii, p. 85, New York, 1952.

I have recently learned that the first nine Books were translated from Greek into French by the physician and botanist Jacques Dalechamps (1513–1588) of Lyons. I have not seen this extremely rare book. It was printed by Pierre Roussin and published by Benoist Rigaud at Lyons in 1572. The only copies I have traced are a copy recorded by Graesse, and copies in the Bibliothèque Nationale, Paris, the Cushing Collection, Yale University, and the Hunterian Museum, Glasgow University. The Hunterian Catalogue gives the date of publication as 1573, but Mr. R. O. MacKenna, the Librarian, to whom I am indebted for details of the copy, considers that the final 'J' in the date is a later addition. An edition of 1566, mentioned by certain biographers, is probably a ghost.

The following typographical devices are adopted here:

Greek words are normally spelt in Latin capitals.

Proper names are given in Latinized form.

Titles of Greek books are given their conventional Latin forms.

My own emendations of the Greek text are indicated at the foot of the relevant pages. Omissions are indicated in the text and/or at the foot of the relevant pages.

Explanatory passages or words added by me to the translation are printed within *square* brackets. Passages or words in *round* brackets are translated from the original but are either scribal additions or additions added by Galen himself as afterthoughts. Modern anatomical terms for structures described by Galen are usually added to the text in italics enclosed within *square* brackets.

The division into Books is the work of Galen himself. The titles of Books and Chapters have no manuscript authority but follow roughly the indications of the Renaissance editors.

BOOK I

[*On Dissection in General and on Muscles and Ligaments of Upper Limb in Particular*]

Chapter I

[*Galen's Reasons for writing*]

Anatomical procedure was the subject of a previous work *215* written on my coming to Rome [A.D. 162] not long since. That was at the beginning of the reign of our present Emperor, Antoninus[1] [reigned 161–80]. I have now resolved to write again on the subject, for two reasons. Firstly because Flavius Boëthus, the Roman Consul,[2] as keen an anatomist as ever lived, on leaving Rome for his native Ptolemais [A.D. 165], urged me to record these 'procedures'. I gave him, among *216* other works, my *De anatomicis administrationibus libri duo.*[3] These were of notes [only] for, while he was with us [162–5], he had made many observations in a short time and had asked me for some such records as memoranda. But since he is now dead[4] and I have no copies (for those I had in Rome were destroyed by fire), at the urging of friends I decided to write others to give them. I was the more inclined thereto because the work would be much better composed, for meanwhile I have made many new observations. For clarity it is enlarged into a more detailed and accurate account.

While Boëthus was still in Rome, I wrote *De Hippocratis et Erasistrati anatomice,*[5] and also *De vivorum dissectione*[6] with *De* *217* *mortuorum dissectione*[7] and added *De causis respirationis*[8] and *De voce.*[9] When he left I was engaged on a long work, *De usu partium libri XVII.*[10] This finished, I sent it to Boëthus, then still alive.

De thoracis et pulmonis motu libri tres[11] I wrote long ago, as a youth. It was for a fellow-student, returning to his own country after a long absence. He wished to display his talents in public, but lacked lecturing ability. He, too, died and thus this book became public property, so that many got hold of it, though it was not for publication. I had indeed written it while still in Smyrna, to be with Pelops,[12] my teacher after Satyrus[13] the pupil of Quintus,[14] before I had made any important or original contribution.

Later I went to Corinth [A.D. 152], to hear Numisianus[15] *218* the most famous pupil of Quintus. Then I visited Alexandria [152–7] and several other places where I heard that Numisianus was living. Next I went home, but after no long time came to Rome [162], where I made many anatomical demonstrations for Boëthus. He was constantly accompanied by Eudemus the Peripatetic,[16] by Alexander of Damascus,[17] official exponent of Peripatetic doctrines in Athens, and often by other important officials, such as Sergius Paulus the Consul, present Governor of Rome,[18] a man as distinguished in philosophy as in affairs. But the treatise that I wrote for Boëthus falls far short in lucidity and accuracy of what I propose now. And so to the opening.

Chapter 2

[*How to study the Skeletons of Men and Apes*]

218 As poles to tents and walls to houses, so are bones to living creatures, for other features naturally take form from them and *219* change with them. If an animal has a round skull, its brain must be round; if elongated, so must the brain be. If jaws be small and face oval, the muscles must correspond. So too, if jaws be large, the creature will have a great muzzle with muscles in keeping. Now of all living things the ape is likest man in viscera, muscles, arteries, veins, and nerves, as in the form of the bones. From the nature of these it walks on two legs and uses its fore-limbs as hands, and has the flattest sternum of all quadrupeds,[19] and clavicles similar to man's, and a round face with narrow neck. With these characters its muscles must accord, for they are extended over the bones, reproducing their size and shape [Figs. 2–4]. So also arteries, veins, and nerves conform to the bones. *220*

Since, therefore, the form of the body is assimilated to the bones, to which the nature of the other parts corresponds, I would have you first gain an exact and practical knowledge of human bones. It is not enough to study them casually or read of them only in a book: No, not even in mine, which some call *Osteologia*, others *Skeletons*, and yet others simply *On Bones*,[20] though I am persuaded that it excels all earlier works in accuracy, brevity, and lucidity.

Make it rather your serious endeavour not only to acquire accurate book-knowledge of each bone but also to examine assiduously with your own eyes the human bones themselves. This is quite easy at Alexandria because the physicians there employ ocular demonstration in teaching osteology to students.[21] For this reason, if for no other, try to visit Alexandria. *221* But if you cannot, it is still possible to see something of human bones. I, at least, have done so often on the breaking open of a grave or tomb. Thus once a river, inundating a recent hastily made grave, broke it up, washing away the body. The flesh had putrefied, though the bones still held together in their proper relations. It was carried down a stadium and, reaching marshy ground, drifted ashore. This skeleton was as though deliberately prepared for such elementary teaching. And on another occasion we saw the skeleton of a brigand, lying on rising ground a little off the road. He had been killed by some traveller repelling his attack. The inhabitants would not bury him, glad enough to see his body consumed by the birds which, in a couple of days, ate his flesh, leaving the skeleton as if for demonstration. *222*

If you have not the luck to see anything of this sort, dissect an ape[22] and, having removed the flesh, observe each bone with care. Choose those apes likest man, with short jaws and small canines. You will find other parts also resembling man's, for they can walk and run on two feet. Those, on the other hand, like the dog-faced baboons, with long snouts and large canines, far from walking or running on their hind-legs, can hardly stand upright. The more human sort have a nearly erect posture; but firstly the head of the femur fits into the socket at the hip-joint rather transversely,[23] and secondly, of the muscles

223 which extend downward to the knee, some go further [than in man].[24] Both these features check and impede erectness of posture, as do the feet themselves, which have comparatively narrow heels and are deeply cleft between the toes [Figs. 7, 16–20].

These are but trifling differences and only slightly interfere with standing upright. But such apes as the dog-faced baboons not only differ very greatly from man in form, but also have an obvious unlikeness to him in their bones [Fig. 4].

Of apes choose, then, those likest to man, and meanwhile read my writings, getting from them an exact knowledge of the bones. For from the start you will gain from having grown familiar with the terms for them. These will be useful for learning the anatomy of the other parts also. Moreover, should you light on a human skeleton, you will more easily recognize and recall all that you have learned. But if you rely on reading, without constantly observing these bones, and on a sudden

224 come on a human skeleton, you may be at a loss. For to recall observed phenomena demands continued familiarity. Do we not readily recognize those we often meet, while passing by those seldom seen? Hence the much-vaunted 'empirical' anatomy,[25] to which some physicians attach special value, must fail to explain the nature of the observations which have been made. For to understand [a dissection] when suddenly seen, one must have observed each part at leisure beforehand, preferably in human subjects[26] or, failing these, in animals similar to man.

In an epidemic of the ANTHRAX in many cities of Asia, a number [of patients] presented parts stripped of skin and even of flesh.[27] I was then still at home [i.e. before A.D. 152], studying under Satyrus.[13] He had been three years in Pergamum with Costunius Rufinus,[28] who was building for us the temple of

225 Zeus Asclepios. Not long before there died Quintus,[14] the master of Satyrus. All of us, who saw Satyrus demonstrating on exposed parts, recognized them explicitly and completely, telling the patients to make this movement or that, such as we knew was effected by this or that muscle, sometimes contracting or displacing the muscles a little to observe a large artery, nerve, or vein lying beside them. We then saw some students, as though blind, unable to recognize the parts, uselessly raising or displacing the exposed muscles (which needlessly distressed the patients), or even making no attempt to observe. Yet others, who had had more practice, knew how to direct the patient to move the part appropriately. Thus I perceived that, in observing wounds, those are confirmed who already know what to expect, but the ignorant learn nothing thereby. *226*

I therefore maintain that the bones must be learnt either from man, or ape, or better from both, before dissecting the muscles, for these two [namely bones and muscles] form the groundwork of the other parts, the foundations, as it were, of a building. And next, study arteries, veins, and nerves. Familiarity with dissection of these will bring you to the inward parts and so to a knowledge of the viscera, the fat, and the glands, which also you should examine separately, in detail. Such should be the order of your training.

As I have already said, you should seek in demonstrations to uncover the part for study as rapidly as possible, and to display it in many aspects, adopting various methods of handling. If you have no ape, bodies of other animals must serve, making *227* clear from the start wherein they differ from an ape, as I shall presently explain.

Chapter 3

[*Distinctiveness of Muscles and Neglect of the Ancients in dissecting Them*]

First read my exposition *De ossibus*[20] so as to have it at your *227* finger-tips, not only as regards the facts, but also the names, for I cannot discuss incidental points during my argument.

Not long ago I wrote also my *De musculorum dissectione*, a separate work.[29] This was at the instance of colleagues who needed memoranda when travelling. They particularly requested this as there had just reached us a tedious compilation by Lycus.[30] It was of about 15,000 lines and contained nearly as many errors, even omitting many muscles. My work is probably but a third as long, but explains all the muscles. It deals faithfully with Lycus, a man ignorant of the function *228* of many muscles and missing some completely. By dissecting an ape guided by my book [*De musculorum dissectione*] any so minded may gain experience, but he will learn better from this present one how to handle the muscles in each part.

On the body let your practice be first to discern the origin and insertion of each muscle, and whether it be uniform throughout its length or diversely compounded. You will find some muscles of a single nature, others of a multiple. The latter may look like several muscles superimposed on one another, criss-crossed in their length. Such observations are useful to you both in surgery and for investigating function. For in operating we must sometimes sever muscles, because of deep abscesses, *229* or necrosis or sepsis. By knowledge of the action of the severed muscle you may forecast the function destroyed and thus escape the charge that the disability is due to the treatment rather than the lesion. Surgical precision, too, demands knowledge of the action of the muscles, for the action of some is so important that, if they be inactive, the whole part becomes useless, whereas others initiate only insignificant actions. It is better to acquire this knowledge beforehand, so as to cut cautiously or drastically according to need.

Muscles are best divided along the fibres. Transverse incisions, that is across the fibres, paralyse them but are sometimes necessary for the extension of narrow wounds which go deep. Such would be a stab wound at either end of a tendon; where *230* there is a risk that, while the parts on the surface close, those deeper may remain separate. Sometimes we are driven to sever the muscles for drainage, for the position of the wound is often such that the injury in its depth disappears from sight. Thus, for example, if a wound be received with the arm completely extended, obviously the patient cannot maintain that position during treatment, and the easiest position is that in which the deep injury is hidden. No medicament can then reach it nor can pus drain therefrom. It is then necessary to incise the wound again, and for that it is essential to know the direction of the fibres and the action of the muscles.

The student must carefully do everything himself, even to removing the skin. My predecessors actually remained in ignorance of eight muscles, because they left to others the flaying of the apes, as at first I did myself. Of these eight muscles two are designed to move the jaws [*platysma faciei*] and two join arms to chest [*panniculus*] [Figs. 11–13]. *231*

They erred also as to the other four and their tendons, for though all pass into tendons which are quite round, yet these expand to the thinness of a membrane, as happens under the sole of the foot and in the hand [in the *plantaris* and the *palmaris longus*]. All the anatomists have maintained, with some show of reason, that these tendons in the hands flex the fingers, whereas those in the leg draw back the heel. For in the foot there is no single muscle which Nature has designed as the origin of this tendon. However there is a bipartite muscle in the calf of which one portion gives rise to this tendon [*gastrocnemius*].[31] In the hands the attachment of the tendon is [more] obvious, though in skinning it is inevitably torn away with the smooth part of the palm [*palmaris longus*]. Finding the tendon plainly extending from the muscle and seeing its lower end torn, and reasoning rather than carefully dissecting, they thought that it, too, moves the fingers like the muscles that lie under it [Fig. 14]. *232*

Many such facts have been discovered throughout the body, which the anatomists disregarded, shirking detailed dissection and content with plausible ideas. It is thus no wonder that they were ignorant of many things in the living animal. For if they pass as unimportant what is demonstrable only by careful dissection, would they trouble to cut or ligate parts of the living animal, to discern the function thus impeded?

233 At first I too had an assistant to skin the apes, avoiding the task myself as beneath my dignity. Yet when one day I found by the armpit, resting on and united to the muscles, a small piece of flesh which I could not attach to any of them, I decided to skin the next ape carefully myself. I had it drowned, as I usually do, to avoid crushing the neck, and tried to remove the skin from the surface, avoiding the organs beneath. I then found, extended under the whole skin of the flank, a thin membranous muscle [*panniculus carnosus*]. This was continuous with the covering of the spinal muscles at the loins as a fascia (SYNDESMON) from the bone of the spine. (I give this name SYNDESMON to all that extends from the bones, just as I call the offshoots of the brain and spinal cord nerves (NEURA), and the extensions (APONEURŌSEIS) of the muscles tendons (TENONTES).) Having found this muscle—the nature of 234 which will be fully and duly explained—I was the more anxious to skin the animals myself, and thus I discovered that Nature had wrought these aforesaid muscles for important functions [Fig. 8].

First I shall consider those muscles under the lower, smooth, hairless part of the hand, since it seems to me better to begin with the hand as a whole, following the order of my *De usu partium*.[10] For my earlier *De anatomicis administrationibus libri duo*[3] had followed the same order as that of Marinus[32] (and this I have mentioned in my *De usu partium*).[33] Now I return to the task after a long interval throughout which I have studied dissection.

Thus I have now much new and more detailed knowledge, particularly in the subjects treated at the beginning of that work. For then I knew nothing of the fine muscles at the 235 extremities of the limbs which flex the first joint of each finger and toe [*lumbricales*]. I thought that this action was performed solely by the membrane which encloses on the outside the tendon running down to the end of their internode [*flexores digitorum sublimis et profundus*]. I also thought the tendons which move each finger sideways [*interossei*] to be analogous to those which extend and flex them, in that they are attached only to the parts of the bones at the joints. Yet that was not the case, for they [i.e. the tendons of the *flexores digitorum profundi*] each extend to the tip of each finger, attaching their own tiny filaments [*vincula longa*] like a cobweb to the bones beyond the joints. These discoveries I made in the hand and foot, but throughout the rest of this treatise there are many comparable points, of which I shall duly speak.

Chapter 4

[*Certain of Galen's Differences from his Predecessors*]

Since it will be thought that on many points I am contradicting eminent anatomists, I think it wiser to say in advance a little on this. Controversy between physicians did not start with me but has long existed among them. For this there are two reasons—first, because some of them had made erroneous statements, but second, merely because they used different ways of expression. Thus some, who agreed in recognition of observed facts, gave an illusory impression of disagreement to readers who themselves have never dissected. I have discussed such matters more extensively in my earlier work *De dissentione anatomica*.[34] Now I shall state briefly only what bears on the present theme. *235* *236*

Some anatomists consider that there are as many muscles as there are muscle-origins. Others neglect the origins but consider the insertions (TELEUTAI), emphasizing the body of the muscles. For them many short heads, coalescing and producing a uniform outline, are not necessarily many muscles. [Even] if the insertions be multiple and have a uniform motion, they say that it is better to treat them as one muscle, and the more if it be impossible to divide them in a linear fashion into several parts. This is illustrated with the muscle in the middle of the lower *237* arm on the outside [i.e. extensor surface].[35] For being continuous with itself and single in the strict sense, it is split at the wrist into four tendons [*extensor digitorum communis* which is, however, variously divided in different species of ape] producing a uniform movement, each extending the relevant finger. With reason, then, all anatomists treat this muscle as one, disregarding the multiplicity of tendons of insertion.

For the same reason, they regard as one the muscle lying next to it which moves the little finger laterally [*extensor digiti minimi*], though it has two tendons of insertion, for when the belly which lies above the tendons contracts it gives the appearance of one muscle. So if, like the tendons, the muscles also *238* which lie above them had a twofold outline, they would have maintained that the muscles that initiate lateral motion in the little finger were two. However, the muscle that gives the other three fingers the same motion [*extensores digitorum II, III, IV*] they do not regard as one. Yet if likeness of motions justifies treatment of them as a unity, surely since all regard the muscle that extends the four fingers as one, they should reckon also as one those that initiate lateral movement.

Moreover, not even when several heads of a muscle coalesce near their origin into one belly with its own outline, do they consider the number of heads. Thus they have all taken as single the muscle in front attached to the arm, which starts from two heads [*biceps brachii*], because it has but one insertion and has necessarily a single motion and uniform outline. But they do not regard as single those muscles which move the calf [*gastrocnemius*], though they accept that they are fastened to the heel by a single tendon [*tendo calcaneus*], because their heads *239* extend a long way before uniting.

If then they be right, though their teaching about other muscles is often wrong, they should not be charged with ignorance on this ground alone, nor need it be suspected that they disagree [on matters of fact] with those who enjoy better doctrine. I shall state in turn two methods of teaching the same subject, which differ in appearance more than in reality.

One may be put thus. The three larger digits, thumb, index, and middle finger, are moved sideways toward the little finger by a single muscle [*extensor pollicis longus*, *extensor indicis* plus *extensor digiti* tertii *proprius*, the last absent in man]. This arises from the bone in the forearm, but produces three tendons of its own near the wrist. These pass into the side of the hands and cause their oblique motion.

Another way may be put thus. Two muscles resting on the forearm on the outside[35] initiate the lateral movement of these *240* three fingers. One muscle is inserted into the middle-finger [*extensor digiti tertii proprius*] and index-finger [*extensor indicis*] with a single tendon, being attached to the bone of the forearm over a very large area. The other muscle extends with a single tendon, just as it itself is single, and draws the thumb as it were towards the index [*extensor pollicis longus*]. Its head is in the upper parts of the arm, near the elbow-joint, and after a short distance it ends in a tendon which extends by the side of the muscle that moves the middle and index fingers.

The two methods differ less in what they seek to express than in their way of expressing it. The second, which says that two muscles are involved, is more accurate, since the muscle moving the thumb obviously has its own outline, but the first is not to be rejected entirely, seeing that the muscles have something in common and lie together, united by thin fibres.

Still more will a false impression of disagreement arise from the accounts of the tendon which moves the thumb and wrist. *241* For here too one can say that the muscle is forked—as in fact the anatomists have said—because it obviously has both a single head and a single outline, though at the end of the radius, by the wrist, it yields two tendons [one for the thumb and one for the two adjacent fingers]. However, anyone concerned about precision would do better to say that there is not one muscle here, but two, however closely united from the head to the point of divisions into tendons. It is fair to treat them as two, both because, if properly separated, they are found completely distinct, and also because they move parts different in nature.

For one tendon moves the thumb, the other the wrist; the motions are alike but the parts moved unlike.

[The anatomists] have made it clear that they generally distinguish muscles by differences in their motions rather than by their places of origin, when they say that there are two muscles bending all the fingers, not one only, although their motion is almost alike in kind, and what is more they have a single origin. For since one head of the tendons bends the second joint, the other the first and third, they say that there are two muscles here. These, they say, are completely united through the whole length of the forearm, until they end in the branching tendons [*flexores digitorum sublimis et profundus*], but are perceived to be double from the difference in their motions. [In the ape the *flexor sublimis* gives off a fleshy branch to the *flexor profundus*.]

242

The most accurate method of teaching looks to these points. Yet one must not quarrel with those who follow a second method for any small departure from the first. It is preferable, when we find a statement made by many accepted authorities that departs slightly from the best method, to accept it temporarily, so as to avoid confusing the hearers by raising an appearance of disagreement. If you insist on precision, either you add to your account, if you are following the accepted method, that it is preferable to suppose that there are, say, two muscles, for the reason given or, if you follow the best method again you will add that these two muscles are really one, on the ground that they coalesce for a large part of their course. It is better that this should be said right away about all the muscles.

243

Chapter 5

[*Muscles of Flexor Surface*[35] *of Forearm*]

243 It is now time to explain how to proceed if one would gain experience oneself and give demonstrations to others. I have already shown the common error of many who claim to be anatomists, in dissecting animals long dead, with parts dry and tense. They stretch the overlying skin, or the membranes or other tissues, and thus displace the underlying parts, or again pull and bend the fingers by the tendon inserted into the palm [*palmaris longus*]. Yet they themselves say that muscle or tendon must be attached to the bone that is to be moved. They speak erroneously (forgetting what they have themselves rightly said) when they assert that the fingers are bent by the tendon even when it has no attachment to the bone.

We must now explain how to proceed, avoiding their errors. *244* Obviously we must first of all remove all the outer skin from the arm and fingers excepting only the palm, then carefully strip the parts in the region of the wrist-joint. The sharp lancet is suitable for removing such tissues so that no membrane may be left behind after removal of skin, just as the blunt is useful for sundering muscles.

The membranes being removed, the first muscle [encountered] is on the surface of the mid forearm [*palmaris longus*]. Of it I shall speak more fully later [pp. 14-15]. You will see ligaments [*retinacula*] lying across the articulations, both on the inside [flexor surface] and on the outside [extensor surface] of the limb. Under them lie the heads of the tendons, on the inner[35] side those that flex the fingers, on the outer those that extend them. On either side of the ligaments on the inner side [of the arm] is a muscle flexing the wrist. The one is in a line with the little finger [*flexor carpi ulnaris*] the other with the index [*flexor carpi radialis*]. On the outside, there is the single muscle *245* in the forearm which extends the wrist [*extensor carpi ulnaris*] as well as two in the ulna* both moving the wrist. The latter move also the thumb, and I said [p. 11] that it was better to describe here two muscles rather than one. The tendons† of all the muscles on the outside which I have mentioned have ligaments transversely round them [*extensor retinaculum*].

* Text says 'radius'.

† Text says 'heads'.

There is also a muscle descending from above the radius [*brachioradialis*] which in the ape does not end below in a tendon, like those so far mentioned, but somewhat membranously. By it this part is turned inwards [i.e., flexed]. No retinacular ligament surrounds this muscle, any more than the muscles inside which move the wrist [*flexor carpi ulnaris*], but it becomes both fleshy and membranous at the lower end of the radius and turns inward near the wrist-joint. You may call the fibrous end (APONEURŌSIS) a 'muscle-tendon' (HYMENŌDĒ TENONTA). This muscle has a middle position, being neither among the muscles of the outside of the limb nor among *246* those of the inside when the hand is in its natural position, for it rests on the whole limb and on the radius. Since anatomists divide the parts in the lower arm into two regions, calling some of them 'exterior' and others 'interior',[35] we must follow their example to avoid the impression of making innovations. This muscle we think should, on the whole, be classed with the exterior muscles.

Another muscle within the forearm, of which I shall speak more clearly later, has a function unlike that of any muscle throughout the whole body, unless we except the calf. It is on the surface inside the hand under the skin, between ulna and radius. It ends, as I have said [p. 7], in a flat tendon, extending under the smooth, hairless part of the hand [*palmaris longus*]. On removing the skin this muscle is seen in the middle of the muscles on the inner side. You may, if you choose, dissect the outer parts first, but let us begin from this muscle which extends under the skin with an expanded tendon [*palmar aponeurosis*].

This tendon begins obviously to widen a little above the wrist- *247* joint. There one had best begin its dissection. It is plainly marked off from the muscles around and under it, being surrounded with fine fibres which you can strip off even with your fingers and easily with a blunt lancet, raising the head of the tendon with the fingers or by inserting a hook. Then dissect it upwards to the joint at the elbow whence it issues. (For this work the blunter sort of lancet is best.) Then, with the upper attachment still adhering, cut it across.

Now pull upward the lower part (which you have severed from the tissues by transverse incision), so as to stretch the 'roots'. Give special attention to what you now do, for not far from its end this tendon extends under the palmar skin [*palmar aponeurosis*]. Here you can proceed in one of two ways. Either remove the attached skin with the flattened tendon, separating the latter from the underlying tissues with a sharp lancet; or free the skin from the tendon, leaving it on the underlying tissues. Either way its nature will become clear. This tendon is set under the inside of all the fingers, having as limit the line where the hairless palm meets the hairy skin. Beyond this tendon you will see flattened vessels (PLATYNTHENTA) and nerves apportioned to these parts [digital vessels and nerves]. Membranes rest on them, which you will remove with them after dissecting the muscles. *248*

Springing from two heads, the tendons that flex the fingers lie underneath, at the level of the ligament [*flexor retinaculum*] to which the heads of the tendons are applied. Of these heads, the one produces four tendons, inserted into all the digits except the thumb at the beginning of the second phalanx. By these tendons the second joint is flexed [*flexor digitorum sublimis*]. The other tendon-head [*flexor digitorum profundus*], lying beneath the former, splits into five parts in the ape, each reaching to the last joint of the digit, and is there inserted. *249*

Each several tendon is surrounded by a strong sheath, tougher than the tendon itself, and like a thick membrane [fibrous flexor sheath]. (You may call this tissue 'ligament' (SYNDESMON) or 'membrane' (HYMĒN) or, compositely, 'membranous ligament', or again 'hard membrane'. And you can name the covering of the tendons 'coat' (AMPHIESMA) or 'sheath' (SKEPASMA) or 'tunic' (CHITŌN). Beyond the division into branches, you will see each tendon, along with the aforesaid covering, drawn in by the tendons lying under it but themselves passing on to the bones of the fingers, and [you

will see] the first and third articulation of each finger bent,
250 as if the tendon were inserted there, and the first bound by the surrounding ligament to the bones.*

It has been said in my *De ossibus*[20] that anatomists call the bones of the fingers SKYTALIDES or PHALANGES. You will observe their attachments (EMPHYSEIS) if you remove the ligament lying around the tendons. The [five] tendons [of the *flexor digitorum profundus*] which lie underneath rest on the bones of their fingers and fuse with the third phalanx without splitting. The four [of the *flexor digitorum sublimis*] that rest on them are attached to the second bone, as I have said above, but as each passes over the former larger tendon, each splits in two, encircles the tendon lying under it, and is attached to the sides of the second phalanx. The thumb is peculiar in that
251 nothing [from the *flexor digitorum sublimis*] reaches it from above nor from the common head, but it forms attachments elsewhere.

Scrutinize the palm and examine in it the tendon which breaks off from the other four [of the *flexor digitorum profundus*] to enter the thumb [*flexor pollicis longus*]. It does not stop at the first joint as do each of its fellows to the fingers, but passes on to the second joint (corresponding to the third of the phalanges). It moves this, as they do, by its attachment to it. It has a separate sheath round it and when you free it of tendons you must cut this sheath lengthwise with a sharp lancet. If you botch the operation and do not cut straight, you will sever the underlying tendon.

For manipulating the tendons from their origins to their sheaths, either let your ape be fairly fresh, before the fingers
252 have time to dry and stiffen and so to resist extension, or freshen them by pouring hot water over them or, if they are only moderately stiff, by kneading and movement. You would learn the function of each more clearly if you were to stretch all the structures around the fingers. Do this with the tendons underlying the [transverse] ligament.

* Three lines of text here obscure.

For the other two muscles by which the wrist is bent, begin to dissect them a little above the wrist-joint, for there they clearly pass into tendons and have the unmistakable outlines of such. By separating them from the underlying and surrounding tissues, both at their upper and lower end, you will see the tendons themselves attached to the articulation of the wrist below and their heads reaching the articulation of the elbow above. One of the tendons [*flexor carpi ulnaris*] is inserted in the straight and cartilaginous bone at the wrist which is in line with the little finger [*pisiform*].[36] This lies beside that process of the ulna that anatomists call styloid. The other tendon [*flexor carpi radialis*] plunges deep immediately after the articulation so that it has been thought that it becomes attached to one of the carpal bones. If you dissect the ligaments on top of it, however, you will see clearly that it reaches the metacarpal of the index, to the base of which it is attached. *253*

These five muscles [*palmaris longus, flexores digitorum sublimis et profundus, flexores carpi ulnaris et radialis*] occupy the whole inner side [flexor surface] of the forearm. If they are removed, those moving the radius will be revealed. Of them I shall speak later.

Chapter 6

[*Muscles of Extensor Surface*[35] *of Forearm*]

Meantime I shall touch first on the muscles on the outer [extensor] side of the forearm, adding only that, whether you remove or retain the upper attachments [of the muscles already dissected], you will not prejudice the dissection which follows. Leave, however, the tendons which pass into the fingers so that there may be revealed the small muscles of the hand. These can be found even before the dissection of the outer parts, though it is better to dissect them last, as I shall later make clear. *253*

Dissect the outer parts thus. After the skin come the super- *254* ficial vessels and nerves. Remove them with the membranes and you will see clearly four ligaments lying obliquely, one which binds the end of the ulna and the radius, the second on the ulna alone below the afore-mentioned, and two others on the radius alone. [These are apparently subdivisions of the deep fascia.] Make a straight incision in them, then fold up on either side, as far as the root of each, the parts of the ligament separated from one another, or else remove them altogether.

Next raise with a hook for its full length first the head of the four tendons [*extensor digitorum communis*] which move the digits (other than the thumb)—it is placed in the midst of the others—secondly, the tendon-head which draws the two little fingers to the side [*extensores digitorum proprii IV et V*] away from the others. This last is divided, of course, into two tendons.[37] (It makes no difference if one says that this draws the fingers to the lower part of the hand, imagining it in its natural

255 position, as Hippocrates taught.) Then you must raise the remaining one, the third, which initiates a like movement in the two* bigger fingers [*extensores digitorum proprii II et III*]. The first head of the tendons issues from one muscle, just like the second. By dissecting the double tendon of the third, the head which moves the two fingers, the index and the middle, [is seen to] issue from one muscle, while that which moves the thumb [*extensor pollicis longus*] from yet another. And thus there will be four muscles under the aforesaid ligaments.[37]

Next comes the muscle that extends the wrist at the little finger [*extensor carpi ulnaris*]. It has its attachment by a single tendon at the back of† the fifth metacarpal. It is surrounded by a rather feeble ligament arising in the [styloid] process of the ulna.

At the thumb region, another strong ligament binds the head of the two tendons [of the *abductor pollicis longus* and *extensor pollicis longus*], the bone of the radius being most beautifully carved at the process into a hollow equal to the thickness of the tendon's head.[38] [Fig. 6.] One tendon is inserted into the meta-

* Text says 'three'. † Text says 'in front of'.

carpal of the thumb [on the sesamoid there], the other into the thumb itself, immediately after the first articulation. Whether you say that these two tendons spring from one muscle or two makes little practical difference, but the preferable view is that the two tendons spring from two closely united muscles. Indeed with care you can separate them, as with the two which produce lateral movement in the two* larger fingers [p. 13].[39] 256

The remaining muscle on the outer side of the forearm [*extensores carpi radiales longus et brevis* treated as one], which extends the wrist, is inserted by a double tendon into the second and third metacarpals, and the head of its tendon is fixed firmly to the radius near the wrist-joint [by the *extensor retinaculum*].

Thus there are eight muscles occupying the forearm on the outer side, or seven if one holds that the three big fingers are moved by two muscles and wrist with thumb by a [separate] one, that is by the muscle by the radius.

Chapter 7

[*Origins of Wrist Muscles*]

How each muscle is attached to the bones in the forearm has been explained in my *De musculorum dissectione*.[29] I shall repeat it here, to avoid gaps in my exposition and, as in that book, I shall also describe the attachments of the higher [muscles] for the sake of consistency. 257

On the outer condyle of the humerus you will find three muscle heads; the highest extends the four fingers [*extensor digitorum communis*]; the lowest extends the wrist by the fifth digit [*extensor carpi ulnaris*]; the middle [extends] the two lesser digits [*extensores digitorum proprii IV et V*].

Under these and deep to them you will find two closely united muscles which belong to the remaining three digits. They arise from the ulna; that which belongs to the two fingers [*extensores digitorum proprii II et III*], from the greater part of its length; that other which belongs to the thumb [*extensor*

* Text says 'three'.

pollicis (longus)], from its upper end. On this there lies the muscle, closely united to the muscle of the wrist, which extends 258 the head of the thumb but itself occupies the whole depth of the region between radius and ulna [*abductor pollicis longus*]. This muscle you should begin to dissect, as with the others, from the wrist [upwards]. As you strip it gingerly off the underlying tissues, note the ligamentous membrane between ulna and radius, throughout their length [*ligamentum interosseum*]. This forms the boundary between inner [flexor] and outer [extensor] side of the limb. You will find this muscle resting on and coalescing with it, or rather, arising from it.

If then you strip this muscle [*abductor pollicis longus*] properly from the membrane which separates one from the other, you will find under it [i.e. under the membrane] a certain small muscle set transversely, extending from ulna to radius [*pronator quadratus*]. Of this I shall speak later, for you must first turn to the muscle that rests on the aforesaid muscle [*abductor pollicis longus*] which lies along the radius throughout its length, always adhering to it, while its upper end is applied lightly to the ulna. Dissect higher up the muscle which lies on the afore- 259 said muscle and beside the radius. From this muscle* a double tendon comes off and is attached to the metacarpals of the index and middle fingers [*extensores carpi radiales longus et brevis* treated as one]. You will find the top of this muscle at the highest part of the outer condyle, reaching a point on the humerus above it.

Consider now the muscle above this [i.e. above the *abductor pollicis longus*] and [above] the radius itself, the muscle peculiar to the radius, which turns the palm upward [*supinator*]. It has an origin above this [i.e. the radius] and continuous and united with the origin of which we have just spoken [i.e. with the origin of the *extensores carpi radiales*]. But here especially the dissection may become confused, since the end of this muscle, becoming membranous, insinuates itself into the muscles of the upper arm. Therefore let it alone [now] and do not search for

* Text here reads 'I said that', a scribal insertion.

it while dissecting the lower arm. When you come to the upper arm, you will first lay bare the muscle in front [*biceps brachii*]. It is then that you will find the origin of this muscle inserted into the humerus by a narrow ligament. The greatest part of it rests on and lies alongside the muscles of the arm there. *260*

Such are the heads of the muscles on the outside of the fore-arm. Of the muscles on the inside, that by the little finger that flexes the wrist starts from the inner condyle of the humerus having some connexion with the ulna too [*flexor carpi ulnaris*]; while that by the thumb has its origin in the same condyle [*flexor carpi radialis*]. Between the two heads lies the origin of the muscle that runs down into the skin of the hand [*palmaris longus*]. Under it again lie the heads of two muscles that move the fingers [*flexores digitorum sublimis et profundus*] filling the entire space between radius and ulna. The smaller [*flexor digitorum sublimis*] is exactly in the middle and springs from the inner condyle* of the humerus; being connected for a short space with the ulna also. The other [*flexor digitorum profundus*] is under this and occupies throughout its depth the whole space between radius and ulna. Moreover, it is attached to both bones [in the ape]. To the ulna it is attached at its forward outgrowth [*coronoid process*] in the elbow region, and this part branches out in the wrist in line with its attachment into the little finger. Another part of it with the same origin moves the four [other] digits and is placed in line with the index. And there is a third part of it which pertains to its own [special] fingers [i.e. I, II, and III]. This part, the belly, occupies the space between radius and ulna. *261*

Chapter 8

[*Insertions of Internal*[35] *and External Muscles of Forearm*]

When you have dissected this muscle, it is time for our exposition of the transverse muscle [*pronator quadratus*] which I postponed. All the muscles so far discussed having been removed, *261*

* Text reads KEPHALĒ for KONDYLĒ.

those peculiar to the forearm become visible. By these the whole hand is supinated or the reverse. There are four: two are seen to reach the upper part of the forearm and two are close to the wrist [Fig. 15].

Of the two at the wrist, one is the transverse* muscle. It lies between radius and ulna [*pronator quadratus*] and issues from the 262 ulna, while the end reaches the radius, to move which is its function. Thus if you place the hand palm upward and stretch the origin of the muscle, grasping it with your fingers, as I told you always to do, you will see the whole hand being turned palm downwards. (Similarly if you stretch from its head the muscle that lies at the top of the forearm, the head of which reaches the humerus [*supinator*], you will make the hand turn palm upward. Thus to these two muscles opposite functions are assigned, though both move the lower end of the forearm.) The yet longer and more fleshy muscle [*extensores carpi radiales longus et brevis*], which lies altogether above this, also moves the hand to the supine position and we therefore reckon it among the outer muscles. The other [*pronator quadratus*], which turns the radius inwards, initiates the prone position [Figs. 14, 15].

The two muscles remaining move the upper part of the radius and are also opposed, their position being oblique. The one comes from the inner parts, issuing from the [inner] con- 263 dyle of the humerus [*pronator radii teres*]. It is there closely united with the head of the muscle on the thumb side which moves the wrist [*flexor carpi radialis*] but starts higher on the condyle. The other [*supinator*] is on the outside, and is smaller. Because of this, its fibres have a more slanting position. And it has a more sinewy insertion on the radius than the muscle on the inside [*pronator radii teres*] which we mentioned earlier, of which the attachment to the radius is continuous with it.†

I have now explained all the muscles that surround the ulna and the radius.

* Reading LECHRION for LOXON, oblique.

† Two lines here unintelligible, followed by four of repetition.

Chapter 9

[*Small Muscles of Hand*]

You now proceed to the small muscles of the hand. Remove all tendons of muscles on the outside, as far as their terminations in each finger, but not those of the muscles inside. *263*

Examine the small muscles beside the tendons which flex the third joint [*lumbricales*] before you cut them away. These muscles take their rise from the four sheaths surrounding the tendons [of the *flexor digitorum profundus*] and reach the sides of the fingers, producing very slender tendons. If, beginning from the fleshy part of the muscle which lies beside the first tendon, you dissect carefully, freeing it from the neighbouring parts, you will find the small tendon extending along the whole finger. Like the tendons from which they arise these muscles are four in number, namely, for the fifth, fourth, third, and second digits [Fig 14]. *264*

The thumb is moved by two other muscles, one drawing it away as from the other fingers [*abductor pollicis brevis*], the other drawing it towards the index [*adductor pollicis*]. That which draws it away to the utmost [*abductor pollicis brevis*] must necessarily be longer, wherefore its head issues from the first bone at the wrist [*navicular* but also from the *radial sesamoid*]. That which draws it towards the index is naturally shorter and broader and has transverse fibres [*adductor pollicis*]. This latter rests on the other muscles that I am about to mention. Its head is attached to the third metacarpal [but also to the second]. *265*

As the thumb is drawn away from the other fingers by the muscle [*abductor pollicis brevis*] that arises from the first of the bones in the carpus [*navicular*], so is the little finger drawn away by a muscle of like kind [*abductor minimi digiti*], which has its origin in the bone of the carpus corresponding to it [*pisiform*], in which is also inserted the tendon which bends the whole wrist [*flexor carpi ulnaris*] [Fig. 14].*

* Here there must have dropped out from the text a passage describing the *contrahentes digitorum*.

These seven muscles [four *lumbricales* and three *contrahentes*] have, of course, not escaped the notice of the anatomists, for there is no tissue lying over them which needs skilful removal for their display. For not only are the muscles that abduct thumb and little finger bare of covering by muscle or tendon, but they actually come to light before the tendons which flex the fingers, if that method of dissection be followed in which we remove the membranous tendon which lies under the palm. Each of the other [four muscles] [*lumbricales*] lies along the four deep-set [flexor] tendons.

266 However, as I have said, it is not surprising that the tendons lying deep at the metacarpus were unknown to them, as they were to me for long. For unless you remove the large flexor tendons and the seven muscles which I have just discussed, none of those small muscles of which I am about to speak can be seen. If, however, these be removed, there becomes visible a continuous fleshy sheet formed from them all. This needs careful dissection so that you may distinguish the separate muscles [Fig. 15].

There are two for each finger [*palmar interossei*]. They reach the first articulation on the inner side and are attached to the sides [of the *phalanx*]. For this reason they make no rigid and unwavering curve, but incline a little to the side, so that each, when contracted, bends the first joint slightly, but the two combined produce a straight and rigid position in each finger.

All the others [*dorsal interossei*] issue from the ligament at the wrist and metacarpus at roughly the same articulation of the bones [as the *palmar interossei*]. Those belonging to the thumb [*flexores pollicis breves* described as two muscles] have *267* their attachment higher than these. They issue not from the aforesaid bones but from the ligament that confines the two tendons of the muscles which flex the fingers [*flexor retinaculum*]. This ligament issues from the bones of the wrist on either side, without being attached to the ends of the ulna, or to the base of the metacarpals. [Fig. 15].

If you remove these muscles also, there will be no others left in the wrist or lower arm. You can then proceed in your investigation of the combination of the bones—their numbers, relations to each other, and their union. Of these enough has been said in my *De ossibus*.[20]

Chapter 10

[*Ligaments of Wrist and Hand*]

Try to dissect with a sharp lancet all the ligaments [SYNDESMOI, 'bonds'] which remain when the muscles are removed. Remember that such structures of their nature have a threefold function. First, that to which they owe their name, as binding [*ligo*, I bind, hence 'ligaments'] bone to bone. Second, they protect underlying structures, as I have said, for the tendons at the wrist [*flexor and extensor retinacula*]. Third, they may cover these same tendons, forming an integument [tendon sheaths]. A fourth use is not peculiar to them. It is that when muscles end ligamentously they may act as ligaments as we have mentioned, but not so as to bind bone to bone, for in their midst they conduct (SYNAPTOUSI) the muscles under them to the bones into which they are inserted. *267* *268*

None of the muscles hitherto discussed has ligaments of this last type, though others have. Of such, as for example the muscle in front of the upper arm [*biceps* and its *lacertus fibrosus*], I shall speak later. And yet some of the muscles of which I have spoken have some general ligamentous character to the eyes of those who can trace the beginnings of things.* Such is the muscle which abducts the thumb [*abductor pollicis brevis*]. This, though small, has something much like a ligament in its attachment to the first of the bones at the wrist [*navicular* but also the *radial sesamoid*]. *269*

Among the muscles previously described some have a tendinous structure according to the third† use [as tendon sheaths]. There are five of these in the wrist, one on the inside which

* Literally 'See the great in the small'. † Text says 'second'.

rests on the two big muscles which bend the fingers [carpal tunnel], and four on the outside. Of the latter the middle belongs to the tendons which move the fingers [*extensor digitorum* compartment],[37] two are at the radius [*extensores pollicis longus et brevis* compartment],[39] and the fourth is in the ulna [*extensor digiti quinti* compartment].

Different from these [and in the fourth class] are certain membranous ligaments round all the joints in the fingers and wrist. Others are firm and coarse, such as those which bind together the carpal and metacarpal bones of which I must speak presently. If all the muscles are removed, these are clearly seen; in fact, while the bones still hold together you can observe

270 the movement of the ligaments of the metacarpus at their union with the carpus. When these ligaments are detached, what seemed a united mass is at once clearly seen to be separated and severed. Because of the shortness of the bones [of the carpus] and the closeness of the joints, their movement is not quite obvious. (Many people think that all these bones* of the wrist are one.) You must separate them at their meeting points by cutting the ligaments. Their junction will be apparent if the tendons are moved before they are dried up, for there is between them a little articular give which indicates clearly to the close observer the places for their severance. If you extend and flex the wrist the junction of the bones is visible. If you make an incision there you will separate them all from one another and see that their appearance is varied.

271 While laying bare these spreading ligaments you will notice another [*medial ligament*] which is round and set opposite the tendon which flexes the wrist on the little finger side [*flexor carpi ulnaris*]. In Book I of my *De usu partium* I have explained how it retains the cartilaginous bone [*pisiform*] which lies there upon the articulation of the wrist. In laying bare the ligaments you will see the tendon of another muscle, that which flexes the wrist by the great [i.e. middle] finger [*flexor carpi radialis*]. This tendon appears to unite with the nearest bone

* Text irrelevantly inserts KAI POLY MALLON = 'and still more'.

of the carpus at that point lying by its side [*trapezium*], but passes through the ligament to the base of the second* bone in the metacarpus. Extreme care is needed not to sever the tendon in baring it, nor to assume that it stops at the point on the first bone of the wrist where it seems to do so to those who cut carelessly.

Observe here also the stylus-like process given off by the ulna in a line with the little finger. Anatomists call it STYLOEIDĒS. *272* If you move round the whole articulation to the side, you will see how it is adapted for movements of the wrist in turning round the whole hand. Observe exactly also the movements of the radius on the ulna which we make when we turn the hand.

Chapter 11

[*Extensors and Flexors of Forearm*]

You cannot observe accurately the movements of forearm on *272* upper arm in flexion or extension until you strip the upper arm of all surrounding muscles. Let this then be done, remembering that we said that the muscle resting on the radius [*brachioradialis*] reaches up to the humerus and that the muscle under it [*extensores carpi radiales longus et brevis*], that is, the muscle attached to the metacarpals of the index and middle finger, also comes up a short way. It is better to preserve the heads of these muscles, or at least that of the muscle resting on the radius [*brachioradialis*], for you will first see it clearly when you lay *273* bare the anterior muscle of the upper arm [*biceps*]. You will expose it, paying attention firstly to the vein running along the whole upper arm [*cephalic*] called 'shoulder vein', and secondly to the muscle which occupies, or rather forms, the highest part of the shoulder [DELTOEIDĒS], for it is the only muscle that lies there.

The incision along the vein should be downward (the skin here being, of course, removed as well as the membranes

* Text says 'first'.

[fasciae] round the muscles). The incision from the highest point of the shoulder should be made with attention to the likenesses and differences of the fibres, from which you will see that the outline of the muscle [*deltoid*] runs to an apex, like a triangle, inserted into the humerus.

This muscle pertains to the shoulder-joint and, alone of

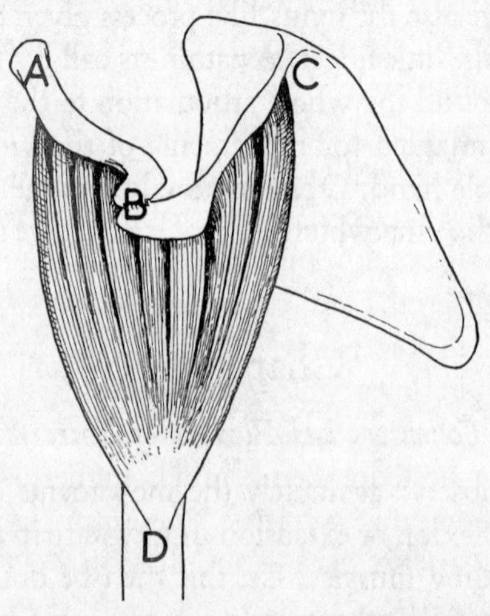

[Reconstruction of Galen's diagram of deltoid.]

those that move it, must now be removed to render visible the double head of the anterior muscle of the upper arm [*biceps*]. 274 [In the figure] let *AB* be the collar-bone, *BC* the spine of the scapula; suppose that the fibres* arise between the first and third of these points and extend at the one end to *B*, at the other to *D*, *B* being the top of the shoulder and *D* the farthest point of the insertion [of the fibres] into the humerus; and that *BD* be the whole [length of the] insertion. Of this muscle we must speak again, when we go through the muscles which move the shoulder joint. For the present, having noted it, remove it and follow what I have to say next.

The anterior muscle of the arm [*biceps*], which is clearly visible beside the 'shoulder vein' [*cephalic*] even without dis-

* Text reads 'muscles'.

section, in all, and especially in athletes, has two heads. One [*caput longum*] is attached to the ridge on the neck of the shoulder blade, the other [*caput breve*] to the process which 275 some call 'like an anchor' (ANKYROEIDĒS), others 'like a crow's beak' (KORAKOEIDĒS). The ligament of each head is strong and nearly round. Follow these heads as they run down through the upper arm. By their union they form this muscle which, unlike them, neither hangs loosely nor is raised from the humerus, but is closely applied to it. It rests unattached as far as the elbow-joint upon the smaller muscle lying beneath [*brachialis*]. There [the *biceps*] gives rise to its APONEURŌSIS, a strong tendon attached to the radius. It has a share in the membranous ligament round the joint [by the *lacertus fibrosus*] by which it flexes the joint, bending it slightly inwards.

If this muscle [*biceps*] be removed, you will find another beneath which also encircles the humerus. [It arises] from two fleshy heads, one at the back of the humerus, the other more to the front, the posterior being much higher [*brachialis*]. You will see them joining to form a single muscle which, passing 276 into a tendon, is attached to the ulna. It flexes the joint and bends it slightly outwards. But if both muscles [*biceps* and *brachialis*] perform their function correctly, the bend of the articulation is inclined neither to right nor left.

There are thus two anterior muscles which flex the elbow. Three others united extend it [*triceps*]. These you must treat as follows:

First dissect the muscle on the inside of the upper arm under the skin [*dorso-epitrochlearis* corresponding to part of *latissimus dorsi* in man] which has its head near the limit of the muscle behind the armpit [*latissimus dorsi*]. (On the nature of this I shall speak in explaining the muscles moving the shoulder.) Its end reaches the elbow-joint at the inner condyle of the humerus. This termination is membranous and thin.

When it has been removed, observe the origin of the two other muscles which extend the forearm [corresponding to parts of *triceps* in man]. Of these one [*caput longum*] springs from 277 the lower side of the scapula, about half-way down the upper part. The other issues from the back of the upper humerus below its head [*caput laterale*]. These, as they run on, coalesce in the upper arm and, continuing, are inserted in the crook of the ulna [*olecranon*] by a flat tendon. If you follow the fibres from above longitudinally, this tendon will be seen to be twofold, deriving its outer part from the first [part] of the two muscles we mentioned and the inner from the second. And if you separate each [part] of the muscle from the other and try to stretch it, you will see that the whole forearm is extended by each but that a difference lies in the lateral inclination to the side, for the former inclines outward, the latter inward.

Another muscle lies under it, surrounding the bone of the upper arm obliquely [*caput mediale*]. This unites with the second muscle and is thought to be a part of it by the anatomists, as indeed it is, if you think of this muscle as single. But it is *278* possible actually to separate them along the fibres. If you do this you will find that this muscle remains fleshy throughout, and is attached to the posterior part of the elbow. If pulled, there seems to me to be a straight and direct tension at the elbow joint, deviating neither to right nor left, though sometimes a little inwards.

I have now mentioned all the muscles in the arm. Having heard them, remember what you ought to know about these and about all the phenomena that you observe in dissection. For some muscles or tendons or ligaments you find vary a little, some in their course and some only at their end. Again, some fuse with their attachments or become attached to what fuses with them, or have other such slight differences. If ever, when you are dissecting a limb, you see something that contradicts what I have written, recognize that this happens infrequently. Do not prejudge my work until you yourself have seen, as I have, the phenomenon in many examples.

Here ends my first book. In the second I shall describe ana- *279* tomical procedures on muscles and ligaments in the legs. I shall add also the disquisition on the nails, which has reference to both limbs.

BOOK II

[*On Muscles and Ligaments of Lower Limb*]

Chapter I

[*Why the Ancients wrote no such Books*]

I commend Marinus,[32] who has written on anatomical procedure, *280* without criticizing my other predecessors who have not. For them it was superfluous to compose memoranda for themselves or others since they practised dissection from childhood under parental instruction,[40] as they did reading and writing. And it was not only professional physicians among our predecessors who studied anatomy, but also general philosophers.[41] *281* One so instructed from his earliest years would no more forget what he had learned from experience than would others the alphabet.

In time, however, the art came to be customarily imparted not only to kinsmen but to those outside the family. Thus the habit of dissection from early years came to be discontinued. For when the Art was communicated to [any] favoured adult it followed that the instruction became the poorer.

How much training from childhood counts in everything has been made clear, I think, by our forefathers, when they called 'educated' (PEPAIDEUMENOI) not only those skilled in the arts and sciences, but all who had gained some reputation in life, just as they called their opposites 'uneducated' (APAIDEUTOI). Hence the Art, being no longer exclusive to the Asclepiad family, was ever degenerating from one generation to the next. Thus, too, arose a demand for memoranda to *282* preserve knowledge.

Formerly, then, there was no demand for accounts of anatomical procedure, nor for the sort of handbooks that were first written, so far as I know, by Diocles [*c.* 360 B.C.].[42] Other early physicians followed him and not a few of the younger school whom I have mentioned.

In addition to their other deficiencies such treatises have not made clear the usefulness of their matter, but fling together indiscriminately things that can be of the greatest service to the Art with others that contribute little or nothing thereto. It is indeed to the good that anatomical theory should be included in books on diagnosis, prognosis, and treatment, as Hippocrates plainly does. But, since there is danger that such studies may perish, because of the little regard that my contemporaries have for the arts and sciences, and further since they themselves no longer have practice from their earliest years, I feel justified in *283* writing these memoranda. Yet had it been possible to preserve the oral tradition, such writing would have been superfluous.

Accordingly I have [here] communicated everything I have learned from the beginning to those who find they need it. Would that it were possible for all to acquire that knowledge. Already I see some who have been taught by me grudging to share their knowledge with others. Should they die suddenly after me, these studies will die with them.[43] Wherefore I have nothing but praise for Marinus[32] for recording his anatomical experience, though I was myself compelled to write another work on the same theme, since I have found his both incomplete and obscure.*

Chapter 2

[*The particular Uses of Dissections*]

283 Almost all anatomists seem to have failed to treat clearly the most useful part of the science. What could be more useful to a physician for the treatment of war-wounds, for extraction of missiles, for excision of bones, for [treatment of] dislocations, fractures with ulcerations, &c., than to know accurately all the

* This last sentence is, in the text, the opening sentence of the next chapter.

parts of the arms and legs, and all, not so much of the internal as of the external parts of the shoulders and back, breast and ribs, abdomen, neck, and head? For it is from these that we have *284* to extract weapons, incising the contiguous areas, excising some parts, evacuating humours in putrid infections and abscesses, and treating ulcers. Again with bones we have to cut out some affected parts or open them up. If a man is ignorant of the position of a vital nerve, muscle, artery, or important vein, he is more likely to maim his patients or to destroy rather than save life.

Certain knowledge, as the number and appearance of the muscles of the tongue, would be additional, but not primary or essential. I say 'additional' since we must inquire closely into such things because of doctrinaire theorizers who, not satisfied with the useful side of natural knowledge, are ever demanding *285* 'For what is this part?' 'Why is it of this nature or size?' An intelligent man may grasp the matter sufficiently by two or three careful dissections by which is revealed what is useful for medical practice and, secondarily, for the knowledge of nature. I of all men am entitled to say that such studies in anatomy are useless for the treatment, diagnosis, and prognosis of disease.

[A gap here in text.] . . . escaped the attacks of unscrupulous sophists who, neglecting to criticize the theory, turn their attack against its authors, professing that their opponents, being ignorant of such studies, bring the charge of uselessness against them. For their sake, so that ignorance on the part of their critics may not provide the sophists with an easy line of attack, I have laboured at the purely theoretical as well as the practically useful part of anatomy. I have given sufficient proof of this in my *De usu partium*, and now I shall describe anatomical procedures on all the parts of the body. But, while doing this, *286* I also distinguish the value of each of the studies [i.e. theoretical and practical] and demonstrate its usefulness.

Anatomical study has one application for the man of science [ANĒR PHYSIKOS] who loves knowledge for its own sake, another for him who values it only to demonstrate that Nature does nought in vain, a third for one who provides himself from anatomy with data for investigating a function, physical or mental, and yet another for the practitioner who has to remove splinters and missiles efficiently, to excise parts properly, or to treat ulcers, fistulae, and abscesses. Now all this [last application of anatomy] is most necessary, and a really good physician must first of all have practice in it, and next in the actions of the inner organs, which are important for diagnosing diseases. For some functions are of greater moment to natural philosophers than *287* to physicians, both for pure knowledge and to show how the artifice of Nature is perfectly worked out in every part.

Chapter 3

[*Why Anatomy is neglected or mistaught*]

287 Yet the anatomists have not done this. They have obviously elaborated with care the part of anatomy that is completely useless to physicians or that which gives them little or only occasional help. But they have given far less care to the part that needs urgent attention and is most useful and necessary for all to know, to wit that concerned with the muscles, nerves, arteries, and veins—not just those round the heart or any of the internal organs, but those evident in legs, arms, and outer parts of the chest, by the spine, breast, ribs, shoulder-blades, abdomen, neck, or head.

I have daily seen those ignorant of such things fearing what was not to be feared, and confident where confidence was misplaced. Such, for example, was he who examined suspiciously the muscle inside the thigh [*gracilis*] as if it were of vital importance, when it has neither a large tendon nor an artery nor a *288* vein, nor does it initiate any of the leg movements[44] as do the muscles that extend or flex the knee. The most useful part of the science of anatomy lies in just that exact study neglected by the professed experts. It would have been better to be ignorant of how many valves there are at each orifice of the heart, or how many vessels minister to it, or how or whence they come, or how the paired cranial nerves reach the brain, than [not to know] what muscles extend and flex the upper and lower arm and wrist, or thigh, leg and foot, or what muscles turn each of these laterally, or how many tendons there are in each, from where they take their rise and how they are placed, or where a vein or a great artery and where a small underlie them.

These things are so necessary to physicians that not even the Empirics, who wrote whole books against anatomy, have dared to condemn such knowledge. Indeed they admit that *289* all such knowledge is most useful, though they maintain that enough of it can be learned from the wounds that occur from time to time. One might well wonder at their temerity, for since even those who have devoted much time to anatomy have failed to bring it to perfection, one could scarcely acquire it from the contemplation of wounds. Perched high on a professorial chair a man can say these things to his pupils without being able to instruct them in the actual practice of the Art. For he begins by being ignorant of the parts of the animal organs, and even those [among the Empirics] thought to be highly expert are acquainted only with the parts clearly visible under the skin.

It is needless to enter into controversy with these men. Nor need we be over-zealous to prove that anatomy 'depending on cases' and on 'observation of wounds'—these are their own terms —is not only unable to teach the precise nature of the parts, but that it cannot do so even when carried out with careful attention, unless accompanied by constant practice on many bodies, aided by instructions which I repeat in the course of this work. One can then disregard those of the Empiric School since they *290* are evidently quibbling. Further censure is due to all the anatomists whose investigations into such matters have been superficial. Failing to recognize many tendons or even whole muscles, what must one suppose happens to them with nerves, some of the finest of which have the greatest power?

Therefore I call on the young to set aside for the present the dissection of brain, heart, tongue, lungs, liver, spleen, kidneys, stomach, larynx, as well as embryos and pregnant wombs, and first to learn thoroughly how the humerus, scapula, and forearm bones are articulated, and to gain knowledge of each of the outer parts in the limbs, what muscles move them, and what nerves, arteries, and veins are in each part. I put anatomical practice on arm and leg before all others, thinking it right that 291 the young should go first to what is pressing and of great advantage to the Art.

This was bound to entail the same arrangement in my exposition as that which I followed in my *De usu partium*, which is not only for physicians but also for philosophers. In that work, since my subject was the bodily organs, I put first the discourse on the hand, for that part is characteristic of man. Now I do it not only for that reason but even more to give the young practice first in what is most necessary. For I see that just the opposite is being done by those who think themselves fit to deal with the subject of anatomy, though they are still ignorant of which of the elbow veins has a nerve, or muscle-head, or end of an artery under it. For this reason they make grave mistakes in venesection. Yet they dissect the heart or tongue of an ox without realizing that these are utterly unlike those of a human being.

Chapter 4

[*Muscles of the Thigh inserted on the Tibia*]

292 In the previous book I explained the practical method in dissecting the arm muscles. I shall now give a similar account of the leg. Until one has learned to recognize these exactly, it is impossible to dissect nerves or vessels or to teach others to do so.

The skin must be removed with great attention to the origin of the sole in the neighbourhood of the heel, lest there be torn with the skin that fascia under it [*plantaris*] by the expansion of which (as I pointed out for the hand) the hairless and inflexible part of the skin is moved.* Leave the skin there, as with the hand, having learned the same lesson [p. 7].

You had best dissect first the muscles in the thigh, and then either those round the leg, or those by the hip which move the head of the femur, and with it the whole thigh. But you may *293* desire to dissect either the leg muscles or those in the hip before those in the thigh. If you want to dissect the leg-muscles first, remove the ends of the muscles springing from the thigh that come down to the leg. If you [want to dissect] the hip-muscles first, then remove the heads that come up beyond the knee [to the femur]. You will find them without difficulty in the way I shall explain, if you start from such conspicuous and well recognized points as ham, knee, or shin. You should mark these well in starting to dissect, after the skin and underlying membranes [fascia] have been removed, for thus the muscles prove most manageable, their outlines being distinguished by the differences in the fibres.

First on the surface under the skin appears a flat tendon [*sartorius*], somewhat fleshy, inserted in the tibia below the knee, where lies what is called the 'shin' (ANTIKNĒMION). This tendon is attached there along the prominent part of the tibia, which is fleshless and uncovered, stretching down from above as a ridge. The upper end of this muscle (which they call *294* its 'head') has a fleshy origin from the middle of the ridge [*anterior superior spine*] of the ilium which is extended lengthwise in the animal. In thin subjects its projection is quite visible before dissection. Moreover, it [i.e. the ridge] forms a boundary between back and front through its length till it ends in an acute projection comparable to that of the spine of the scapula at its summit [Figs. 5, 16].[45]

The muscle runs from the ilium to the inner region of the thigh, gradually turning askew. It then descends to the knee-joint, passing round the inner condyle of the femur. Turning back thence, it is attached to the tibia slantways, at the part where it is fleshless and bare [Fig. 16].

* Text HYPOBEBLĒTAI DERMA TŌ KŌLŌ.

Traction on this [*sartorius*] muscle from its origin brings the leg into the position that boys use in the palaestra in 'changing 295 legs', when they throw the other leg on the thigh.[46] This will be plain to you if a large part of the flesh on the leg be removed, and still more, if you cut off the foot at the joint. [For though] after death large muscles can, when pulled, exhibit their functions without the flesh being cut away, this is impossible with small ones until most is removed.

If you attempt to dissect the [thigh] muscles first, it is best to remove the ends of any muscles associated with the leg. For thus you will see this [*sartorius*] muscle acting of itself, to move the femur and, in conjunction with the calf muscle, to draw up the leg as already mentioned. Beyond the point where this [*sartorius*] muscle becomes tendinous is another insertion [*gracilis*, larger in ape than man] in the strict sense of a tendon passing into the tibia. If you follow this to its origin, dissecting away the overlying muscle, you pass through the surface parts of the 296 thigh on the inside as far as the pubic bone, where it has its head. The front of the [*pubic*] bone, extending vertically downwards, is gently rounded [in the ape]. The bones called 'pubic' (HĒBĒS) here meet and fuse through cartilage. There these two muscles, one for each leg, are in contact at their origins. You can learn their action from their place of origin, from their course on the inside of the thigh, and from the area of insertion on the tibia. But, even apart from this evidence, you can find by the use of your hands how they move the leg, for if you pull in the direction of their origin, you will see the leg raised and rotated inward. You must recognize such distinctions in the dead animal, having removed most of the parts that bend the joints and, if possible, leaving the bones bare of flesh.

Beside the two muscles just mentioned [*sartorius* and *gracilis*] 297 there is also engaged, in the same conjunction on the inner side of the tibia, a third attachment of a flat tendon [*semimembranosus proprius* of the ape]. It slopes gently downward to the site of the oblique muscle [*sartorius*]. You will find it if you follow gradually, as with the two former, the part of the muscle that produces the tendon. At first it extends from the inner side of the tibia and knee, then, moving up slantwise along the ham through the back of the thigh, it reaches the outer and lower part of the ischium, at the hairless and fleshless part of the ape's rump [*ischial tuberosity*]. Springing from this, it passes obliquely through the thigh; then, within, it reaches the tendinous conjunction that we have mentioned, rolling the leg backward, as one might say, as dancers often do. (Note here this common characteristic of muscles, that if straight-set they cause a straight movement, and if oblique, an oblique movement.) Among the thigh-muscles, none is more transverse since it starts from the outer side of the ischium and is attached to the inner side of the tibia. The tibia is thereby pulled backward and upward and rotated, a very complex motion. These three muscles [*sartorius*, *gracilis*, and *semi-membranosus proprius*] are joined to the tibia by tendons, which you will have first to remove if you want to dissect the leg itself for it is impossible to see any of the underlying structures clearly while they are on them [Fig. 16]. *298*

There is another muscle [*biceps femoris,* which in the ape has only one head], the fourth of those which descend to the tibia. Its insertion is not on the inside like the others, but only on the outside and plainly to be seen, being fleshy and broad and attached along the outer parts of the tibia. Traced upward, it becomes narrower* as it approaches its origin which lies at the farthest point outside the ischial bone. This origin is also outside that of the previous muscle. Attached there, its action is clear from its position, for it draws the whole leg outward with a simple motion. This is obvious by trial, for if you pull the muscle towards its head, the leg follows [Fig. 17]. *299*

In the case of a certain excellent runner, we saw this muscle [*biceps*] ruptured about the middle while the man was racing. After that its place was empty and hollow, for the parts of the torn muscle had moved, the upper being pulled toward the origin, the lower toward the tibia. When pain and inflammation

* Text says 'broader'.

had subsided, walking did him no harm and, taking heart, he began running again. Feeling none the worse for this, he actually restarted racing and was again victorious. This is not surprising, because in running we do not need the sideways turn of the [knee] joint, but it suffices to extend and flex it. Whence it follows that even the aforementioned three muscles in front of this [*sartorius*, *gracilis*, and *semimembranosus proprius*] do not initiate motions in the leg that are essential for everyday use of the limb, even in running.

There is [in the hip region] a fifth muscle [*semimembranosus* 300 *accessorius* of the ape, unrepresented in man] in addition to the four I have mentioned. It does not reach to the tibia like the first three, but [goes] to the lower head of the femur and to the place of origin of the muscles of the leg on the inner side. It can be dissected not only from this point, but equally well from its attachment higher up. It is well to manipulate it at both points of contact. If you begin below, you will track it up to its head through the back parts of the thigh as far as the ischial bone, for the origin of the muscle is united with that of the third muscle [*semimembranosus proprius*] of my exposition, as is most clearly seen at that point. If you begin from above, you have as guide the head of the muscle dissected before [*biceps*].

[Here has dropped from the text an account of the *semitendinosus*. Its origin in the ape is associated with the *biceps* on the ischial tuberosity. It descends, posterior to the *semimembranosus*, to its insertion below the tuberosity of the tibia [Fig. 17].]

Four muscle heads in a row thus spring from the ischium. Outermost is that of the flat muscle torn by the runner [*biceps*]. Second is that which rotates the leg outward [*semimembranosus proprius*]. Third is that now in question [*semimembrano-* 301 *sus accessorius*, Fig. 16] which is [part of] the second and also turns the whole limb gently outward—a motion like to but less than the second.* And next to this is the fourth [*semitendinosus*]. All these [four] heads issue in a row from the ischial tuberosity.

* Text reads 'third'.

When you begin dissecting from above, seek to move downward through the hinder and inner region of the thigh, that will bring you to its condyle, where issues a muscle of the calf on the inner side [medial head of *gastrocnemius*]. You will see its head embracing and gripping part of the ligament round the joint. If you stretch this muscle at its head, the tibia is seen turning backward and somewhat inward on the thigh. This is because of the association of the head of this muscle with the inner and hinder part of the calf (GASTROKNĒMIA) [Fig. 16].

Chapter 5

[*Muscles moving the Knee-joint*]

The thigh muscles are now under discussion. If you remove all those I mentioned, you will find large muscles still remaining in front of, behind, and inside the part. Dissect those in front first. They all extend the knee but are variously placed and have different origins [Fig. 16]. *302*

There are four of them [making up the *quadriceps femoris*]. The highest [*rectus femoris*] springs from the ridge of the ilium in a line with the muscle first mentioned [*sartorius*], issuing from the parts underneath it. Next is one much larger, lower down, and on the outer part of the thigh toward the buttock [*vastus lateralis*]. From this head comes the biggest of the anterior muscles of the thigh. It is continuous and united with another which runs from about the middle of the thigh to its lower end [*vastus intermedius*].* Another tendon [*vastus medialis*] also reaches the same place as the muscle [*rectus femoris*] which was just said to spring from the ridge of the ilium. The two are seen to be united toward the knee-cap, the 'mill' (MYLĒ) as it is called. Here they are combined as a very strong flat tendon which covers the whole of it in front. This tendon *303*

* Greek text here inserts two irrelevant lines.

[*ligamentum patellae*] extends into the tibia, being itself very strong and inextricably attached to its front part beyond the articulation [Figs. 16, 17].

When you have severed these [attachments of the *ligamentum patellae*] three* muscle-heads will be clearly seen beneath. One [*vastus lateralis*] arises from the great trochanter, and the neck of the femur. The second [*vastus intermedius*], below the former, comes from the anterior region of the femur. It runs down straight through the front parts of the thigh as far as the

304 patella, remaining entirely fleshy. The third [*vastus medialis*] starts higher up, and ends by the inner side of the thigh, acquiring a more membranous end. Their ends combine and make one, wherefore the anatomists pronounce them a single muscle, though it has three heads† which generate a very strong tendon. Why of all the muscles to the knee these should be the most powerful extenders is obvious. For unless they act vigorously it would be impossible to stand upright and, were all the others destroyed, these alone could suffice to maintain the tension.

Flexion of the thigh is to be classed as a less energetic action. That movement is comparable to what happens when we raise a leg, sustaining the whole body's weight on the other firmly planted on the ground. For this reason Nature did not assign this leg-lifting function to so many or to such large muscles. Of those already mentioned there is actually one only [*semitendinosus*] in contact with the head of the calf muscle (which, I said, has come into being to bend the leg), and this does not so much bend it as turn it inward, for its bending action is both

305 slight and obscure [Fig. 17].

People think that the 'large muscle' [*adductor magnus*] flexes the [knee] joint by itself. That muscle, however, which occupies practically the whole postero-medial part of the thigh, draws the leg after it little if at all, because its end only just reaches the parts round the knee-joint, while the ligament [of the joint]

* Text says 'two'.

† Text here adds 'just like those on the surface, of which I have spoken', the meaning of which is not clear.

lies all round it. It is not in the least degree inserted in the tibia, but they were driven to represent this muscle as the cause of the bend at the knee because they were ignorant of another muscle [*popliteus*], concealed in the joint, which could effect the flexion itself or had more power to do so than any other. It cannot be seen until you remove the muscles that move the calf. Therefore I do not speak of it now, but in the due order of dissection I will explain its nature when it is laid bare.

Chapter 6

[*Muscles of the Hip*]

When the muscles round the thigh have been cut away, except *306* only the large one [adductor mass], you may dissect both those that move the hip-joint itself and those round the leg. Suppose that we deal first with those that move the hip-joint. Among them, we said, is the great muscle of the thigh [*adductor magnus*]. (Some think, mistakenly as I explained [p. 42], that it moves the knee-joint.)

Starting from this muscle, examine [*a*] the fibres which come from the back of the femur [at the *linea aspera*] and pass up toward the ischium [*adductor magnus*, posterior division]; and [*b*] the fibres on the inner side [*adductor longus*] which reach the inner part of the pubic bone [i.e. the inner part of the pubic angle], for the muscle arising from that whole region is thus attached to the innominate bone by its union with the lowest part of the pubic bone. By the vertical fibres behind, it bends the hip-joint. (If it move the knee-joint at all it will do so by these and by no others, whereas those [fibres] which you will see carried up from the side parts to the pubic bone adduct *307* the thigh.) Sometimes this muscle [*adductor magnus* in the ape] seems to present two or three different divisions, forming, as it were, two or three muscles, and sometimes only one or two. At all events, it has a certain contour attached to the inner part of the femur in its middle and upper middle region [Fig. 16].

Sever this muscle [adductor mass] from the pubic bone with care, leaving intact the underlying muscle which occupies the great foramen [*obturator externus*]. This [latter] muscle passes into a tendon, of which I shall speak later. In separating the great muscle from the pubic bone, spare not only that muscle which occupies the foramen but also that set low down which in these animals is throughout of dark colour [*pectineus*]. It issues from the deeper parts of the pubic bone and is united to the lower part of the small trochanter by a tendon strong in proportion to the size of the muscle. The tendon is *308* implanted in the inner part of the trochanter; it is fleshy throughout and not merely sinewy.

Another muscle [*iliopsoas*] produces a yet stronger tendon of attachment. This runs down, continuous with the muscle just mentioned [*pectineus*] to the remaining part of the small trochanter which it embraces. It comes from the parts above, arising both from the ilium and from both loin-muscles. Obviously this muscle cannot be examined without cutting through all the muscles in the region of the body-wall (EPIGASTRION) and removing everything that lies on the loins. You will [then] see clearly that it is the only muscle in the loin region that is threefold. In its inside portion [*psoas minor*], by a strong ligamentous tendon, it reaches down to that part where the pubic bone ends next the ilium. In the outer part [*iliacus*], by another short, and much lighter aponeurosis, it arises from the ilium. The other [and third] part [*psoas major*] moves downwards between the aponeuroses, amalgamating with the muscle that *309* attaches to the whole ilium within [*iliacus*] and producing the aforesaid tendon which unites with the small trochanter. From its position you realize that it flexes the thigh and rotates it inwards. If you put actual tension on it, you will see it producing this effect, the opposite to that of the back part of the big muscle [*quadriceps*] that we spoke of before [p. 41].

It is obvious that the small, livid muscle [*pectineus*] initiates oblique motion towards the inside in the thigh.

In this region you will find no other muscle attached to the femur, but proceeding to the external muscles, you will find them all attached round the head of the bone near the great trochanter. The first among these is set on the surface under the skin [*tensor fasciae latae*], springing from the whole straight ridge of the ilium. This part [of the muscle] is entirely fleshy, but it becomes membranous and soon a membrane in the strict sense and of a ligamentous nature [*tractus ilio-tibialis* of ape]. It is placed upon the higher parts of the ilium which tend to slope backward, being continuous with the end of the spinal muscles. *310*

Where this membranous part [of the *tensor*] ends, there is a second fleshy process, opposite the one first mentioned, namely, that from the ilium. This process issues from the side parts of the coccyx, embracing also the back parts [*gluteal fascia*]. You must remove it, tracing the fibres downwards and stripping it off from all the underlying tissues, with a blunt lancet. These tissues lying between coccyx and inside* edge of the ischium are membranous and resistant, rather than fleshy. But all which passes toward the hip-joint [*gluteus maximus*] and is continuous with it is fleshy, and fuses with the [membranous] head that issues from the coccyx. For a short way, then, strip off these tissues, too, from the underlying structures, together with those that correspond to them that issue from the ilium, and also their membranous centre [i.e. from the dorsal fascia over *311* the sacrum]. Thus you will lay bare the top of the femur and find the twofold termination of the muscle, one [part] uniting with the back parts of the femur set roughly in a line with the fibres from the ischium to the coccyx [i.e. the tract known as *gluteal fascia* in man], the other [part] passing into a flat membranous tendon which embraces the front muscles of the thigh [*tractus ilio-tibialis* of ape] coalescing with the fascia which we said before ran down to the knee [*fascia lata*, traceable to patella and leg in apes] [Fig. 17].†

When this muscle has been removed, there remains another [*gluteus medius*, larger than *gluteus maximus* in *Macaca* though

* Text reads 'outside'.

† Here follow seven lines devoid of clear anatomical meaning.

less marked in *Semnopithecus*]. It is strong and fleshy throughout and issues from roughly the whole back of the ilium and embraces to some extent also the neighbouring bones [namely those of the sacrum]. Its tendon is attached to the apex of the
312 great trochanter, extending even in front.

In dissecting this muscle you must pay attention to a certain small muscle [*gluteus minimus*] which arises from the outer and lower parts of the ilium. You may think this to be part of the 'large muscle' [*gluteus medius*] unless you examine its outline carefully. Not only has it an origin continuous with it [i.e. with *gluteus medius*], but it is also continuous with it as far as its insertion into the great trochanter. Further, its continuity is rather more in the inner parts than elsewhere. It also extends the thigh with a slight inclination outward.*

Another muscle [*piriformis*], dark in colour [and very robust in *Macaca*], is hidden there under the 'large muscle' [*gluteus medius*], having itself a like position. It is more easily discerned than the muscle mentioned before [*gluteus minimus*], because of its hue. This muscle arises from the inner lateral parts of the sacrum [i.e. from the transverse processes of the last two sacral vertebrae, being somewhat different in man], and it is clear that it can rotate the head of the thigh to those parts. It is inserted in the great trochanter lower than the 'large muscle' [*gluteus medius*]. These three muscles [*gluteus medius*, *gluteus minimus*, and
313 *piriformis*] are thus all attached to the great trochanter.

Next there are two others [*obturatores externus et internus*] that are completely hidden, which rotate the head of the femur outwards,† being attached by strong tendons in the hollow [*digital fossa*] by the large trochanter. Both arise from the pubic bone and occupy the [*obturator*] foramen, the one inside, the other outside. They pass out by the neck of the femur and both alike approach the trochanter at the aforesaid hollow. The posterior muscle [*obturator internus*] is attached higher than the anterior [*obturator externus*]. When you cut the latter from the pubis, try

* Text says 'inward' but the actions of the glutei are very complex.

† Reading EXŌ for ESŌ.

to preserve the common [*obturator*] membrane which underlies both. It occupies the whole foramen. Many muscles arise [in the bone] here, which pass to the bones lying beside the foramen on either side.

You will loosen the outer muscle [*obturator externus*] without difficulty. But if you wish to observe clearly the inner [*obturator internus*], you must sever the *symphysis pubis* with a strong lancet. You will do this easily, for a cartilage lies between, drawing and binding the pubic bones together. If you cut along this, the incision will not be difficult and, the bones once severed, the muscle comes plainly to view. This is easier if, having separated the bones, you grasp the ilia and forcibly bend them outward. Thus they are loosened and parted from the sacrum, so that the whole is everted and the inner portion of the pubic bone displayed. *314*

For the present it suffices to remove the attachment of the [*obturator internus*] muscle here. Later you will hear, in the anatomy of the rectum, how first to lay bare the covering membrane [? *pelvic fascia*, ? *levator ani*] which looks like a kind of wrapping. Yet it is not a wrapping of this muscle but is a sort of thin elastic membrane* running down to the anus on either side. Like the previous muscles [*obturatores*], it was quite unknown to all the anatomists, but when we come to the anatomy of the rectal region these muscles will be more fully discussed. *315*

The muscle that is now under discussion, that within the pubic bone [*obturator internus*], produces at the great trochanter a motion opposite, but like in result, to that of its anterior fellow [*obturator externus*]. Both turn the head of the thigh outwards,† the one through the front parts of the articulation, the other through the back parts. Such then is the anatomy of the muscles moving the hip-joint.

* Literally 'membranous muscle'.

† Reading EXŌ for ESŌ.

Chapter 7

[*Muscles of the Leg*]

316 It is now time to pass to the muscles in the leg. These can be dissected, as I have said, after those in the hip, but also before, if you remove the muscles in the thigh that run down into the leg. When they are gone, two muscle-heads [*gastrocnemius*] are clearly visible. They arise from the back of the femur at the roots of the condyles. Thus their heads encircle these condyles. For this reason, each attaching tendon contains a rounded cartilage [*sesamoid* in apes][47] which it shares with the most convex part of the condyle. Passing through the ham to the calf, the heads join and become one.

At this point a considerable strand splits off from the outer head. This becomes a muscle [*plantaris*, larger in apes than in man] ending gradually in a flat aponeurosis under the sole, as I explained for the hand in Book I. Lay this muscle bare in two different ways, as I said [p. 7], and you will see that it is like in form [to that in the hand] and is united to the muscle at present under discussion [i.e. to *gastrocnemius*].

From the two muscular heads in the calf, there springs a tendon [*tendo calcaneus*] which lies beneath and adjoins the aforementioned muscle [*plantaris*]. It is inserted into the end of the heel at the back and can pull the heel that way.

317 Continuous with this muscle you will find an attachment higher up, belonging to another muscle [*soleus*], mostly of dark colour, which springs from the fibula* at its highest part. These muscles at the back of the calf, whether you choose to count them as three [the *triceps surae*] or four [including *plantaris*], all reach the heel [*tuber calcanei*] and underside of the foot.

There are other muscles continuous with them, not exactly at the back, but rather to the side and within the leg, which reach to the underside of the foot [*flexores digitorum fibularis et tibialis*]. At the point where they yield tendons, a ligament

* Text says 'tibia'.

[*flexor retinaculum*] is laid over them which passes out of the tibia into the calcaneum. If you divide this with a straight cut, as in the hand, and follow the tendons, you will find them all inserted into the digits. Yet it is not, as in the hand, that one moves the middle joint and the other the first and third, but both move all three. The hallux is excepted, for the tendon that moves it reaches the second and third joints as with the hand.

318 The divisions of the heads of the two muscles that I have spoken of [*flexores digitorum tibialis et fibularis*] are not always distributed in the same way, for often the one moves the toe corresponding to the index and the little toe, the other moves the middle and the fourth toes, while both, united in a common tendon, move the big toe. Sometimes again it is their fusion that varies. Thus the heads of these tendons are between calcaneum and tibia and they differ only in that one [*flexor digitorum fibularis*] is placed at the lower end of the talus where it lies beside the calcaneum. This head has a ligament of its own apart from the common [*flexor retinaculum*] ligament.[48]

A third tendon [*tibialis posterior*] arises at the very end of the tibia and is fixed firmly on it, while it is bound by a ligament [of the *retinaculum*] which again is peculiar to it. This tendon itself bends the whole foot backwards, as do those inserted in the heel. The end of it fuses with the first bone of the tarsus on the inner side [*navicular*].

When each of these muscles has been dissected, turn to those on the outer side of the leg, of which there are three, so far as *319* origins go, but in respect of tendons of insertion and motions induced—to which above all you must attend—there are many more. When you have removed the membranes there under the skin, you will see a ligament like that on the outside of the hand, under which passed all the tendons which extend the fingers [*extensor retinaculum*]. This ligament is much longer and stronger* than that [in the hand], particularly if you consider the difference in the limbs. For the ligaments in the foot, as Nature has made them more numerous, so are they stronger,

* Text says 'more slender'.

being meant for more energetic functions. This ligament is slightly aslant and not at right-angles, like that in the wrist. It is attached to the end of the tibia and to that of the calcaneum. You must cut it, too, along the axis of the limb and, stretching the parts to their origins and baring the underlying tendons, begin the demonstration of the muscles as entities. They lead
320 you down to the tarsus and up to the leg.

First you will see a muscle [*peroneus longus*] extending along the fibula to its upper head. The end [of this muscle] is secured by ligaments and inserted in the tarsus in the line of the big toe, reaching out a little beyond to the inner and lower region [of the foot]. You will see a second muscle [*flexor digitorum fibularis* or *flexor hallucis longus*] lying beside this and thought to be part of it, as it has a common head above and lies along it on the outside throughout the leg, but its tendon is inserted into the head of the first phalanx of the big toe [and into digits III and IV]. So, if you recall the dissection of the hand, the parallel is clear between this twofold muscle and that in the hands that is common to wrist and thumb [*flexor digitorum profundus* and *flexor pollicis longus*].

Continuous with this is another thin muscle [*tibialis anterior*] set in the region between fibula and tibia. It is inserted into the side part of the big toe as a whole, being exactly parallel to the small muscle in the hand which is thought to be a part of the muscle that gives the three bigger fingers their
321 oblique motion on the outside. But this tendon in the foot, when it approaches the hallux, passes through a ligament having the same function as the small rings on chariots.*[49]

After these muscles, consider the tendon-head lying under the [transverse] ligament assigned to it [on the dorsum, i.e. *extensor digitorum longus*], like these aforementioned heads [on the inner side]. They are plain enough to an attentive observer. If you start from it in a downward direction you find four tendons which extend the four toes, comparable to those on the dorsa of the hands. Over this muscle you will see another

* See p. 52. The insertion is inaccurately given.

[*extensor hallucis longus*] of which the origin is on the fibula and the insertion at the end of the tarsus in the great toe a little above the inner side. You may see the head of this muscle bound by a certain ligament that arises on the inner* side of the tibia and inserted into the neighbouring fibula [corresponding to a part of the *anterior talo-fibular ligament* in man] which is like many another slender ligament which retains muscle insertions.

Chapter 8†

[*Muscles arising from the Fibula*]

The muscles [just described] lie toward the front of the leg. *322* Other three from a single head are in the outer part. They have a ligament in line with them which runs down from the fibula to the heel [*superficial peroneal retinaculum*]. When it is loosened, you will see that there are three tendons of the muscles. One, of a considerable size [*peroneus longus*] passes gradually to the outer region of the tarsus and from there, passing aslant across the sole, reaches the head of the first bone [*metatarsal*] of the big toe. It obviously bends it at the articulation. Where it makes the turn, as it were, round the tarsus, travelling down from the upper parts to the lower, you will find a [*sesamoid*] cartilage [*os Vesalianum*] coalescing with the tendon. . . .‡

The foot of an ape differs from that of man because this animal has toes different in nature. For human toes are much smaller than the fingers, while the toes of apes are larger, like the toes of creeping animals, and are deeply cleft and separated. It is by these the ape climbs so easily, as do weasels, mice, *323* martens, &c.

. . .§ As I said, you will not find this tendon [of the *quadratus*

* Text says 'outer'.

† The text of this chapter is much disturbed.

‡ Here should come descriptions of the *peroneus brevis* and the *peroneus minimi digiti*, but they are missing from the text.

§ Here a hiatus in the text.

plantae] in the human foot [which is very different from that of the ape] but the thin tendon lying alongside it which springs from the small muscle, drawing the little toe outwards [*abductor digiti minimi*], you will find in human beings, as you will the next which bends back and turns upwards the whole foot [*tibialis posterior*] in that part. The latter has a close parallel with that in the lower arm in line with the little finger [*flexor carpi ulnaris*]. Its tendon sometimes becomes cloven on the side of its origin and the tendon that draws the little toe outward [*abductor digiti minimi*] passes through the parts of it. If it chance not to be split, the membranous ligament that surrounds it receives, between itself and the tendon, the other which passes to the little toe, performing the same service for it as the small rings on chariots through which they thread the reins. Of like *324* nature is another ring formed by a ligament in the big toe which serves as an outlet for the tendon. . . .*[50]

These three muscles have a united origin. The first-mentioned in the tarsus forms a connexion with the lower parts of the foot from the upper parts of the heel, being set under the skin near the surface, having originated from delicate ligaments attached to portions of flesh. The second has its beginning where the head of the above-mentioned muscle ends, and not far from its beginning this second muscle ends in a round tendon, being itself thin throughout. The third turns the whole foot upwards and springs from the remaining part of the heel.† This muscle stretches up the foot with an inclination towards the inside, whereas the muscle that coalesces with the big toe bends it outwards, and when both are stretched at once, they extend the foot straight backwards.[51]

* There is a small hiatus here.

† Reading PTERNĒ for PERONĒ. Here three lines of repetition.

Chapter 9

[*Muscles of Foot unknown to Galen's Predecessors*]

These muscles were dissected by our predecessors, if not with complete thoroughness and accuracy, at least fairly well. Those I shall now discuss were almost entirely unknown. *324* *325*

The first of notable thickness and strength, if not length, is hidden in the joint behind the knee [*popliteus*]. You will find it after removing the muscles at the back that run down to the calf [*gastrocnemius*] which were earlier subjects of dissection in my treatise [pp. 40–41]. This [*popliteus*] muscle lies between the heads of the other, occupying almost the whole breadth of the leg there.

Its origin is a very strong ligament arising from the outer condyle of the femur. You will find it if you dissect the ligament of the articulation which, springing from the outer parts of femur and fibula, fastens them together and binds the whole joint [*arcuate popliteal* and *lateral ligaments*]. The muscle is [partly] hidden under the ligament and ascends obliquely from the fleshy substance of the calf across the back of the knee to the condyle where its head is.

Its head is formed at the condyle within and in front of the [capsular] ligament that binds together the whole articulation. *326* If you pull on its head you will see the leg bend. As this muscle is itself short the tibia—surrounded by much flesh—is attached short. If you remove the flesh [of the leg] and lay the foot bare, you will readily see the tibia drawn back, with a slight outward swerve, by the ligament and muscle in question.

It is not remarkable that this [*popliteus*] muscle remained unknown, for its head is hidden. But for the muscles in the foot, I cannot say why they were overlooked, particularly by those who examined the seven intrinsic muscles of the hand. For in that too they missed the muscles lying deep down on the bones [*interossei*], as I have already said, though not the conspicuous seven.

In the foot there are four kinds of muscle (not two as in the hand), three in the sole, and one in the upper parts upon the tarsus.

The latter [kind, on the dorsum] involves two muscles [*extensor digitorum brevis* and *extensor hallucis brevis*]. They produce
327 oblique movements in the toes, analogous to those produced in the fingers by the muscles on the outside [i.e. dorsum] of the hand.

Those underneath the foot, which are seven, as with the hand, give an oblique movement to each toe. Of these [seven], as in the hand two emerge from the first bones at the wrist, so in the foot two from the first bones in the tarsus draw away [digits I and V] from the other toes [*abductor hallucis* and *abductor digiti minimi*]. The other five [muscles] will be mentioned later.

The others in the lower parts are small muscles [*lumbricales*], springing from the flexor tendons [of the *flexores digitorum fibularis et tibialis*] before they are cleft in each of the toes. The function of these muscles is to bend the middle joint of each toe. Other smaller muscles [*contrahentes*] are attached to the tendons already split. They have an exact parallel with the muscles in the hand that initiate an oblique movement in each finger. They, too, are four in number.[52] When two muscles are added that I have already mentioned, which draw back the ends of the toes as far as possible, their total becomes seven.

328 A third kind is that of the muscles in the feet [*interossei*] beneath those attached to the bones, analogous to those in the hand that remained completely unknown. These of course you will see if you remove all the tendons, as with the hand. Their whole arrangement, number, and function corresponds to those of the muscles in the hand that I have previously mentioned. Two, set in front of the first articulation, bend the toes to some degree, together making a balanced movement, but each separately swerving* slightly toward the side. Sometimes they are so continuous with one another that there seems but one muscle in each toe. When these muscles have been dissected, there is no other left in the limb.

* AMBLYNŌN.

Chapter 10

[*Some Ligaments of Leg and Foot*]

As with the arm you examined the ligaments of the bones, so *328* now examine those of all the exposed joints and first of the hip. This has one ligament embracing it [*capsular ligament*], as with all joints. A second, hidden in the depths of the joint [*liga-* *329* *mentum teres*], ties the head of the femur to the hollow in the hip-bone [*acetabulum*]. It is so tough that it could be called a 'cartilaginous sinew'.

Examine the ligament that encircles the articulation, to find whether all parts of it are equally thick and strong, or whether some exceed others. Do likewise with the knee-joint and further with those in the foot, keeping even tension on the ligaments, for if you let one part shrink while you stretch and distend another, the latter will appear weaker. In these articulations you will find no great projection of the parts in the embracing ligament though some will be seen in the foot, as I shall indicate.

The knee-joint, however, has several other ligaments [besides the capsular]. One is deep down [*cruciate*] comparable to that hidden in the hip-joint but twofold in the knee.* There *330* are two others at the sides [*collateral ligaments*]. The outer [of these]—which I mentioned in describing the muscle behind the knee overlooked by the anatomists [*popliteus*, p. 53]—links femur and fibula. The lower end of it towards the fibula is placed under the insertion of the muscle [*peroneus longus*] the tendons of which, passing round the outer side of the tarsus, reach, I said, the first joint of the big toe. This [*fibular collateral*] ligament is carried rather to the front of the fibula than to the side. The inner [*tibial collateral*] ligament is thinner and weaker than the outer. It arises likewise from the condyle of the femur and likewise is not attached exactly at the side of the tibia, but somewhat anteriorly.

In the knee-joint are other cartilaginous ligaments [*menisci*] encircling each condyle of the tibia. They meet where the

* Text reads 'thigh'.

hollows of the tibia adjoin. They produce a single strong carti-
331 laginous tendon in that region, inserted into the part between the condyles of the femur [*anterior cruciate ligament*]. Dividing the joint—for it lies between the cavities [at the head] of the tibia and the condyles of the femur—it slips away in course of time and the space between the cavities at the head of the tibia appears as empty, though it was higher up when the animal was alive.

I shall examine in their turn the remaining ligaments in the foot, first mentioning those you removed to observe the tendons. Some of them do no service to the articulations themselves. [Such are] those in one portion of the bone, like that [*flexor retinaculum*] which embraces the tendon-head at the back which flexes the toes, and that which is attached at the end of the tibia and grasps the tendon that dorsiflexes the whole foot [*extensor retinaculum*]. Moreover, the bones, into which these tendons are inserted, have ligaments which* extend from one [bone] to
332 another, as does the ligament on the surface from the end of the tibia to the calcaneum [*deltoid ligament*], which both holds together the tendons beneath it and at the same time clamps the bones. Thus the ligaments in front which fasten the tibia to the fibula [*superior extensor retinaculum*] both bind these together and serve as a shield for the tendons lying beneath, just as the antero-lateral ligaments [*superior peroneal retinaculum*], guarding the tendons there, not only protect and clamp them securely but also fasten and bind fibula to calcaneum. Thus such ligaments are shared between the bones themselves, which they unite and the muscles beneath them.†

You will find other ligaments which are peculiar to the articulations as such and are more fibrous. You will recognize these [as mostly] hidden in the depths, though some are extended on the outside like those that guard the tendons. Thus there is a longish ligament [*anterior talofibular*] not strong like the others—which springs from the same root as the ligament
333 in front [*anterior inferior tibiofibular* ligament]. The latter is

* It has been necessary to remove a negative here and to make some other adjustments in the text to obtain sense.

† Here three lines of repetition.

attached to the fibula. The former does not, like the latter, itself bind tibia to fibula, but at a lower level it passes towards the outer region and down through the frontal projection of the talus almost hidden by it. Its end reaches the bone of the heel [*calcaneofibular ligament*]. Under the origin of this ligament, there is another [*lateral talocalcaneal ligament*] issuing from the end of the fibula* continuous with the [*capsular*] ligament encircling the whole articulation. Its end is not much behind the [*malleolar*] process, immediately crossing the joint towards the fibula.

Next that ligament, at the bottom of the tibia, is a more fibro-cartilaginous ligament [*deltoid*] through which the tibia is united to the inside surface of the talus, just where the tibia receives it. In the same way another on the outside joins fibula to talus [*posterior talofibular ligament*]. A third, issuing at the very foot of the neck in the talus [portion of *posterior talofibular ligament*], passes into the calcaneum. And a fourth, in the front parts, binds the head of the talus to the navicular *334* [*talonavicular ligament*].

All these four ligaments connect the navicular to the surrounding bones and are fairly fibro-cartilaginous, as are those that bind deep down the joints at hip and knee. Thus in the foot the talus, being articulated with four bones, its fibro-cartilaginous ligament passes down to each in the depths, outside to the fibula, inside to the tibia, below to the calcaneum, in front to the navicular.

As all the bones of the carpus are embraced by a strong ligament, so, but to a greater degree, a strong ligament embraces all the bones of the tarsus. Some of them are united with each other by certain other natural junctions, small but firm.

Chapter 11

[*On the Nails*]

It remains to give an exposition on the nature of the nails. *334* This [exposition] has two parts, one applies to all bodies made

* Text reads 'tibia'.

335 of homogeneous particles (HOMOIOMERIA),[53] the other to the nails alone. Some think that they come into being as a mingling of bone, sinew, and skin, [all HOMOIOMERIA], to which some add flesh. That the nails partake of the nature of all these is clear, but it is impossible to see that their substance has come into being out of them, for every homoiomerious body is formed so by nature from the matter that is the substrate of the animal. The lower arm is not generated from the upper as are nerves from brain, nor is the wrist [generated] from the lower arm, nor are the bones of the fingers [generated] from it [the wrist]. For there is no small difference between joining with a thing [as bone to bone] and growing out of a thing, as branches from trunks and twigs from branches, or as arteries and veins are divided off [from their trunks]. For what grows from a thing must have its nature, as an offshoot of its substance. Nerves are offshoots from brain-substance, but a nail is no such offshoot
336 from the tip of finger or toe, but is of another kind of substance, as are the stone and tiles and bricks of a house.

The manner of construction of the living creature is like that of the external objects that men fabricate, putting together different substances into one [whole]. They fasten them together, making that which they form out of them. Yet a brick does not spring from a tile or a stone. Rather there are certain substances invented for combining them, as clay and glue and nails and bolts and ropes. Sometimes the method is one of mere juxtaposition, as with things nailed in or fitted in. So with the works of Nature; some things she fixes in, as teeth in gums; some she puts together as with a buckle (GIGGLYMOEIDĒS), as the bones at the cranial sutures; some she attaches as with glue, as those joined by a cartilage; some as with clay, as those joined by flesh; and some as with rope, as those joined by a ligament.[54]

The nails she has united to the ends of the last internodes by
337 a ligament and by a natural junction with flesh and skin, laying the former underneath throughout and making the latter grow round the whole root outside. Not only a nerve, but also

an artery and vein reach the very root [of the nail]. From these the nail derives sustenance, life, and sensation—as do the other parts—but none of them [the parts] comes from the conjunction of these three tissues, still less from their mingling together, as Erasistratus conceived.[55] He advanced an opinion which was clearly at variance with the observed facts, for the substance of the organs is obviously different from the essence of these three, as I showed in the third book of my work on the anatomy of Hippocrates.[56]

Stomach, bladder, and uterus are each so made by Nature. Each has its nerve for sensation, with vein and artery for sustenance and life, all demonstrably distributed through them, like irrigation channels through a garden. But this is not so *338* with the nails, for they grow up from below, like the hair. Like hair, it is well that they be continually renewed and growth never cease, for they are worn away.

The nails, being a different kind of substance, were joined to an artery and vein and nerve at their root to ensure life, nourishment and sensation. And they were fastened to the bone and the skin so as not to hang loose, for they, too, had to be a part naturally united to the whole organism, like the others. But if, on the ground that they are harder than sinew and skin and softer than bone, it be urged that they are compounded from the substance of these, then it must be said that everything else has come into being so; cartilage from bone and ligament mixed; ligament from cartilage and nerve; nerve again from brain and ligament. For nerve is intermediate between these two combinations, not that it was made what it is by the mixing of the brain with ligament, but by compression alone.[57] For ice too is produced from water when congealed by cold. Let them say then that ice too comes from water and stone, *339* completely mixed with one another, if they think that everything that is intermediate between two bodies, not having their function or structure, is produced by a 'mixture' of these two.[58]

BOOK III

[*Nerves, Veins, and Arteries of Hand and Foot*]

Chapter I

[*Need for Anatomy of surgically accessible Parts*]

340 Those who neglect practice in the Art and rather regard sophistical theories, concern themselves little with the exact nature of the limbs. But how can they treat dislocations, whether simple or compound, or fractures and sphacelus of the bones; how can they even open abscesses (APOSKĒMMATA),[59] or excise *341* gangrenes, or remove a missile or splinter properly if they have not learnt enough to open a vein correctly? I expect beginners to practise all such methods [of study] first because I see their necessity, and second because, if the time needed to learn them is but short, as they think, then the shame of ignorance is so much the greater.

The limbs then are made up of bones, ligaments, muscles, arteries, veins, nerves, and the wrapping of them all, to wit the skin. As to the nature of the latter the professed experts in anatomy were mistaken about certain parts, notably as to the palm and the sole. Because of such ignorance a certain surgeon of repute, excising a sphacelation in the wrist, rendered the palm insensitive. Not long ago, being present with another practitioner who was treating this part, I showed him the region where the tendon attached under the hairless part of the hand *342* begins to widen [into *palmar fascia*], and suggested that he take care not to sever it. Thus the patient retained his power of feeling. For should the tendon mortify and you have predicted the consequent loss of sensation [from injury to the median nerve], you will escape reproach. So too if the tendon be severed by some sharp missile as happened in one case, the physician will escape blame if he foretell the event.[60]

It is thus proper to know these facts about the palm of the

hand, and the sole of the foot, and many other things as to arteries, veins, and nerves. First, sensation and movement in all the fingers or toes do not depend on the same nerve. Secondly, of all the nerves that run down into them, in the upper limb through arm and forearm, and in the lower through thigh and leg [a small hiatus here] . . . and when sometimes they cut a nerve in the thigh, they make some of the fingers and toes insensitive or immovable. This happens to them because of their ignorance of the nerves.

343 There are thousands of other mishaps because some practitioners do not know the veins and arteries well enough to avoid injury in operating. So, when they are excising bones or opening abscesses, they cut through important veins and sometimes, by severing large arteries, they are confronted by uncontrollable haemorrhage. Again some, in opening a vein, may cut an artery, being ignorant as to which of the veins in the limbs have companion arteries.[61]

The case of my patient deprived of sensation in the little fingers [digits IV and V] and half of the middle finger [i.e. parts supplied by C.7 and 8] is known to all because of his celebrity as a sophist. Doctors of the third [Methodist][62] School were treating him and making a fuss over the fingers, as if they alone were affected, while the condition had origin at the point where the nerve first emerges from the spinal marrow. The Methodists were putting applications on the fingers, using [preparations of] a kind first 'relaxing' and then 'constrictive'—as they were pleased to call them—without bothering about the 344 antecedent cause. They recognized only that a state of insensibility and numbness had arisen in the fingers—as by mere chance—and that it was worsening little by little.

The patient, failing to improve with drugs, communicated the nature of the treatment to me. I asked him if he had had any blow on the upper or lower arm. When he denied this, I asked him the same of the upper part of his spine. He replied that he fell out of a carriage three or four months before and, in being thrown to the ground, was struck in that part of his back by a projecting stone. He suffered severely, but in six days the pain left him, though on the fifteenth day he had a slight sensation as of insensibility and numbness of the fingers. This went on increasing up to the present, unrelieved by drugs. I reasoned that the consequent inflammation in the root of the nerve to the affected fingers had as sequela an induration which, though itself 345 painless, had produced insensibility in the fingers to which the nerve was distributed. Accordingly I transferred the treatment from the fingers to the site of the original blow and thus cured the trouble.[63]

A whole day would not suffice me to describe all the conditions of this kind that I have seen in the feet and hands, in wounded soldiers, in gladiators, and in many civilians—accidents in the many changing circumstances of life—in which those ignorant of anatomy always cut a poor figure. For, on the one hand, in their operative procedures, they may sever some nerve, small indeed but with no small power, thereby destroying in some underlying part the power of sensation, or motion, or both, or, on the other, failing to foretell the result of wounds, they are held responsible for the injury.

I perceived that the knowledge of the limbs and of other outer parts is most necessary and is utterly neglected. I resolved 346 therefore to add successively to the anatomy of the muscles in the limbs (which was my first task) that of the arteries, veins, and nerves, and so to encourage the young, engaged in dissection, to practise primarily on those [outer] parts. For they daily see practitioners, learned as to the number and nature of the cardiac valves, of the lingual muscles, and the like, yet ignorant of the anatomy of accessible parts, making the gravest errors in prognosis and local treatment, whereas those familiar with this branch of anatomy, yet ignorant of what the others know, are as constantly successful.

Chapter 2

[*Precautions in removing the Skin*]

Let us now set out the proper way to dissect the vessels and nerves in the limbs; but first as to the arm as a whole. We may begin with the saying of Hippocrates that 'The human foot is composed of many small bones, like the "end of the arm" (CHEIR AKRĒ)'.[64] He said 'foot' without qualifications, but to CHEIR he added AKRĒ, since the limbs are not like in their nomenclature, though of similar construction, for as femur is to lower limb, so is humerus to upper, and as foot is to the lower limb, so is hand to upper. The part starting at the joint by the wrists and split into fingers, is called CHEIR AKRE, just as the end of the lower limb with which we walk is the 'foot'. I shall use this nomenclature, calling the whole limb CHEIR without qualification, and when I want to designate the end of the CHEIR from the wrist [downwards], speak of the CHEIR AKRĒ. *346* *347*

This limb begins, of course, at the shoulder-joint. The neck of the scapula is articulated there with the head of the humerus, so that if you cut off the whole arm there, you can conveniently dissect it separately. You have often seen me demonstrating its parts. *348*

The first step in the procedure is to remove the skin from the underlying tissues. This is not to be done anyhow, as do curriers who, along with the skin, take away the membrane [fascia] beneath through which the nutrient veins reach it. You must leave the membrane and sever the skin from it, using a sharp lancet from the first. Taking a selected part of the limb in your hand, remove the hair so that sufficient skin is bared for the first cut, for you will thus incise the better. It is natural at the first attempt either to leave part of the skin uncut, or to sever the underlying membrane with it. By trying a second or third time, increasing or tailing off the depth of the cut, you will soon learn the right measure. *349*

[Here follow two displaced pages of a trivial discussion of terms, a translation of which would be purposeless.]

351 You must incline the lancet toward the skin when separating it from the membrane. If you turned it towards the membrane, you would injure it, while to pierce the skin does no harm. This operation is rather tedious, so, if you are demonstrating the parts of the arm to another, remove the skin before he arrives. If your colleague, who participates in the dissection, wants to show it to others, do the operation in his presence. For the work needs great precision and calls for one who really wants to know and does not mind taking trouble. Many a time I have left the task to a colleague, only to find the membrane 352 torn in some places and in others adhering to the skin. Where that happens, none of the veins and small nerves under the skin can be found, and this especially in the ape. It is true that in such large beasts as horses, donkeys, mules, and cattle they do not wholly disappear, yet if the membrane be torn from the continuous tissue beneath, clear apprehension is no longer possible. In small animals, however, [the superficial veins and nerves] are completely destroyed if one of these accidents happens to the membrane [fascia].

Therefore when the whole arm has been bared of skin, leave the membrane still entire upon the underlying tissues. In this membrane, before it has time to dry, examine the surface veins and nerves. These do not show equally in all cases, either because they are naturally so small in some apes, as in some human beings, or again because the adiposity varies. In thin animals the nerves are more clearly visible; in the fat they are 353 concealed. When the ape is full-blooded, the superficial veins can be clearly seen; when bloodless, they are indistinct. Nevertheless, in all cases try to observe and remember the 'roots'[65] of the nerves on the surface and their course, so that in making an incision you cut along them. Thus the nerves severed will be few or none, but if you apply the lancet transversely you may divide many. Try especially to avoid 'roots', realizing that, as with a tree, in cutting a branch or twig, you harm the plant but little, while if you sever the crown of the root, you ruin the whole plant. So with the nerves. If you divide a 'root' the region which derived sensation from that nerve will be rendered insensitive.

If you remember the anatomy of the muscles as expounded in Book I, you will learn here, too, to find without difficulty the origins of the nerves distributed through the skin. But if you have forgotten, leave this present book for the nonce and return to Book I. As soon as you have a clear realization of the posi- *354* tion of the muscles, turn to what follows. Assuming that you will do this, I shall proceed.[66]

Chapter 3

[*Nerves in Upper Arm*]

In Book I the nature of the muscle that embraces the top of the *354* shoulder [*deltoid*] was explained to you. Of it Hippocrates wrote: 'As for the upper arm, were one to strip the shoulder of flesh, he would strip the area over which this muscle extends.'[67] I expect you to keep this muscle in mind with reference to the part, for there the shape of a [Greek letter] DELTA is produced, and some have called the muscle 'deltoid'. The part in question encircles the head of the humerus and this is the starting-point of the arm itself. The deltoid muscle, triangular in form, has its attachment at its apex to the humerus.

When you see clearly the apex of the triangle in the outer side of the arm, by raising your eyes you will see a number of little nerves, fine as hairs, springing from the depths [upper lateral *355* cutaneous branches of the *axillary* (*circumflex*)]. They are like twigs of a little bush, springing from one stem but at various angles. As some grow straight and others oblique, so is the course of such nerves from their origin, some passing along the limb, others to the sides. They reach beyond the middle of the upper arm. [These include brachiocutaneous branches of the *radial*.] The outer parts below are enmeshed with little nerves from another root which also rises up from the depths and is spread abroad, embracing the outer and lower nerves of the regions round the elbow-joint [lower lateral cutaneous and posterior lateral cutaneous branches of the *radial*].

For the most part, you must take for granted such subcutaneous nerves and small veins as I shall describe, because their continuity is not preserved. Further, their position, number, or calibre is not always exactly determinate as they are for 356 the larger vessels and nerves. Their origins, however, are always from the same vessels and nerve [trunks] as the two just described as 'like little bushes' [p. 65].

One of these [large] nerves [*axillary*] comes from that which is intertwined with the deltoid, the other [*radial*] from the largest of those that go to the upper arm. This [latter] twines round the muscles at the back [of the humerus] and passes to the outer side of the limb and reaches the lower arm by the higher of the processes of the humerus called KONDYLĒ [*lateral epicondyle*].

Of the [former] nerve [*axillary*] a small portion penetrates to the spot mentioned [i.e. outer side of upper arm], while the remainder of that which is distributed to the deltoid comes through entirely to the skin [as the *upper lateral cutaneous*]. These then [i.e. *axillary* and *radial*] are the two sources of the cutaneous nerves in the upper arm on the outer side.

The skin in front receives small nerves [*lower lateral cutaneous*] in its upper region from the first branch (EPIBASIS) of the second nerve [*radial*] that enters the upper arm from the spine, and, in the region below, in front of the elbow-joint, from 357 another nerve [*musculocutaneous*] of those from the spine which is alone from the beginning, of which more anon. But the skin of the upper arm within and behind, up to the ends of the shoulder-blade, is enmeshed with another nerve [*intercostobrachial* (*intercostohumeral*)] which emerges from the second intercostal space. This nerve also reaches the upper arm, like all the others, through the armpit. Whoever wishes to examine them exactly must first cut away the small muscle that was overlooked by anatomists [*pectoralis minor*, see pp. 122–3], for under it pass all the nerves assigned to that region [Fig. 23].

First on the surface, but under this muscle, lies the nerve [*intercostobrachial*] which I said emerges from the second inter-costal space. It divides completely into branches to the skin of the upper arm on the posterior and inner sides.

Next, deeper down, when glands, membranes, and vessels are removed, lies a succession of large nerves. A cutaneous nerve [*cutaneus brachii medialis*] descends on the upper arm to the spot where the head of the small muscle [*pectoralis minor*] lies in apes. It starts from the very large muscle there, *358* which moves the outer part of the armpit [*latissimus dorsi*], and it ends in the back region of the elbow, at the inner parts. Where it passes into the arm it is immediately divided into three; its higher branch twines round certain parts in the inside of the upper arm as far as the articulation behind; the next part round the whole back region of the skin; the third round all the continuous tissues up to the shoulder-blade. The skin of the upper arm then contains the starting-points of the nerve of which we have spoken. That of the lower arm I shall deal with shortly. If you first examine the nature of all the nerves in the upper arm, it will be much easier for you to dissect and learn about those in the forearm, not only on the surface but in the depths.

[Deep nerves of upper arm, Fig. 23.]

As the upper arm starts from the shoulder-joint, it is as well to sever it [there] and dissect it separately. Begin the operation at the humeral [*cephalic*] vein and the front muscle with two heads [*biceps*]. The latter, as you have learned [p. 28], arises from strong tendons and is inserted by an aponeurosis into the *359* beginning of the radius. Where the two heads are just uniting you will find the first nerve [*musculocutaneous*] passing along the humerus. At that spot the large muscle in the armpit at the back [*latissimus dorsi*] is attached to the humerus by a strong flat tendon. Next [to this tendon] there is attached to it [i.e. to the *humerus*] the tendon of the largest of the muscles from the breast [*pectoralis major*], being fleshier than the aforesaid muscle. Next to it again is the attachment of the muscle of the top of the shoulder, called DELTOEIDĒS.

[1. *Musculocutaneous nerve.*] The first nerve, then, that comes from the spine through the armpit to the upper arm, enters it at the attachment of the tendons of the posterior muscle of the axilla, the largest of those that move the shoulder-joint [*latissimus dorsi*]. Then at its entrance it passes under the anterior
360 muscle [*biceps*] of which the heads are here still separate. Passing under the inner head it gives a branch to each head. Thence it goes straight down, in contact with the fibres of the inner and more slender head which arises in a ligament from the anchor-shaped process [*coracoid*]. The heads coalesce and make a single united anterior muscle which, as you learned in Book I [p. 28], flexes the elbow-joint. You will see this tendon clearly if you cut both tendinous heads above and separate them to the straight part where they unite. With that part the nerve, too, travels down.

As you do this another muscle [*brachialis*] is exposed. It is much lower than the former [*biceps*] and rises only a short way on the humerus which is hidden by it. It hides also, as I said, the tendon of the first muscle [*deltoid*].

In their course the two tendons [of the *biceps*] send forth sometimes from one of them, sometimes from both, APONEURŌSEIS [sometimes a *lacertus fibrosus*] into the heads of the
361 smaller anterior muscles of the forearm. . . .

[2. *Axillary (circumflex) nerve.*] [The passage on this nerve is missing. Ten lines are substituted on the Median and Ulnar nerves, irrelevant here.] So now, leaving these nerves, go back to the beginning of the arm.

[3. *Radial nerve.*] After the two nerves I have spoken of there is a third, near the second. It makes a deeper penetration into the upper arm along with the great vessels, artery, and vein, which pass through the axilla. This nerve is split up along with the vessels to enter the large muscles of the upper arm [*triceps*, differently divided in ape and man] which extend the elbow-joint, and it gives branches to both, making its way slantwise to the outer region.

This [*radial nerve*] is the largest of the nerves entering the upper arm. (You hear anatomists habitually designating as 'large' a nerve, artery, or vein without indicating differences in length but only in circumference [misleadingly] as though they had used the term 'thickest'.) Where this nerve passes out round the humerus and through the region at the back and pushes beyond a little above the elbow-joint, a branch [is seen] to make its way out to the skin. Of this I have spoken already in the section on the cutaneous nerves of the arm [p. 66]. How the remainder of the third nerve [*radial*] reaches the forearm and how it there divides, you will learn later in the section on that part. *362*

[4. *Ulnar nerve.*] Most parts of the upper arm having now been laid bare, examine [one of] two nerves remaining on the inner side, where the aforementioned three entered [the armpit], a little deep to the third. This other is seen first of them all, even without the dissection of the muscles in the upper arm, being on the surface under the skin. I have already mentioned it in the anatomy of the superficial nerves [p. 65], and postponed explaining its complete distribution till I came to the anatomy of the lower arm. Yet this nerve begins its division in the upper arm above the elbow-joint [in the ape, with branch to *m. epitrochleoanconeus*] and is carried through practically the whole bend, already divided into many branches, for only the higher parts of the bend lack a branch from it, while the anterior superficial parts of the upper arm, above the elbow, receive their branches from this nerve. [Either the text is confused or Galen here describes an abnormality in which the *medial cutaneous* nerve arises from the trunk of the *ulnar*.] *363*

[5. *Median nerve.*] There remains a fifth nerve of those that come from the spine to the upper arm. Like the others, it passes through the inner side. This nerve gives no portion of itself to any part in the upper arm, either superficial or deep. In thickness it resembles the second [*axillary*] just as the first

[*musculocutaneous*] resembles the fourth [*ulnar*]. You will esti-mate the second and fifth [*axillary* and *median*] as about three
364 times as thick as the first and fourth [*musculocutaneous* and *ulnar*]. Thickest of all is the third [*radial*].

You remember that I said another nerve [*intercostobrachial*, p. 66] enters the skin of the upper arm, emerging through the second intercostal muscle. So that among the nerves from the spine to the arms there are two that divide as cutaneous branches only [the second being *cutaneus brachii et antibrachii medialis*], and five* distributed deep down to all the muscles of the limb, with a few delicate branches to the skin.

Chapter 4

[*Nerves to Forearm and Hand*]

364 Leaving the upper arm, pass now to the forearm. If you sepa-rate the skin from the membranous tissue, as I have said, you will see the first beginning of a nerve [*ulnar*]—fourth of those mentioned in the upper arm—which supplies most of the inner side of the forearm, extending to the lower part, and to much of the outer part [*medial cutaneous*, sometimes in the ape a branch of the *ulnar*]. That part of the forearm on the radial
365 side, both back and front, receives the branches from other nerves, anteriorly from that first mentioned [*musculocutaneous*], posteriorly from the third [*radial*]. (An account of the cutane-ous nerves in the hand will be added to the anatomy of the big muscles [of the forearm].)

You saw five nerves (i.e. 1, 3, 4, and 5, pp. 68–69 and *cutaneus brachii et antibrachii medialis*], in dissecting the upper arm, passing through the bend of the elbow into the forearm, but only one [the last named] is dispersed into the skin, being split above the bend at the elbow.

Four then remain. The first, of which I gave an account be-fore in the anatomy of the upper arm, reaches the middle of the

* Text says 'four'.

articulation at the elbow [*musculocutaneous*]. A second, which is lower, reaches the inner and lower condyle [*medial epicondyle*] of the humerus where it is at its flattest and least convex [*median*]. A third nerve [*radial*] which, I said, is above those that go to the whole arm, reaches the forearm touching the radius in association with the outer and upper condyle [*lateral epicondyle*] of the humerus. The remaining nerve [*ulnar*], the fourth of those that reach the forearm deep down, has its place between the point of the elbow and the inner and lower head *366* [*medial epicondyle*] of the humerus.

If you trace the natural attachments and positions of the muscles and dissect them as you learned in Book I, you will observe the distribution of them all [i.e. the nerves]. You may start from any of them, though it is perhaps best to keep the same order as was employed for the upper arm.

The nerve to the forearm through the middle of the bend at the elbow [*median*] produces there a very delicate branch [*ramus anastomoticus*]. This runs by the side of the vein [*v. medialis antibrachialis*] which extends along the approximate middle of the surface throughout the forearm, and meets at the wrist the artery with plainly visible pulsation [*a. radialis*]. And yet this nerve, which is the highest of all those mentioned, gives another very delicate branch to the head of the large muscle peculiar to the radius [*flexor carpi radialis*], and next to this branch another, carried along the remainder of the forearm* by the radius, very like a spider's web [*n. interosseus anterior*]. After passing underneath the vein—which is split off from the humeral [*cephalic*] and across which we cut—what is left of the nerve I am de- *367* scribing passes aslant† to the large muscle peculiar to the radius [*flexor carpi radialis*] and is carried out of the upper parts between the four already mentioned slender muscles [*flexores digitorum*]. . . .‡

* Text says 'shoulder'.

† Text adds 'gradually on the surface'.

‡ Here are eighteen lines, most of which fit neither human nor simian anatomy. They are, in any event, out of place.

368 Let us now speak of the outer nerve [*radial*] first, so as not to interrupt the exposition of the two remaining nerves, distributed through the anterior parts of the forearm and fingers. This nerve, after it has given off the branches in the upper arm [to the *triceps*] of which I spoke earlier, is carried down towards the elbow-joint between the smaller of the anterior muscles in the upper arm [*caput medialis tricipitis*] and the head of the large muscle peculiar to the radius [*flexor carpi radialis*]. It sends its first branch into the outer parts of the forearm, and it is distributed on the surface under the skin there [*n. cutaneus antibrachii dorsalis*] and in the wrist. And it yields other branches as it passes through the articulation at the wrist, and yet others again where it enters at its head the muscle that extends the wrist by the bifurcate tendon [i.e. the tendons of the *extensores carpi radiales longus et brevis*]. One of these is split into the head 369 of this muscle, the other goes forward undivided. . . .* Its end passes through to the wrist in line with the bigger fingers, being split up on the dorsum to enter them under the skin. It spreads through two fingers and half of the middle finger, sometimes uniting at the end of the radius with a small branch of the above-mentioned nerve which extends to it.

The rest of the third nerve [*radial*] inclines towards the outer region of the forearm. It is carried aslant through the depths, first to the bifurcate muscle of the wrist [i.e. the tendons of the two *extensores carpi radiales*] into which, I said, it enters at its origin, before producing the aforesaid branch. It is then through the muscles of the radius verging on the outside of the elbow [*brachioradialis* and the two *extensores carpi radiales*]. It gives certain fine branches to both and to the muscle extending the four 370 fingers [*extensor digitorum communis*] and after that to the muscle that initiates the oblique motion in the lesser fingers [*extensores digitorum proprii*], and then in its turn to the muscle that bends back the wrist at the little finger [*extensor carpi ulnaris*]. It produces all these branches at the origin of the aforesaid muscles, not far from the [elbow] joint. Thence it is carried along the

* Six lines here are anatomically unintelligible and are omitted.

bipartite muscle which moves the thumb and the wrist [i.e. the two *extensores carpi radiales*] and gives manifest branches to it also. In the course of this journey, the tendon of the muscle that gives the thumb its lateral motion [*abductor pollicis longus*] lies very close to it for some distance as far as the wrist. Next it has for neighbour the muscle that moves index and middle fingers in the same fashion. What remains of this nerve is distributed to the articulation without reaching the fingers. The largest of the terminal branches enters the depths of that region where lies, I said, the ligament that hides the origin of the tendons extending the four fingers.

This then is the mode of dispersal of the nerve by the outer *371* condyle [*lateral epicondyle*] that reaches the forearm from above. It was, we remember, the third of the nerves from the axilla to the arm.

The remaining two nerves [*ulnar* and *median*] are distributed to all the muscles on the front of the forearm. In dissecting these [muscles], as you learned in Book I, you will follow up the course of all the nerves that enter them, starting at the elbow-joint. You will find branches going from both nerves into the flexors of the fingers, and indeed into all the other muscles except that which was said to be the second to go to the upper arm [*axillary*]. The fourth of the nerves which, I said, runs between the point of the elbow and the lower condyle [*medial epicondyle*] of the upper arm into the lower arm [*ulnar*], gives a certain portion of itself to the muscle that bends the wrist at the little finger [*flexor carpi ulnaris*]. You will find the remaining nerve [*median*] giving a portion of itself to the muscle that moves the radius there [*pronator teres*] and then, as it advances, a part also to the higher of the muscles flexing the wrist [*flexor carpi radialis*] and to that which passes into the *372* palmar fascia [*palmaris longus*], and a delicate part deep down to the small muscle in the radius there [*pronator quadratus*.]

The two large nerves [*median* and *ulnar*] take their course through the forearm between the muscles that flex the fingers [*flexores digitorum sublimis et profundus*], resting on one and lying under the other, and they give of their substance to both [untrue of *ulnar*]. When these muscles end in the tendons, the remainder of each of the nerves reaches the wrist and metacarpus, being dispersed through the tissues there and the inside parts of the fingers, the higher [*median*] to the two big fingers and the half of the middle finger on the side next the index, the rest to the middle finger and the remaining little finger. 373 The higher of the nerves is expended there. The lower [*ulnar*] sends a considerable part into the outside of the hand on the surface under the skin, reaching the finger-tips of the inner two and a half fingers. The remaining half of it with the thumb receives the whole end of the nerve I mentioned [*radial*]. There is no muscle on the dorsal aspect of the hand as there is on the palmar side.

Chapter 5

[*Veins of Axilla and Arm*]

373 A single artery but two veins enter the arm. One of these veins is obvious even before dissection, for it lies on the surface, between the skin and the underlying muscles. Of these [muscles] one arises from the acromion, becoming triangular there [*deltoid*]. The other forms the fleshy part of the breast [*pectoralis major*]. Both are inserted by strong aponeuroses along the front of the humerus, not far from the shoulder-joint [Fig. 9].

The 'shoulder vein' [*cephalic*] then lies on the surface between these two [muscles], along the inside edge of the deltoid, and reaches the end [of the muscle]. Thence it is carried down in 374 the outer region of the upper arm, in contact with the larger of the anterior muscles [*biceps*] along the line that bounds it laterally. When near the elbow it separates from this muscle and mounts on the large muscle at the bend of the radius [*brachioradialis*]. There it splits into three parts, roughly equal. One plunges into the depths: observe the position and course of this in examining the surface veins. The second [*median basilic*] reaches the bend of the joint uniting to a part of another vein [*basilic*] that is carried into the forearm. The third and last inclines towards the outer region of the forearm and divides there.[68]

Before it splits into three at the elbow, the large 'shoulder-vein' [*cephalic*] can be clearly seen next the skin throughout the upper arm, nowhere sinking in the depths but outstanding and conspicuous, particularly in athletes who are naturally thin *375* and muscular. Throughout the upper arm it distributes delicate branches into the skin and superficial muscles. This you will see in dissecting large, full-blooded apes, and other creatures of the six different kinds of four-footed creatures of which you learned [p. 97].[69] When it mounts on the muscle of the radius [*brachioradialis*] at the elbow-joint, the three divisions into which it is split are sometimes equal, sometimes unequal; sometimes one is larger, sometimes another, but none ever greatly exceeding the others.

The branch [of the *cephalic vein*] to the outer region of the forearm gives off branches that are more clearly visible than those in the upper arm, and it is entirely consumed [in the forearm in] anastomosing with other veins to be described. Whence they come, you will now learn.

The vein which traverses the axilla [*axillary*], which is much larger than the 'shoulder vein' [*cephalic*], together with the corresponding artery divides into branches all along the arm.

These two vessels [vein and artery] are in contact through *376* the armpit into the upper arm, and the nerves and the branches into each muscle are united with them by a single natural outgrowth [*axillary sheath*]. When they have passed through the upper arm, coursing along the larger of the anterior muscles [*biceps*], the artery goes on to the muscles in the forearm, passing now into the depths as it was at the start. The vein, however, divides into two near the joint. One branch goes deep with the artery and divides [into *venae comitantes*] throughout with the artery. The other [*basilic*] runs obliquely down subcutaneously. It is plainly seen in thin people and those with large veins. You will see it more clearly if you constrict the arm with a bandage.

The first branch of this vein [*basilic*] is seen running down aslant to the bone [*ulna*] of the forearm. It courses between the inner condyle [*medial epicondyle*] of the humerus and the bend

377 at the elbow but, mounting on the forearm [below], it goes forward with it to its end. The second branch arising with it runs above the forearm for a little but at once divides. Of the branches the lower reaches the [*cephalic*] vein, which I said runs along the bone of the lower arm. The higher, often passing outside, sometimes comes to the same vein in the forearm and, reaching it, is consumed by final division into branches. The vessel stretched along the forearm reaches its end with certain branches extending to the lower region of the wrist, sometimes visibly, sometimes indistinctly.

[Here follow five pages of very elaborate description of the veins of the forearm and hand. Since these are, in fact, highly variable, and since their variations are without significance, the translation of these pages would be unprofitable.][70]

383 All these veins [in the lower arm] can be seen clearly even before dissection in many men who are both thin and full-blooded, and have large veins, but the surrounding air should

384 be warm or the man have just had a bath. You must compress the part with your hand where you wish the full veins to be clearly seen. You should do this often and in many subjects. Its usefulness is considerable, and that for two reasons: first, for the knowledge of the vessels themselves, for no phenomenon is accurately and quickly recognized unless often seen.[70] (This is proved by [identical] twins for they are indistinguishable to strangers but are easily distinguished by intimates.) And secondly, to convince yourselves of the close similarity of the bodily parts of men to those of apes.[71]

All these veins that you see in man without dissection, you will see in the ape during dissection. Clearly then these animals are like men in respect of the deep veins as well. I want you

385 to have frequent practice on them, so that if you have the

luck to dissect a human body, you will be able readily to lay bare each of the parts.[72] This is not everybody's luck, and it cannot be achieved at short notice by one unskilled in the work. Even the greatest experts in anatomy among the physicians, and even when examining the parts of the body at leisure, have obviously made many mistakes. For such a reason even those who sought to dissect the body of a German enemy, who had been killed in the war against Marcus Antoninus, could learn no more than the position of the viscera. But one who has practised beforehand on animals, and especially on apes, lays bare with the utmost ease each of the parts for dissection. It is easier for a careful man, previously practised in dissections, to gather something quickly from examination of a human body, than it is for one who is inexpert to discover the obvious even at his leisure.[72]

For men have often rapidly observed whatever they wished in bodies of men condemned to death and thrown to wild beasts, or in brigands lying unburied on a hillside. Again, extensive *386* wounds and ulcers, reaching deep down, have exposed many parts which were recognized by the experienced as having the same structure as in the bodies of apes, and yet they were of no service to the inexperienced [see p. 4]. By constantly dissecting bodies of exposed infants,* they were persuaded that man has the same bodily structure as an ape. In the course of various surgical operations that we perform, sometimes removing mortified flesh, sometimes cutting out bones, the likeness becomes apparent to the practised eye. But some are so careless of the highest standards that they will not learn, even what can be ascertained precisely, before dissection.

Chapter 6

[*Venesection*]

What I have just said [in Chapter 5] as to the veins in the *386* lower arm and hand can all be ascertained in man before dissec-

* Literally 'By frequently dissecting many bodies of exposed children'.

tion* in many cases. Thus, for example, after the dichotomy of the vein through the axilla to the front of the elbow-joint, the [branch] vein that reaches the bend has an artery lying under 387 it for some distance. This, in thin subjects with strong pulses, you can recognize by touch and by its movement. If therefore you let blood in one in whom this vein is clearly visible, you must keep well away from the artery. And where only the part resting on the artery is visible and the rest is out of sight, you must be particularly careful.[73]

First [observe that] when you bind the arm, the place round the artery swells into a sizable lump; secondly, cut one of the other veins which I shall mention and never this one when this area is distended, knowing that so broad and strong an artery underlies it. When it is swollen to the fullest extent, raise and stretch round it the vein that rests on it. Thus the artery becomes emptier, where the vein is stretched round, so that if one apply the lancet with the usual degree of force employed in pressing it down and lifting it [as in venesection], it would quickly pass through [the vein] and pierce the underlying artery. Therefore 388 it is best to discard this [vessel] and pass to a neighbouring vein, particularly one of those running down towards the ulna.

If none of these be visible, then pass to the vessel [*median basilic*] that arises from the venous junction in the bend of the elbow which, I said, extends to the top of the radius. If not even that is visible, [pass] to the vein [*median cephalic*] which comes to the bend at the elbow from the 'shoulder vein', and if it be not visible and if blood needs to be let from it, the vein that comes to the bend from it must necessarily be cut instead. If not even that be visible, [choose] the vein that stretches up aslant to the radius; if not even that, the vein from the armpit 389 running into the bend at the elbow [*basilic*]. This last vein is most useful for disease of the parts below the collar-bone, the 'shoulder-vein' [*cephalic*] for parts above.[74] But they have the second and third place after those I mentioned. Since the vein that runs up to the top of the radius [*median*] is common to

* PRO TĒS ANATOMĒS.

both, I give it the third place in both limbs. The first and second places are taken by the right and left median.* I have now said all that is to be said about the superficial veins throughout the lower arm to the fingers. 389

Chapter 7

[*Deep Veins of Forearm*]

Now investigate the deep veins, after removing the superficial veins at the bend [of the elbow]. When these are gone and the muscles dissected, as you learned, you will see the deep veins conjoining like the superficial. Moreover, after their meeting they separate again and run as a pair through the lower arm to the wrist, parallel with one another. The lower one runs along the ulna, the higher along the radius, accompanied by the arteries supplying branches to the muscles. 389 390

A certain portion of the lower [*ulnar*] vein, when it reaches the small muscle of the radius [*pronator quadratus*] emerges on the inner† side where, dividing, it unites with the superficial veins there. Moreover, the part of it which remains deep joins deep branches of the superficial veins on the inner side of the ulna.‡

I said that two [superficial] veins run into the arm, one through the armpit, considerable enough in size [*basilic*], and the one much smaller, yet itself large, which they call 'shoulder vein' [*cephalic*].

Chapter 8§

[*Deep Arteries and Veins of Arm*]

A single artery [*axillary*] reaches the arm with the vein that goes through the armpit [*basilic*]. Both emerge from the chest 391

* Ten repetitive lines here follow.

† Text says 'outer'.

‡ Here a brief repetition is omitted.

§ It would seem that Chapters 7 and 8 should be united. The first sentence of Chapter 8 repeats the last of 7.

along with the ninth pair of nerves from the spine [T.1 contributing to lower trunk of brachial plexus, Fig. 23]. They enter the upper arm where they are reached by the third nerve [*radial*]. From there, giving important branches to all the muscles of the upper arm, they [i.e. *brachial artery* and *vein*] are carried straight down to the bend of the elbow. The vein, however, at the end of the upper arm, divides in two. One part goes to the skin but the deep part is carried to the bend with the artery, taking with it in addition a third part of the 'shoulder-vein'. Then, dividing in two with the artery which is similarly divided [into *radial* and *ulnar*], it is carried along and distributed, thus divided, to all the muscles up to the beginning of the fingers.

In feeling the pulse by the wrist joint, we touch the higher *392* artery by the radius. In thin people the artery between index and thumb [*arteria metacarpalis dorsalis*], which has its origin from that [in which the pulse is felt], can be seen moving too. The movement of the lower artery [*ulnar*] which runs along the bone of the forearm towards the little finger, cannot be distinguished clearly unless the man is quite thin and has a strong pulse. For Nature keeps the arteries down, nowhere bringing a branch conspicuously to the surface, which, as I indicated earlier, is the case with veins and nerves. Thus it is not remarkable that you cannot find any artery on the back of the finger-ends, for there is none at all there. But the front [of the hand] since it has many muscles, has also many arteries, [some] reaching each of the fingers.

You will see all the arteries at the wrist, with their companion veins that come from the inside parts, when you have cut away the broad tendon [*palmar fascia*]. For their position is between this tendon and the tendons bending the fingers, along with the *393* delicate nerve that I mentioned before. . . .*

I have now described all the [vascular] structures of the arm.

* Here five lines of obscure meaning and construction.

Chapter 9

[*On the Care needed in investigating Nerves and Vessels*]

You must not read of each of the phenomena that you observe *393* as you would read the *Historiae* of Herodotus, for mere enjoyment's sake, but you must store them in your memory so that you may know precisely the nature of all the parts of the arm.

Some parts have neither artery nor nerve, nor large vein, while some have one, two, or all three. Potency in arteries and veins is proportionate to size, but not so for the nerves, for in some parts a small nerve has great power, for example, those dispersed through the muscles that move the thumb and, next to them, those that move the index. For if they alone were preserved in their natural state, while the others [in the hand] *394* were paralysed or quite destroyed, the man would not be maimed in the full sense, or his hand entirely useless. If the middle finger be added to these, there will be little wanting to the functions of the hand, even though the small fingers be destroyed. But if, while the four remain in a healthy state, something were to happen to the muscles that either flex or extend the thumb, all functions of the hand would go, for the activities of muscular opponents are always vitiated together. When the muscles that extend the thumb are detached, the muscle the natural function of which is to flex it, having done its job for the nonce, flexes it [for good]. Later it will not be able to do so, for it is impossible again to contract a muscle that remains contracted, unless it be first extended.

Therefore make yourself thoroughly acquainted with the nerve of each muscle and especially of those having an important function. Thus if it be necessary to remove a missile or splinter by cutting through or round a structure, or again, if we are to excise some putrified part or gangrenous bone, let us spare the important vessels and nerves. *395*

I know of a slapdash practitioner who in one case excised a large part of the muscle in the outer region of the upper arm, without greatly harming the limb. But he later applied the lancet freely to that region inside the anterior muscle where the fifth* nerve [*median*] mounts on it. In the phrase of Hippocrates, he was 'expert with a foolish facility'.[75] With one swift circular cut, he not only severed the third nerve [*radial*] but the two in the front of it [*ulnar* and *median*] and, in addition, the [*brachial*] artery and vein, for all these lie there together. Dismayed for the moment by the haemorrhage, he attended only to that, putting ligatures round the severed vessels. A little later, however, the patient was unable to move any part of his hand and had no sense of touch over most of the limb. He shouted at the physician, these very words, 'You have cut my poor nerves'.

396 This healer had indeed made the whole limb useless with one incision. Others have done the same to other parts of the arm and leg from ignorance of the nerves. I pass by, for the present, all the mischief they have done in blood-letting, by [their] failing to understand the parts to be watched in each of the veins at the elbow, of which I have spoken also in my book *De mortuorum dissectione*.[7]

For all these reasons you should dissect the arm of an ape frequently. If you observe something unusual in it, this too may be of use to you. Thus in dissecting an ape I once observed a little nerve [*cutaneus antibrachii medialis*] resting on the vein at the elbow. The observation of these things has proved useful in the case of certain well-known physicians who were blamed for having severed a vein, since immediately after the incision a numbness along the hand was sensed and this affection ever after remained. But I made clear to these critics that such an idiosyncrasy in the bodily frame was sometimes found, and *397* thus freed the physicians from censure. I persuaded those who were accusing the physicians not only by calling on others as witnesses for their testimony, but also by pointing to a record of the phenomenon in the vein I have just described, in the anatomical notes I had taken of each subject dissected. . . .†

* Text reads 'third'.

† Here ten irrelevant lines on the superficial nerves of the arm.

Chapter 10

[*Nerves in the Thigh, Fig. 24**]

The dissections that I have explained having been successfully *397* performed on the arm [we turn to the leg]. Four cutaneous *398* nerves will be seen at the beginning of the thigh. They are equal in number to the large nerves to the muscles, for they descend from them.

[*a*] One runs down from above, from the anterior muscles to the whole skin surrounding them and is distributed there [*cutaneus femoris lateralis* (L.3 and L.4)].

[*b*] Medial to it lies a nerve that passes through the groin [*n. femoralis, rami cutanei anteriores*] on to the large, narrow muscle [*sartorius*].

[*c*] The third [*cutaneus femoris posterior*] near the KOKKYX, as it is called, is more difficult to examine than the afore-mentioned.

[*d*] The fourth [*genitofemoral*], which is even harder to examine than the third, is at the perforation of the pubic bone by the groin.

There are very small nerves like spiders' webs passing out to the skin, some stouter than these and some like strong hairs, and yet others thicker with the 'roots'[65] quite clearly visible. Those stretched on the anterior muscles [group *a* above] with a strong membrane over them are seen to arise at the mid-front region when the surrounding skin is scraped off. Those that pass through the groin [group *b* above] on to the delicate and narrow muscle [*gracilis*] cohere and twine round the inner *399* region of the thigh and leg. They run along with the [*saphenous*] vein as far as the inside attachment of the astragalus [*n. saphenus*]. From the nerve which passes out near the coccyx [group *c* above] almost the whole of the back and outside part of the thigh receive the branches. The end [of the thigh] at the knee is excepted, for there another nerve [*cutaneus surae lateralis*]

* The nerves (Fig. 24) of the lumbo-sacral plexus are different in ape and man.

passes out by the broad muscle [*biceps femoris*]. So at its end a single small part, as I have said, of the nerve, passing out through the perforation of the pubic bone [group *d* above], twines round the rest of the inner region of the thigh.* Additional nerves twine round the outside parts of the thigh [*cutaneus surae lateralis*], because the inside receives branches from the nerve [*saphenous*] that runs along the [*femoral*] vein.

The remaining part of the back of the leg has a nerve of its own [a branch of *cutaneus surae lateralis*], split off from that which twines round the calf. The front part receives a portion of the nerve that twines round the anterior muscles of the leg.

400 When you have examined the small cutaneous nerves, dissect all the muscles round the hip, as you learned in Book II [p. 43]. When they are separated from one another, the branches of the large nerves are seen clearly. They run, as all these nerves do, between the muscles, giving their branches to them. You will see four origins, as you did for the cutaneous nerves which are branches from the deep nerves and, being so soon observed, will lead you to discern the larger nerves. But, even apart from the surface nerves [acting as guides to them], the origins of the large nerves are readily discovered when the muscles are being dissected.

There are three origins of [large] nerves of comparable size which I shall mention first, and there is yet a fourth, the largest, which is bifurcate, of which I shall speak later.[76]

Of the three nerve-stems [of comparable size], one [*n. femoralis*] is divided up for the anterior [flexor] muscles only.

The second [*nn. flexores femoris* peculiar to ape and innervating hamstrings] runs along the large vessels, giving fine web-like branches to them and to the adjoining muscle. It is in *401* contact beneath with the largest muscle of the thigh [*adductor magnus*] and above with the delicate narrow muscle [*sartorius*] which we dissect first among the muscles of the thigh.[77]

The third and last nerve stem [*obturator*] passes out through the large perforation of the pubic bone and through the two

* I have rectified some disarrangement of the text in the above paragraph.

small muscles that occupy it, one outside and the other inside [*obturatores externus et internus*]. These [last] among the muscles moving the hip-joint have been overlooked by the anatomists, as you learned. This nerve is divided in two before it traverses the muscles. One of its parts, running up higher, is dispersed through the muscle that springs from the pubic bone [*gracilis*] which was the second that you learned to dissect. The larger and lower, passing out through the perforation and the small muscles beside it, splits up to enter the biggest muscle of the thigh [adductor mass] and sends out some very delicate offshoots from itself to the small muscles lying beside it [*gracilis*].

When you have examined these three nerve origins, pass to the fourth [*sciatic*], which belongs to two large nerves [*tibialis* and *peroneus communis*] running down to the leg and dividing into branches to the tips of the toes. This will be in plain view 402 when the buttock muscles have been dissected. With these you were made familiar in Book II in the anatomy of the muscles of the hip-joint.

Along with these let there be dissected the heads of the three* muscles round the hip which I described as arising from the ilium [the *glutei*, pp. 45–46]. The large nerves [*ischiadic*] are visible lying under them, passing out from the inner parts of the sacrum, along with the delicate little nerves that spring from it. These [latter] are dispersed through all the muscles round the articulation on the outside [*piriformis*, *gemelli*, *iliacus*, *psoas major*, and *psoas minor*] and the first muscle of all on the surface which draws the articulation backwards [*gluteus maximus*], the yet larger fleshy muscle beneath it [*gluteus medius*][78] and the small ones underneath that. One of these springs from the bone of the ilium [*gluteus minimus*]; another [*piriformis*], which is always of a dark colour, from the sacrum; and a third goes from the pubic bone to the large trochanter of the femur [*obturator internus*].

The delicate nerves are used up in entering these muscles, and sometimes give branches to heads of the aforementioned 403

* Text says 'four'.

muscles. But after that, only the largest nerves are seen coursing through the back of the thigh, giving a very large branch to the broad muscle [*gluteus maximus*] and one, plainly visible, to the other three [*glutei medius et minimus* and *piriformis*] and sometimes to the largest muscle at the thigh [adductor mass, wrongly]. The broad muscle [*gluteus maximus*] receives a nerve above at the head like the others, and also another after that, but the great nerve [*ischiadus* = *tibialis* plus *peroneus communis*] pursues its course [unbranched] through the middle of the thigh. From this [united] nerve issue those that pass through to the skin as I said earlier [p. 84]. Such are the nerves in the thigh.

Chapter 11

[*Nerves of Leg and Foot*]

403 Consider now the nerves in the leg. Only two large nerves enter the leg. These are plainly visible at the back of the thigh, as I have said, when the broad muscle [*gluteus maximus*] was dissected [p. 85]. One enters it; the other [*ischiadus*] is prolonged very far. The latter nerve* comes in close contact with the knee-joint and passes back to the inner side of the leg.

404 It reaches the beginning of the leg, and there the nerves [*tibialis* and *peroneus communis*] first separate, the smaller [*peroneus communis*] to the outer muscles, the larger [*tibialis*] to the inner. The outer and smaller nerve passes to the leg under the very head of the fibula. The inner and larger nerve plunges at the top of the calf between the heads of the twin muscles [*gastrocnemius*] which, as you learned in Book II [pp. 40–41], spring from the femur. A large remainder of this nerve passes to the under parts of the foot. Delicate ends belonging to the other nerve [*peroneus*] are distributed to the upper parts of the tarsus. A certain portion of it [*ramus anastomoticus*, absent in man] reaches the other nerve that runs through the calf [*tibialis posticus*] near the lower end of the tibia.

* Text reads 'muscle'.

A single large nerve [*plantaris*, double in man] reaches the underside of the foot and is distributed through its parts. This is a remnant of the large nerve which is distributed to the back muscles of the leg [*tibialis*]. It descends to the underside of the foot along with the tendons flexing the toes. It was remarked that a part of the anterior [*peroneus*] nerve is fused with this nerve, for small nerves from it reach the upper parts of the foot. *405*

The remains of three small nerves [reach the foot]. One runs alongside the vein at the inside parts of the leg [*n. saphenus*]. The second [*suralis*] runs on the surface at the back of the calf, which I just mentioned as entering the calf between the [paired] muscle from the femur [*cutaneus surae medialis*]. A third small nerve [*cutaneus femoralis posterior*] springs from the large main nerve [*ischiadus*, wrongly] itself, which, running down the calf by the muscle along the fibula, reaches ultimately to the foot, being distributed to the outer tarsus by the lesser toes, just as the aforesaid nerve, which I said runs along with the vein through the whole limb, stretches out its ends to the greater toes.

Between these are other remains of each of two big nerves [*ramus superficialis* of *n. peroneus* and *ramus plantaris* of *n. tibialis*] which, I said, twine round the anterior muscles of the leg. These reach the middle parts of the tarsus. One is on the surface just under the skin, on the ligament at the tarsal joint, dispersed through the parts by the skin of the tarsus alone. That set deep under the ligament [*medial* and *lateral plantar branches* of *n. tibialis*] is distributed to all the muscles on the tarsus the tendons of which, as you learned, initiate the oblique movement of the toes [p. 49]. *406*

Chapter 12

[*The Two Veins of the Leg*]

A small vein from the pubes reaches the leg, nourishing a small part of it. I shall speak of it later. Another vein, a very large one, is distributed through the entire limb, running from the *406* inner part of the groin. Certain irregular branches from it pass to the skin. Such veins some physicians call SPORADIKAI. Those distributed through the muscles have a [more] fixed origin and position, but as in the arm they are not always of equal size.

I shall now mention all the branches usually visible of the 407 large vein, which is the main source of all those in the limb. At its origin a branch on the surface under the skin runs into the front and inner surface of the thigh, dispersed in various patterns. Next, three or four other delicate sporadic branches are distributed through the skin. At the middle of the thigh another important one, like the first, shows itself beside the narrow muscle [*sartorius*] wherein a vein is rooted. There are two or three other small sporadic branches. Next there is a branch of considerable size on the inner side of the knee, and next another which is bifurcate, and after it several others of like nature. All these are superficial but certain others correspond to them in the depths.

The first [deep] vein after the groin is distributed to the two anterior muscles [*vastus lateralis* and *vastus intermedius*]. After it is another deeper and rather large branch, between the largest muscle of all [*adductor magnus*] and the inner of the anterior muscles [*vastus medialis*]. From it many veins go to almost all 408 the muscles round the thigh. Next comes the vein that I said is dispersed under the skin and after it another, also from the great one to the anterior muscles [*quadriceps*], passing through the depths to the outer region of the thigh. After it comes another considerable branch, which passes rather deeper down to the largest muscle [adductor mass] and those lying beside it *semimembranosus* and *semitendinosus*]. After these there is that mentioned before in the enumeration of the superficial branches, which passes by the inner side of the knee to the end of the leg, being divided freely in the skin [*internal saphenous*]. Near this branch you will see others from the large vein dividing up into the lower parts of the largest muscle [*adductor magnus*] and through the whole articulation to some depth.

Sometimes the large vein [*femoral*] divides at once, sometimes division does not take place until the beginning of the calf, when a vein [*short saphenous*] passes round through the under parts of the joint to the outer region. There beside the fibula it becomes bifurcate. One part of it divides up on the surface in the inner parts of the fibula to the ankle. The other part, carried through the depths of the outside muscle [*companion vein of peroneal artery*], gives branches to each, and passes through between tibia and fibula near the lower end, so that the convex end of the tibia* is embraced by the end of this and by the end of the superficial vein. *409*

Sometimes when the large vein divides in the ham, this vein arises from the other one of the parts. But however it divides and whatever its condition, the large vein is divided at the ham and with one part passing through the calf reaches the end of the tibia at the ankle, and thence passes to the sole between tibia and fibula there. The other part passes to the shin and divides into several veins, all running in the front part between tibia and fibula, their ends going as far as the tarsus, the foot, and the toes, joining with one another and the veins lying beside. . . .† *410*

Chapter 13

[*Arteries of Lower Limb*]

The largest artery [*femoral*] coming through the groin passes into the thigh at the same spot as the large vein. In thin subjects with a strong pulse you will find its movement perceptible to the touch there. Both vessels run through the inner region of the thigh, covered by‡ the narrow muscle along the thigh [*sartorius*]. Into it, as into all the others round the thigh, pass branches of the artery proportionate in size [Fig. 18]. *410*

* Text says 'fibula'.

† Here for two and a half pages Galen sets forth an elaborate plan of the superficial veins, which hardly accords with anatomical facts and is devoid of interest for the modern reader. I omit them.

‡ Text says 'lying on'.

As in the upper limb, so in the lower, veins go along with the arteries that pass into the muscle. Yet arteries do not accompany the superficial veins, but always come through the depths to the muscles. Every vein in the thigh and along the leg, that 413 I said divides deep down to enter a muscle, has an artery lying beside it, but not so any of the superficial veins. This is clear from the fact that in well-covered persons the pulse is never perceptible in the leg unless at the tarsus in a line with the second toe. We often feel the artery lying there, when we cannot feel that in the wrist.

There are other arteries in tarsus and foot, which often show the pulse in thin subjects, when one is swollen to its full extent. At the wrist on the outside [that is on the dorsum] I said that no artery is found, because there is no muscle there. It is for the small muscles on the dorsum of the tarsus [*extensor digitorum brevis*] that the artery I mentioned just now is distributed there, just as it is for the muscles under the foot that a small artery [*plantaris lateralis*] accompanies the aforementioned vein, and reaches this spot. They move down into it through the space between fibula and calcaneum.

As to the artery [*a. obturatoria*] passing into the thigh through 414 the perforation in the pubic bone which they call THYROEIDĒS [THYRA, hole, door, gate], you may assume that all I said a little earlier about the vein is said of it, for it is disbuted to the same three muscles as the vein.

BOOK IV

[*Muscles of Face, Head, Neck, and Shoulders*]

Chapter 1

[*Function and Order of Anatomical Works*]

In the *De usu partium* my aim was to explain the structure of all 415 the human organs, so far as it concerns the Art. I followed this principle with the best of the older physicians and philosophers. Therefore I began with the hands because these are possessed only by human beings. The legs naturally came next, 416 since in them also man has something that animals lack, for he alone walks quite upright on them.[79] It was shown that the ape is a ridiculous imitation of man, walking like one, and yet defectively in most important ways and falling short of straightness in the structure of the legs. So, too, the thumb, which controls the action of the human hand, is incomplete in the paw of the ape.

In the present work, my aim is twofold; first that each bodily part, the actions of which I explained in the former work, may be accurately observed; and second to promote the proper end of the Art. For since I see contemporary Physicians, reputed serious students of anatomy, making little of the more useful part of it and cultivating the more pretentious, I sought first to demonstrate this to the young and to encourage them to pursue the more useful. This I have done in the beginning of Books II and III. The recapitulation there of the [contents of the] treatise 417 [*De usu partium*] included practically all the customary dissections of the limbs and superficial parts of the body, as to muscles, vessels, and nerves. For it is from them, and not from liver, heart, or lung, that we extract missiles and splinters and it is in them that we treat fistulous ulcers, derangements of the humours, suppurations, and septic infections.

I wished both my works to be arranged alike throughout, as [they are] in the first two books. But I observe that the enthusiasm for the less valuable part of anatomy daily increases, while almost everyone neglects the more useful part. Therefore I decided to encourage the young to study what is more urgently necessary and that not by argument only, but by the scheme of instruction. What I want them to learn first, I set down first in this discourse. Therefore, after the account of the limbs in the previous [three] books, in the two that follow I set down the superficial anatomy of the whole body, in so far as it refers to muscles, beginning from the face and head.

418 Among those muscles that are united with the surrounding skin of which the anatomists overlooked the most important element, are the two broad and delicate muscles ending in the jaws and lips and arising from the cervical spinous processes [*platysma myoides*]. From these there springs a membranous ligament with the fibrous strands common to all muscles but which links the substance of the two muscles [of the two sides]. Many fibrous strands also pass up from the spine of the scapula as they do from the clavicles, and end in the face [Figs. 11, 12].

These muscles must be severed in due course in accordance with the nature of their fibres. Those ignorant of them, when they cut at large across them, dividing the fibres, cause the mouth to be drawn to the opposite side. These cases have been overlooked by all, and I shall say a little about them later, but those interested in practical anatomy have recognized the muscular substance under the skin of the forehead [*occipito-frontalis*] and its action. *419* They state that the brow region is drawn up by it, and that the skin on the forehead derives its motion from it. Yet most surgeons do not know this, and ignorantly incise the forehead transversely rather than vertically. The result is that they make too large an incision there, particularly near the eybrows, and the skin continuous with them is drawn down to the eyelids and weighs down the eyes by resting on them so that they do not open properly, and their activity is thus impaired. As the direction of the fibres is downwards from above, so is it with the muscles moving the jaws.

Is it not then disgraceful that people ignorant of many such facts should [idly] inquire if there be not some cartilaginous or bony element in the pineal gland? or if it be possible to find a cartilage or bone in every heart or only in a large one? Such questions I see engage the attention of present-day physicians more than do useful problems. For these reasons I resolved to add other two books to the anatomy of the limbs—thus making a quarter of the whole work—and then a fifth [book] after that. When the whole anatomy of the muscles has been fully discussed in them, I shall return to the order followed in the *De usu partium*.[10] That is I shall speak first of the organs of assimilation, then of those of respiration, then of the parts in the brain and spinal marrow, then of the reproductive organs, and lastly of investigation on the foetus. *420*

Book XVI in the *De usu partium* is on arteries, veins, and nerves. I explained there what is common to all and useful to be known about these, whereas what is the nature of each is expounded in this present work *De anatomicis administrationibus*. For this reason I must now treat of them very exactly, for many details were omitted in my earlier work *De anatomicis administrationibus libri duo*.[1] Why it seems to me better to give an account of arteries, veins, and nerves at the end of each treatise I shall explain in that book where I describe the procedures by the good use of which one may gain experience. *421*

Chapter 2

[*The Five Kinds of Muscles of the Mouth*]

Now we must proceed to the anatomy of the muscles. First as to those that move the mouth (GNATHOI) with the lips, the jaw being unmoved. It is possible to clench the teeth and draw the corner of the mouth towards either side of the neck. In this *421* action the skin is stretched toward the junction of acromion and clavicle. These muscles [*platysma*] can open the mouth on either side towards the neck, just as other muscles called MASSĒTĒRES ('masticators'), attached on the flat surface of the lower jaw [*ramus*], move it round either way. The tem-

422 poral muscles [on the other hand] do not swing the jaw. Their natural function is to draw it up in biting on anything or in nibbling or in shutting the mouth. It is these muscles that Hippocrates calls MASSĒTĒRES[80] but I shall always call them 'temporal' (KROTAPHITAI) to avoid two meanings of one word. I shall call MASSĒTĒRES those lying on the jaw and moving it either way [Fig. 13].

All known living creatures except the crocodile move their under jaw, while the upper remains unmoved.[81] The actions [of the lower jaw] are three, chewing, shutting, and opening the mouth. The movement of the mouth first mentioned is distinct from these, since it can take place when the lower jaw is at rest. It is distinct also from the movement of the lips which is affected by yet other muscles. Thus there are five activities connected with the mouth, and five kinds of muscle, all of which I shall describe in turn, beginning from those discovered by myself.

In all the types of animal that physicians dissect, as being not

423 very unlike man in nature, there are muscles, both broad and thin, which are intended by Nature to draw the jaws sideways. The types of animal that do not differ greatly in their nature from man are, roughly speaking, six in number, of which I have already spoken [p. 97].[69] Here I treat of apes because of all animals they are most like man.

Apes [for dissection] should be drowned, that no organs in the neck be damaged as they are by strangling. A straight incision must be made with a sharp lancet along the neck from chin to breast, the lancet being pressed so evenly on the skin that nothing else is severed. You will easily accustom yourself to do this, not only here, but throughout the body, by shaving the part you intend to cut.

Practically all the skin on the body has a membrane [dermis] lying under it which is removed with it in skinning. Here is a broad and delicate muscle [*platysma*] with many fibres which have a [general] direction corresponding to the associated vessels.[82] These fibres end at the lips and their origins are mani- fold, for they arise from all the neck vertebrae, from the scapulae and from the clavicles. Those that come from the cervical vertebrae run rather more transversely. Those that run up from the clavicles are nearly vertical. Most of them reach the point of the chin and are inserted into the lips, alternating with one another, as purses are drawn up [by their strings], some passing from left to right of the lips, others the reverse way [Figs. 11, 12]. *424*

The membrane from which the fibres originate is not like that of others in thickness or strength but proportionately stronger, for it is formed of the substance and has the nature of ligaments which spring from bones, being hard and insensitive. Hence this membrane and all those like it should be called 'ligaments', since such they truly are, and 'membranous' for clarity as having the delicacy of membranes. This ligament springs from the ends of the spines of the cervical vertebrae and binds them all to the muscle. *425*

Naturally, when the animal is skinned, this muscle [*platysma*] disappears, stripped off with the ligament like a membrane. You can make a double test on one animal by shaving off the skin from the muscle on one side and removing skin with muscle and ligament to the vertebrae on the other. If you keep the mem- brane* stretched, you can examine in the delicate ligament the numerous fibres in a row, one after the other, like the fibrous cords. They are best seen in either old or newborn animals.

Both [old and newborn] lack fat, which accumulates on membranes, ligaments, tendons, and sinews, and indeed on all avascular and cold tissues. In the newborn the fibres are small, the ligaments powerless, and the muscular substance soft, and so perhaps such subjects are better avoided in the present inquiry. *426*

* Text says 'skin'.

Those thin from age are the most suitable, for their flesh is scanty and dry and the fibrous element even more dry and yet well developed. But if it be a choice of unsuitable animals, select the newborn rather than the large and fat, for nothing so obscures dissection of fibres as fat.

In this muscle [*platysma*] examine the position of the fibrous strands which run up, from the regions I have mentioned, to jaws and chin, for they guide you to the origins of strands that come from many regions. Those in the front and side of the head rise up from the underlying muscles; others coming from the back, springing from the spinous process, have their *427* origin as you may see along with the delicate and flat ligament there [Figs. 11, 12].

It is well to insert a threaded needle to put a loop round each strand close to the lower jaw, then, stretching out the strand by means of the thread, remove the fibrous strands on either side of it. Do this to each strand, so that, when the muscle is cut out, the fibres are left intact, so that their origin may be seen when you remove the thick muscles underlying them. It suffices to do this on one side. On each [side] cut away the ends of the fibrous strands running down to scapula, clavicle, and spine, strip the muscle from the underlying tissues and draw each portion of it towards the end so as to see the animal's jaws following the portions of the muscles pulled on by them. Either the animal must be still warm and lately dead, or else the surrounding air must be summer-like, or you must throw warm water on it, for if the parts round the jaws have time to cool they become *428* difficult to move, growing stiff as hide.

This muscle arises behind from the spine continuously. Thence it runs to the base of the bone of the occiput, then passes under the ear, touching its attachment, and thence it passes to cover the masseter muscle, uniting ligamentously with the upper jaw bone. Thus the two sides, so to speak, of this part of the muscle [*platysma faciei*] are completely defined. The three remaining divisions are not thus separable, since for the most part the spine of the scapula bounds the part of the muscle there [nuchal part of *platysma*], but sometimes a small part of the fibrous strands passes from this, too, into the lower regions. The same may be said of the clavicular [portion], but none of the fibrous strands are so sharply defined as the aforementioned boundaries.

Most of the anterior parts of these muscles in apes so conjoin that they appear one. In some animals the straight sides of these muscles are separate from one another; in some they are *429* in contact through a few oblique fibres, particularly in the region of the larynx. These muscles are separate from one another in proportion as the animals are long in the neck. If you remove these muscles, you can demonstrate either those from the nucha or those in the face.

Chapter 3

[*The Six Kinds of Quadrupeds. The Lips and their Movements*]

I stated earlier that the parts round the mouth have five dif- *429* ferent movements. I think I had better go over them all. Let us start with the lips into which, I said, pass certain interlocking fibrous strands of the thin flat muscles [*platysma*]. In apes the interweaving of these strands is plain to view, while in animals longer in the neck it is less plain in the degree that the neck is longer. Those with the longest neck retain little trace of *430* interchange of these fibres, for in them antero-posterior fibres disappear and the oblique or transverse perform the whole function without their help.

In these animals the lower jaw is also longer than in the ape. Of all animals man has the shortest jaw in proportion to his whole body. After man, the ape, then the lynx,[83] then the tailed ape, and then the dog-faced baboon. Their neck, too, is as long and they all have a collar-bone like man. Some of them stand more erect than others. All [can] walk with their weight on two legs, some worse, some better. No other known animal walks thus. After these comes the bear class, then pigs, then what are called the 'jagged-toothed' (KARCHARODONTA, roughly the carnivora) then two other classes of animal, namely the horned cloven-footed ruminants and the hornless, with uncleft feet and undivided hooves. As for the other classes of animal, biped and quadruped, omitted from these six classes, there is no difficulty in finding to what to liken them.

431

The lips have a special character of their own, for in addition to the variety of their motion, for which they came into existence, it is not possible to conceive a more perfect bodily substance. You can turn them out and aside, draw them in, stretch them lengthways, tighten them or slacken them at need in eating, drinking, speaking, or performing any other activity. Since they are attached to the skin and the flat muscles [parts of the *platysma*] that we have discussed [p. 7], you may place their origin wherever they will no longer follow the skin, as you strip it off. Further, the lips are joined with the bone of the jaw as well, for they have a third ingredient in their composition, a porous substance [presumably mucous membrane]. Thus their nature is composed from this substance, from the skin and from the flat muscle—three ingredients mingled.

432

They derive their sideways movements from the flat muscles through their transverse fibres. The movement downwards and upwards comes from their whole substance and, for the sake of these movements, Nature has penetrated the mandible with small [mental] foramina and given them nerves [*inferior dental*].[84] These holes are near the end[85] of the jaw on either side of the junction [of the rami]. Through them emerge what is left of the nerves to the sockets of the teeth, from which the gums and the teeth and the surrounding membranes derive sensation [Figs. 11, 12].

While stripping the lips from the under jaw, be careful not to cut the nerves. They run upward from beneath in accord with the nature of the lips. By the action of these nerves the lips are drawn down.[86] They are brought together by strands passing into them out of the thin flat muscles by the fibres coming up from the clavicles. Acting like a purse, pulled either way by the muscles at the side, the lips increase in thickness as they lose in length [and vice versa]. It is as if you were to put a finger on either side, pressing them and reducing their *433* width or, again, increasing their height and thickness as you diminished their width. So the tension of the muscles, pulled opposite ways at the same time, draws the ends towards the middle, their spongy nature contributing greatly to this result. For all substance of this nature is both emptied and filled easily, contracting when emptied and expanding when filled. More is said of it in my work *De motibus dubiis*.[87]

Just as nerves are supplied to these [i.e. lower lips] from the lower jaw [from *mental* branch of *mandibular* division of V],[86] so are they to the upper lips from the upper jaw [from the *infraorbital* branch of *maxillary* division of V],[88] also passing through fine foramina in all animals. If these foramina are not visible, you will find them in a larger specimen of like kind. (I call a horse *like* in kind (HOMOEIDĒS) to a horse, an ape to an ape, a dog to a dog. Call them HOMOGENĒS instead of HOMOEIDĒS, if you will.[89])

These [upper lips] are moved in the same way as the lower. *434* They are drawn up by the afore-mentioned nerves which move certain delicate muscles peculiar to the upper lips.[86] They are pulled sideways by the fibrous strands of the flat muscles that come down to them. They are drawn together by the interwoven fibrous strands. In large animals you will see clearly some of them reaching the origin of the lips and stopping there, and some intertwined with each other [Fig. 12].

In exposing the lips, mark by means of ligatures the nerves below that traverse the masseter [*zygomatic*, *buccal*, and *mandibular* branches of VII] advancing to the side parts of each lip, so that you may examine their origin again. And examine closely whether certain anatomists have been right or wrong in saying that each of the lips is moved by two muscles, each running obliquely to the lips, into the upper from above and into the lower from below, or whether rather each muscle is of somewhat cuticular nature reinforced by muscle fibres.

Chapter 4

[*Masticatory Muscles*]

435 It must be shown clearly that the muscles moving the alae of the nose [*nasolabiales*] are of a like nature to that of the flat muscle [*platysma*] that was discovered by me. Here, too, there lie under the skin naturally united fibrous strands by which they are moved and fibres of such a nature are even more characteristic of the skin of the forehead [*frontalis*]. But the alae of the nose are conjoined and fused with the upper lip [through the *levatores labii*], without being provided with any special muscle for this purpose [Fig. 11].

Move upwards gradually to the cheek, stripping off the skin from the tissue there. If you do this, you will see clearly the masseter muscles with the nerves [branches of VII] extending over them and ending at the mouth. Before dissecting the masseters, raise these nerves with hooks and free them from underlying tissues up to their end behind the ears, and leave them there. Remember to examine round the foramina of the skull whence they spring [*stylomastoid foramina*].

But first proceed [*a*] to the masseters, [*b*] to the muscles within the jaw in the mouth, and [*c*] to the temporal muscles, 436 for these three pairs of muscles move the under jaw. The temporal muscles, along with the muscles inside, draw it up, while the masseters turn it to the side. You must dissect each of them thus. Cut the strands of the masseters extending from upper to lower jaw, consecutively so as to observe how they fit into one another. Divide those on the surface, drawing them up with hooks, stripping and dissecting them to the upper jaw, whence they spring, until you come to the underlying [fibres]. These have a different direction, for they fit into each other and do not run straight down. Wherefore it is necessary for the lower jaw not only to be extended and brought to the upper, when animals are chewing, but also for it to run slightly aslant, sometimes forward and sometimes backward, for such is the action we need in chewing [Fig. 13].

Each masseter forms two muscles, coming each from its own head to a common end. The insertion is in the lower jaw which is to be moved. One of the heads you will see in the cheek, *437* strong and sinewy, embracing the substance of the fleshy part with a powerful ligament; the other lies along the whole jugal bone and is not at all sinewy. The former draws up the jaw slightly to the front, the latter is for the opposite movement, and its nature is to draw the jaw backwards to the degree that the former draws it forwards. If you stretch the heads in turn you will see the movement plainly.

As to how you are to do this, give me your attention now. The principles I am going to state apply to all operations for examining the movement of a part in a dead animal. We must remove all the flesh from those bones on which the investigation is being made, keeping intact only the muscles that move them. Dissect these muscles also right up to their heads. Cut these away from the bones from which they issue and draw *438* them towards you, laying hold on them with your fingers, pulling them to the site from which they arose. If you do this aright, you will see the movements of the bones that have antagonistic muscles inserted into them.

Thus you must remove all tissues round the lower jaw and, laying it perfectly bare, observe the movements of each masseter. You will see them even more plainly if you not only strip everything else from the lower jaw, and particularly all that issues from below, but also the temporal muscles themselves which you can dissect either after the masseters or before. Either way it is necessary to excise what is called the ZYGŌMA. When it is away, the whole temporal muscle is clearly seen inserted into the process of the mandible called KORŌNĒ [*coronoid*] by a broad tendon.

Moreover, now that the ZYGŌMA is removed you will see

the relations to each other of three muscles, to wit, the masseter, the temporal, and the muscle hidden within the mouth [*pterygoid*], which is contiguous to them.

439 The masseter is in contact with the temporal in several places, and more extensively with that [muscle] which is hidden within the mouth [*pterygoid*]. Thus if one were to say that it [the *pterygoid*] were part of the temporal, one would hardly err, for the temporal, being attached all round the [*coronoid*] process of the lower jaw, is in union with this third muscle [*pterygoid*]. The latter has its origin by the wing-like (PTERYGOEIDĒS) outgrowth of the skull [*lamina pterygoidea lateralis*], and is below attached to the flat parts of the lower jaw where there is a place made slightly hollow to afford access to the muscle. At its origin there is a great hollow round the wing-like outgrowth of the skull [*pterygo-maxillary fossa*].[90]

It is not possible to examine this muscle till you have loosened the lower jaw, either removing it from the skull at the joint, or by severing the end where lies the junction of its two parts. The temporal muscle is visible enough if you but excise the ZYGŌMA.

Hippocrates says that the lower jaw is compounded of two 440 bones joined together at the end.[91] This has been said by all others who have expounded the nature of the bones with accuracy, yet it is not possible to demonstrate the junction in all apes, for in most of them it will look to you as if the lower jaw were a single bone. In dogs the junction is seen clearly, and in them it is easiest to divide the jaw at this point. Dogs have the three muscles of which I have just spoken, and all the kinds of animal mentioned above [p. 97] have them, and they produce the same movements, the masseters being double, but the others being single [p. 101].

You must find by trial in what animals the lower jaw is easily cleft, and so proceed to the apes.[92] If you want to practise on them from the start, you will divide the jaw at the point with an excision knife. Paying attention to this lower end of the 441 jaw-bone and to the junction of the front teeth called 'incisors', split the jaw with a scalpel at the mid-point. When you have drawn the parts asunder, examine from within the third muscle attached to the flat part of the lower jaw [*buccinator*]. You will see it clearly when you have stripped off the membrane that covers all the parts round the mouth [buccal mucous membrane]. Following up its fibrous strands you will get a clear view of the [*pterygoid*] muscle arising from the hollows of the skull produced by the pterygoid (wing-like) outgrowths.

As for the masseters, when they have been prepared beforehand, as I have described [p. 101], after you have laid bare and cut away the temporal muscles so that at no point is the lower jaw moved up or retracted, you can observe clearly how they move it. But if you wish to dissect the temporal muscles first, you must remove both [masseters] and, having bared the muscle of both skin and membranes, examine the fibrous strands to see how, starting from many regions, they all converge on the tendon. Then cut away all the origins [of the temporal] and stretch them out vigorously. You will then see *442* the lower jaw following and the mouth closing. So open it with your own hands and then draw the temporal muscle upwards to see the lower jaw following it once more and the mouth closing again.

When you have observed these [reactions], cut away [the *temporal*] till you can see the muscle [*pterygoid*] inside the mouth, fusing with it at many points. Before you cut it, you will see the masseter adhering to it here and there. This also should now be cut out so that you can see the inner [muscle, i.e. *pterygoid*] before the separation of the lower jaw. Detach this either at the articulation or at the junction—so that when it is turned back the inner muscle is visible. If you divide it at both places, you will make accurate examination yet easier. It is clear that in the case of this muscle, too, its origin lies by the skull and its insertion at the lower jaw, where it is attached at the flattest point *443* on the inner side where it is somewhat hollow.[93] It emerges from the skull at the hollows beside the pterygoid bones. Once you have cut out the whole of this muscle together with the half of the lower jaw, you will be able to examine all the parts at the mouth, first the gums round the sockets of the teeth and then the sockets and the teeth themselves.

Chapter 5

[*Discussion of Eye-Muscles postponed*]

443 Since my intention was to examine the muscles first, let us proceed to them. We should begin with those round the eye, but I put off treating those in the eyelids even in my *De usu partium*[10] till after the discussion *De motibus dubiis*.[87]

Dissect the inner muscles in the eye region, either excising first with a circular cut what lies around them, or cutting out 444 the eye as a whole. It is not, however, necessary to dissect the eye of a an ape when you have ample opportunity for such an operation on the larger animals. Therefore let us postpone discussion of the globe of the eye, also, to that part of the present work in which I shall describe a dissection* of such parts as can be examined separate from the rest of the animal. (For we can remove from the body the brain, eye, tongue, larynx, lung, heart, liver, spleen, kidneys, womb, bladder, testicles, bowels, or stomach.) Meanwhile, as we planned from the start, let us rather consider in detail the larger muscles that fasten part to part, yet are not themselves included in any one part, for it is not possible to conceive even the nature of such muscles apart from the animal as a whole.[94]

Chapter 6

[*Muscles of Forehead and Neck, and Movers of the Head*]

444 Let us now think of ourselves as stripping off the muscle-like skin on the forehead. I have said before that a flat muscle is set under the skin here and naturally united with it. If you dissect

* ANATEMNEIN TŌ LOGŌ = to dissect in discourse.

it to its origin you will see it becoming progressively thinner. *445* As you strip off the whole skin from the head, you will trace certain outlines of muscles round the ear which, in other animals, you will see not as mere outlines but as complete muscles.[95] Since as you do this the skin round the head is removed, while that round the neck was removed when you exposed the thin and flat muscles [*platysma*], it is time to dissect those muscles that are connected with the head and then those in the neck. As there is some dispute about the origin of these muscles I shall mention their junction with each bone as it comes up for consideration, sometimes saying that they join with a bone (SYMPHYSIS), sometimes that they arise from it (EKPHYSIS), or grow into it (KATAPHYSIS), or are inserted into it (EMPHYSIS).

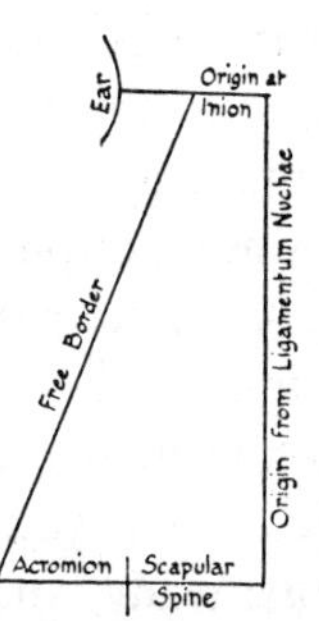

[Diagram of cervical part of trapezius muscle of Macacca]

First of all a flat muscle is seen on the surface, nearly triangular, such as what geometers call trapezoid. You will grasp my meaning more clearly if you cut a right-angled triangle with a straight line parallel to the lowest side (BASIS). Of the lines that join these two, one is at right angles to both, the other is oblique. The line at right angles to both springs from *446* the spine (AKANTHA) at the neck. The base of the figure is the whole spine of the scapula. Parallel to this is a small line on the skull at the nape, near the first vertebra. That which unites it and the end of the base is the fourth side of the muscle, the oblique one, which runs towards the so-called AKRŌMION and joins for a short distance the end of the clavicle there.[96] In dissecting this muscle, begin from the highest line of origin which starts from the middle of the skull at the nape and extends transversely towards the root of the ear at the side [Fig. 10.]

It is clear that here is a single muscle running on either side of the spine yet neither division [of the muscle] reaches the ear, but each falls short of the ear by the distance that it proceeds

from the nape. Make a transverse incision by the first origin, freeing it from the skull. Then thrust a hook through it and dis-
447 sect it from the underlying tissues. Proceed downward along the boundaries indicated, namely, the spinous processes of the cervical vertebrae and the slanting side of the trapezius, reaching the clavicle near the AKRŌMION.

Suppose that this is done: the muscle is now visible, inserted into the sharp ridge on the scapula. The question which I had previously postponed now arises, namely, as to the muscles that fasten together parts which are [both] movable [that is, which is origin and which insertion]. The shoulder-blade makes extensive movements, and the head as great. If, in a freshly killed animal, you remove the flesh from them that the response may be ready, and if you try to pull on both in turn, by this muscle, either end will equally follow the other.

It is best, however, to hold that this muscle [*trapezius*] is produced by Nature for the shoulder-blade and not for the head, for these reasons. First because when it [the muscle] is severed in the neck, the scapula drops down and can never again be raised. (This should be done in the live animal.)
448 Secondly, because there are other muscles that move the head laterally, while only this one draws up the shoulder to the head. Thus, if we deprive the shoulder of this, it will want such motion altogether. Yet it obviously has this motion and since some muscle causes such [motion], it must be this. Third, in long-necked animals this muscle does not reach the head but is exactly triangular, for the line that joins the lines that bound the right angle begins at the lower parts of the neck and ends before it reaches the skull at the nape. For Nature, that does nought in vain,[97] would have been active to no purpose in bringing up to the head a muscle which could have raised the scapula even if it had ended lower down, by movement of the neighbouring spine in such animals, and the extension to the neck would be unnecessary. Fourthly, evidence that the
449 scapula is moved is that a nerve comes down to this muscle from the brain [a branch of XI]. If one cut it, the movement of

the scapula is paralysed but not that of the head. Yet the book of Lycus[30] maintained that the head is drawn down to the shoulder by it, for he was ignorant both of the nerve and of all else of which we have spoken.

But it is not my intention to criticize Lycus or any of my predecessors unless incidentally.[98] For I know that any diligent reader anxious to discover the truth will find the books of other writers crammed with errors. For truly Lycus overlooked one pair of the muscles moving the lower jaw, namely, the pair inside the mouth [*pterygoids*], just as he ignored the flat muscles in the neck [*platysma*], along with those just mentioned [concerning the *trapezius*]. He is ignorant of many more of the facts to be stated next. Sometimes he is alone in this, sometimes the others share his ignorance. I therefore invite all who meet with these books to judge of the points in question, making themselves eye-witnesses of anatomical operations. For it is my express purpose in writing this work to enable diligent readers *450* to teach themselves, if they lack instructors, since the friends who urged me to write it as memoranda can, even without it, recall what they learned from me, unless they slip into indolence. Hence I shall forbear to criticize my predecessors so that the argument may proceed the faster while I state only actual facts.

The second pair of muscles [*rhomboideus, pars capitis*, not present in man] is comparable in length to those already mentioned [i.e. to occipito-scapular part of *trapezius*] for, starting from the same region of the bone of the skull at the nape, they are inserted into the upper angle of the base of the scapula. Their breadth is considerably less. For these muscles are narrow and weak compared to those which appear so large even before dissection that in athletes they raise a swelling in the neck [*sternomastoid*][99] [Fig. 10].

Begin to dissect the delicate muscle that we are discussing [*rhomboideus, pars capitis*] in the same way as the first, that is, from the middle region of the skull at the INION [*external occipital protuberance*]. For lying under those mentioned before and like them, they have a transverse origin there and like them 451 they extend along the spinous processes through the neck and are easily stripped off from the underlying tissues. But the former [fibres of *trapezius*] run thus throughout the neck and to the scapula; whereas the latter, when they approach the scapula, cohere with the muscles lying beside it on either side, and where they reach the scapula produce a round tendon which runs along the inner parts of the base [*vertebral border*] as far as the middle. They too draw up the base of the scapula towards the INION.[99]

The muscles dealt with before draw up not only the base but the whole scapula. When they are removed, if your examination be as careless as that of Lycus, you will think you see the so-called 'spinal muscles' extending [evenly] over the whole neck, but if you look closely you will see many other pairs of muscles there, not only in apes but in all other animals, differing as plainly as could be from the spinal muscles.

They [the spinal muscles] arise from each of the upper cervical vertebrae through powerful ligaments. They are attached to neighbouring vertebrae, their strands running a rather short course. On the other hand, those pairs mentioned before [*trapezius* and *rhomboideus, pars capitis*] 452 extend the head by fleshy projections throughout the neck, being of no mean length in most animals. The sinews run up from below along these, as if they ended in the head instead of having their starting-point from it.

The first of these muscles [*splenius*] is a flat pair arising from the skull at the INION transversely like those first mentioned. (It makes no difference whether we call it a KATAPHYSIS (a growing to) or an EKPHYSIS (a growing out of).) They are triangular: one side is the line mentioned on the INION; the second line is that of the cervical vertebrae; the third line unites these. Their fibres are oblique, slanting from the INION to the spine [a very different and much stronger muscle in apes than in man].

In the contrary direction to these, the fibres of the muscles under them run slanting forward towards the transverse processes of the vertebrae. Since they all tend towards this region 453 [of the INION], they form a single sheet on each side. Their outlines—usually treble, sometimes double—will make you think that it is not a single muscle but three or two. Yet when three seem clearly visible, you will see one extends to the spines of the vertebrae, a second to their transverse processes, and a third in between. [This seems to describe the triangle formed by *obliquus capitis superior*, *obl. cap. inferior*, and *rectus cap. post. major*.]

As to the actions of these muscles, one can, of course, infer them from their fibres, but it is possible to strip all the surrounding tissues from the skull and to draw it backwards by these muscles. It is obviously stretched up and bent backwards by all of them, but by each of those just mentioned with an inclination to the side. On the other hand, the combined oblique actions of the muscles give a direct resultant. When a pair, whether of those lying above or those below, is stretched simul- 454 taneously, you will see the head in equipoise, by moderate tension brought to a settled condition of erectness, while more violent tension imparts a backwards flexure to the animal's spine. It has been made clear that you should attempt such observation of the movement after all the flesh has been removed with the skin of the head and face.

You will begin the dissection I have described of the three pairs of these muscles from the bone of the skull at the INION into which they grow, for they are easier to dissect from there. Continue to their lower end, which may be rightly called either 'origin' or 'insertion'.

Chapter 7

[*Four Small Muscles behind the Skull and on the First Two Vertebrae*]

When these [muscles] around the articulation of the head are 454 removed, three other pairs of small muscles become apparent.

I shall speak of those when I dissect the muscles lying under the pharynx.*

In reality the muscles behind are not three but four (apart from the small ones hidden by the articulation at the side of the first 455 vertebra, on which account they escape notice). The fourth pair of the small muscles behind was overlooked by anatomists for the following reasons. The first vertebra does not have the structures at the back which produce the spinal process, and, moreover, it is the most slender of all the vertebrae. On this account it has surrounded itself with the second [vertebra] so as to form a close association. For these reasons and because the muscle that fastens the first vertebra to the head is so small [*rectus capitis posterior minor*], another [and larger] muscle is laid outside fastening the second vertebra to the head [*rectus capitis posterior major*]. Thus the small muscle is hidden. The muscle lying on it behind begins from the vertebra below [*axis*] and ends in the skull at the INION near its middle. [The muscle is relatively much larger in the ape than in man and has a wide insertion on the occiput.] For that reason also the two [larger] muscles which are straight are in contact with each other and cover the whole articulation. Until they are removed, the small muscles cannot be seen, though they are just as straight and spring likewise from the skull and are in contact 456 with others in the same way as those on them. They are inserted in the back part of the first vertebra just as those above them are inserted in the back part of the second.

The reason that the first vertebra does not have a posterior process is certainly because the skull had to be attached to the second vertebra so that the head could be thrown back. Thus no process could have been set underneath among the muscles there, such as the other vertebrae have, for they would have been pierced or crushed by it. In dissecting the two pairs of muscles you must handle them in two ways. Either sever the muscles from the second vertebra, then pull on them and follow their course with the lancet to the head. This is the easier method.

* I have transposed this and the next sentence.

Or start from the head and work to the vertebra. If you do not touch the strands of small underlying muscles, you will see them with their own outline, but if you touch and cut them anywhere, you will think that they coalesce with the muscles on them. However, the attachment to the first vertebra will be clearly visible in either operation. *457*

These two pairs of muscles merely draw the head back. The third [*obliquus capitis superior*] fastens it to the transverse process of the first vertebra. It is oblique, having its origin from the skull continuous with the former but retreating to the sides. Thus the smaller pair along with the whole first vertebra has been overlooked by anatomists, for the first two give the false impression of arising from a single vertebra, since the spine of the second lies in a line with the transverse processes of the first.

And just as the middle parts of the first vertebra are hidden, because it lacks a spine, because it is feeble at that point, and because four muscles are superimposed on it, so the lateral parts of the second vertebra have been almost obscured because the first surrounds it there with robust transverse processes. *458*

The third pair [of muscles] initiates sideways movement of the head along the line of its fibres, for the nature of all the muscles is, by contracting, to approximate the structures to which their ends are attached. I have discussed all such points at greater length in my book *De motu musculorum*[100] with which I advise all who would gain anything from it to make themselves thoroughly familiar.

There remains [for consideration] a fourth pair of muscles [*obliquus capitis inferior*]. They lie at an angle to the third. They fasten the first vertebra to the second and their ends reach the transverse processes of the first and the spinous process of the second. These three muscles [*obliquus capitis superior, obl. cap. inferior*, and *rectus cap. post. major*] form an equilateral triangle, the first, third, and fourth under discussion. The second is invisible until the first is removed, but the other three are plainly visible.

I used to wonder how this Lycus,[30] whose book has just been

459 published after his death, recognized in his anatomy of the muscles only one of the pairs which fasten head to first vertebra. What I have just said proves plainly that all overlooked the first vertebra, and when we dissect the nerves this will be pointed out again. But it is strange that, when they had a precise view of the first pair of muscles, they did not observe the third and fourth, for all are equally visible to one dissecting the muscles common to the neck and head. But as they actually write their view that the muscles of the neck are parts of the spinal muscles, I think that they cannot have attempted to dissect them. Having decided that there were certain muscles peculiar to the articulation of the skull, they put full trust in reasoning apart from dissection. And so they wrote their notes as if from actual observation, for it is not possible for anyone who had seen the muscles common to the second vertebra and the head to be ignorant of the others. Not only did they ignore 460 observation, but the movements of the head on the first two vertebrae they regarded as insignificant.

Chapter 8

[*Movements of First and Second Vertebrae*]

460 The nature of these movements and their relationship with each other and with the joints in the head I have described in my treatise *De ossibus*.[101] Anyone who approaches the present work before gaining experience in that is building on sand. Assuming that my readers are acquainted with that subject, I shall now discuss the movements that involve the first and second vertebrae.

The first and second pair of the four muscles I have spoken of simply extend the head backwards on the neck. When they act, the condyles (KORŌNĒ) of the skull are clamped on the facets of the first vertebra and the occipital bone is fixed firmly on them, but none the less touches also the second vertebra, which is itself the utmost limit to the backward flexure of the head.

When the head nods forward again, it moves to the front and rests upon the anterior arch (APOPHYSIS) of the first vertebra, and the condyles float free in the facets, separate from the back parts [of the atlas]. Should the head get forward beyond the first vertebra, Nature provides no active aid. Not only are the muscles that pull it down capable of bringing such danger in bending it, but its weight also sinks it down. Nevertheless, there is a safeguard since the anterior arch of the first vertebra prevents the head from slipping too far forward, fixing and raising the head just before it goes too far. So much for Nature's lesser security. But she has a much greater defence in the second vertebra. Coming from it is an upright conical process [*odontoid*]. For Nature here fixes the lower [vertebra] by means of the front parts, carving out a small hollow in the first vertebra [*odontoid facet*] where lies its anterior arch. Behind this the end of the rising process [*odontoid*] of the second vertebra is mounted. From it issues a strong apical ligament which is inserted into the skull. Another ligament, transverse to this, is produced from the first vertebra itself. This binds to a nicety the conical end of the second vertebra.

461

462

If you want to observe these phenomena, it will be easier if the small muscles are removed. If you excise the posterior arch of the first vertebra you will see clearly the said two ligaments performing the service for the skull that I have described. The one ligament holds it back, that which springs from the apex of the tooth or peg (PYRĒN or whatsoever else it may be called) on the second vertebra. The transverse ligament holds and fixes this tooth, keeping it inflexible.

Lateral bends of the head are made by the oblique muscles. They incline it to one or the other of the condyles, to whichever the muscle stretching it leads. There the head is firmly fixed in the facet [of the *atlas*], pressing the condyle into it, and floats on the other and higher condyle mounted in the opposite facet. In this movement the head turns the second vertebra with itself in the direction it moves by means of the ligament. So that Nature with good reason attached it [the *axis*] to the first

463

vertebra by another pair of oblique muscles that have the function of righting its turns and bringing it back to its original position [*obliqui capitis inferiores*].

Chapter 9

[*Muscles uniting the Skull with Sternum and Clavicle*]

463 Enough has been said on the muscles of the head [attached] to INION and neck. Next must be discussed those that bind the head to sternum and clavicle. All the muscles discussed having been removed, we can deal with these and also with the muscles binding scapulae to spine. But since I have spoken of the dissection of many of the muscles springing from the head, it would be better to add those that move the head anteriorly.

It is clear, I think, to all that, reaching down to the sternum and the first parts of the clavicle from two starting-points, one lying behind the ear, the other under it, these muscles [*sterno-* 464 *mastoid* and *cleidomastoid* which are separate in the ape] either move sternum or clavicle with thorax towards the side of the head, or advance the head. It is not less clear that it is impossible for them to impart this motion to the thorax. So it is the head that is advanced by them.

You must recognize that general principle applying to all muscles. Those that have a straight position initiate a simple motion, those that do not, a composite motion. All the aforesaid muscles that spring from the head have a straight position and [produce] a simple motion. Those running down into the scapulae draw them up; of those that run into the neck, some bend it back straight, some move it slightly obliquely. The muscle springing from the back parts of the ear and coming down to the end of the collar-bone at the sternum [*cleidomastoid*] does not lie in a straight line and as its position so is the motion that it yields. So with the muscle following it, that 465 is attached to the sternum [*sternomastoid*]. You will find their attachments in the region of which I spoke, that of the one [*sternomastoid*] continuous with the first muscle common to the neck and head [*splenius*], reaching the ear along a transverse line, that of the other [*cleidomastoid*] at the root of the ear. This tendon is narrow, hard, and fairly round; the other is fleshy like all the rest I have described as springing from the bone of the skull at the INION [Fig. 13].

The attachments of these muscles to the aforesaid parts are with double ends. The muscle under the root of the ear, having become twofold as it moves forward, is inserted in the sternum with one of its ends, with the other in the part of the clavicle articulating with it. The end of the muscle is fleshy, that which enters the sternum more bloodless, harder, and ligamentous. The other fleshy muscle makes a similar attachment with the clavicle to that with the skull. It is united and continuous with the aforesaid fleshy attachment. Yet it is not at- *466* tached to the whole collar bone as some have thought but stops near the middle. This I have observed continually but not the three attachments each with its own outline in all cases, though in one case their termination was seen to be twofold. Perhaps it is better to call their ends at the clavicle bone not 'insertions' but 'origins' or 'heads', and their ends in the skull 'terminations', if they really move the skull. But for the sake of system I give the name of 'origins' [EKPHYSEIS] to the attachments above on the head and 'insertions' [KATAPHYSEIS] to those below by the clavicle, like my predecessors in anatomy [Fig. 13.].

Chapter 10

[*Muscles which move the Scapula*]

These muscles having been removed, we pass to those of the *466* scapula. There are two by the spine [*rhomboidei*] which alone, I hold, draw the scapula backwards—Lycus made little of its other movements—and a third [*atlantoscapularis*, absent in man], having its origin from the first vertebra and terminating *467* in the end at the acromion, and a fourth, long and thin, which fastens the scapula to the bone called hyoid at the beginning of the larynx [*omohyoid*, with no central tendon in apes] [Fig. 10].

When handling these muscles proceed thus. Behind the head of the animal, when you have examined the spinous processes, pass from the second vertebra to the third. Examine the attachment of a muscle from the side parts of it, for if you detect it you will find it easy to follow the attachments as they spring from all the succeeding vertebrae [*longissimus capitis*].

When you have examined the five [vertebrae] of the neck, as I have indicated, you will find a superficial muscle near the thoracic inlet. This hides the rest of the muscle that arose from the five vertebrae of the neck and arises also from the seven of the thorax [*longissimus capitis* and *cervicis*]. So that you must first remove the muscle on the surface, which is placed lower, to observe that which comes down from the neck. Cut away from the low-set muscle first the attachments to the twelve thoracic

468 vertebrae and then strip it off as far as its insertion into the scapula and then treat the other in the same way. [This can only mean the *trapezius*, which below its origin in the cervical vertebrae, is treated as a separate muscle.] When the low-set muscle [*rhomboideus minor*] on the surface is visible, inserted into the root of the process at the shoulder-blade, and another [*rhomboideus major*], growing into the whole base, draw each to its own origin along the line of its fibres to learn their functions. You will see the scapula drawn towards the spine by both, the higher [*rh. minor*] inclining it towards the neck, the other [*rh. major*] to the lower parts of the spine. If both are pulled on, the scapula moves back, without deviation, to the first seven vertebrae of the thorax, to which they are attached.

After these, pass to the muscles arising from the first vertebra. To this [*atlas*] there are two transverse processes from which a number of muscles issue. Two of these we have already dissected [*obliquus capitis superior* and *obl. cap. inferior*], one going up into the skull, the second moving to the second vertebra, set

469 transversely to each other. Next to these, at the end of the transverse process are two other large muscles, the one extending to the shoulder-blade [*atlantoscapularis anterior*, unrepresented in man], high through the neck, not fixed quite fast or mounted on the other, but bounding the large flat muscle, first mentioned [*trapezius*], which I said is attached to the spine of the scapula.[102] The other muscle, with origin from the transverse process of the first vertebra, will be treated of in Book V.[103]

When you have cut it [*atlantoscap. anterior*] from the first vertebra as far as the shoulder-blade, dissect it till you find its insertion into the end of the ridge of the scapula at the acromion. Pull on its insertion in the line of its fibres to see the high part of the shoulder-blade drawn forward and upward to the side of the neck. This muscle is fleshy and roundish. It is inserted into the third part of the ridge of the scapula at the highest part near the acromion.

The authors of treatises on the dissection of the muscles were mistaken about this [*atlantoscap. anterior*] muscle, as about many *470* others. So it was with Lycus,[30] some of whose anatomical works have now reached us. I did not see him while he was living, though I was familiar with the pupils of Quintus and was not deterred [in seeking him] by the length of a journey either by land or sea. Lycus had no reputation among the Greeks while alive but, now that he is dead, some of his books in circulation are greatly admired. I have nothing to say about the others. I have not met with them. But the anatomical books, at least those I have so far read, I found to contain many errors. However, as I said, my aim is not to criticize my predecessors unless incidentally, but to record only anatomical observations, on which Marinus has compiled one large work. This is obscure in interpretation and faulty in observation.[32] Let us then proceed to the task before us without bothering about the errors of our predecessors.

A long thin muscle stretches out from the parts at the larynx to the scapula [*omohyoid*], pulling it towards the front of the neck. It goes to that part of the bone which at its upper side *471* approaches the root of the anchor-like process [*coracoid*], but the attachment varies in different species of ape. Its upper attachment, being a little above the larynx, I shall describe in the account of the dissection of that part. As you cut away this muscle, realize that you are still leaving one that moves the scapula which cannot yet be observed [*serratus anterior*].

Leave it then for the moment. But we would say only that, of the muscles ranged round the scapula, that move it, some are peculiar to itself, some shared with other parts. The six muscles mentioned before belong to it alone; two of them are beside the spine [*rhomboideus* and *trapezius*]; two others extend to the head [*splenius* and upper *trapezius*], as does a fifth which springs from the first vertebra [*atlantoscapularis anterior*]; then a sixth is fastened to the hyoid bone [*omohyoid*]; and yet another, shared with the articulation of the shoulder, dragging the scapula downwards [*serratus anterior*]. Of this I shall speak in its proper place.

Chapter 11

[*The Twin Muscles that open the Mouth*]

472 Since our task is to explain how the parts of the animal should be laid bare, let us return to the structures continuous with those previously described, for the sequence of the parts in the course of dissection controls the order of teaching.

After the removal of the muscles discussed, those opening the jaw would be seen [*digastric*]. They take their origin from the stonelike [*petrous*] bone of the skull and extend up to the very end of the jaw [i.e. the chin], so that the muscles of the two sides meet. They have a special character in that in mid-course the fleshy element vanishes and each becomes avascular, as though 473 interwoven of the subtlest fleshy fibres. If you sever their origin and dissect their body to the chin, preserving the junction to the jaw, and then draw them towards their origin, the jaw will follow and the mouth will open.

Of course all such operations should be carried out after the skin has been removed, and while not only the ligaments round the articulations but also the muscles are still fresh and therefore soft. The most accurate scrutiny of each muscle is possible when all the others have been removed and only those muscles remain, the movements of which are opposed to those that you are examining. Flesh forms the largest part of the substance of muscles. When tendons and nerves are mingled with the flesh, we have a muscle. I have spoken of this in my *De motu musculorum.*[100] Those who intend to follow this present work must read it all.

The function and use of the muscles of which I have spoken being made clear, I must state that it is not necessary to look for another pair opening the mouth. Nature is content with that pair which I have just mentioned, for she has opposed it alone *474* to the three that shut the mouth.[104] The cause of these and of all the other [muscular] phenomena has been set forth in my *De usu partium.*[10]

BOOK V

[*Muscles of Thorax, Abdomen, Loins, and Spine*]

Chapter 1

[*Muscles uniting Thorax to Humerus and Scapula*]

475 Our next task is the separation of the scapulae from the thorax to reveal the muscles of respiration. My account will be of the one side only, for the two correspond in all ways.

Remove the skin round the chest from the underlying tissues. Examine first a muscle of the surface above the others [thoracic *476* portion of *panniculus carnosus*]. It starts from the region of the nipple, extending obliquely upward to the shoulder-joint. This muscle is freed from the underlying tissues by 'excoriation' (DARSIS). People use this term when tissues are linked by numerous delicate, web-like connexions. These, if separated in the living animal, keep each its own even and smooth appearance, nowhere torn or lacerated. In tissues naturally united, however, and especially in muscles, division produces a rent in the sundered parts and moreover a lancet is always needed for their separation. Those held together by web-like fibres, on the other hand, are parted well enough by the fingers. For you, however, it is better to use a lancet on them too, for thus you will see clearly what you do; since the fingers obstruct scrutiny of the tissues. Blades shaped like myrtle leaves (MYRSINAI) *477* are the handiest.

You must separate this muscle, running up from the false ribs, by stretching its fibres with a hook and then dissecting it gently. Its origin is more closely attached to the underlying tissues than are other muscles. When loosened, you can pull on it with confidence. Dissect it to the shoulder-joint, observing whether the muscle hangs loose or lies upon the tissues at the articulation.*

* There is probably here a gap in the Greek text. See p. 130, line 6, and note 109.

Now pass to another and much larger muscle [*pectoralis major, pars sternalis*]. It runs to the same joint but springs from the whole sternum and has the nipple lying on it. This muscle is twofold, its fibres crossing each other like the letter X. Some run up from the lower parts of the sternum to the higher part of the joint. Others run from the higher parts of the sternum to the lower part of the joint. They cross at the fleshy part of the armpit. The hollow there is produced by two muscles, namely this and another which is stretched along the ribs [*pectoralis abdominis* generally minimal in man]. Of it I shall speak presently. *478*

Because of the crossing of the fibres and consequent difference in their activity, it is possible to say that the muscle springing from the whole sternum [*pars sternalis*] is really two muscles united, for the fibres from the higher part of the sternum bring the humerus to the thorax without pulling it downward, while the other fibres give it an oblique downward movement.

Think of four consecutive movements that you have often seen me demonstrate. First and foremost is a [simple] adduction of humerus to thorax by the muscle of which we speak. Second is bringing humerus to thorax along with the surrounding flesh and inclining it gradually downwards. The first is the act of the higher [*pectoralis major, pars clavicularis*], the second of the lower, fibres of this muscle [*pectoralis major, pars sternalis*]. The third movement is the action of the first muscle [*panniculus carnosus*] which began by the nipple. The fourth movement is the drawing of the humerus over the ribs. This also is twofold, for [*a*] it continues the movement of the first muscle and partakes of the nature of the second, being a combination of adduction of the humerus and of laying it on the ribs, while [*b*] it pulls the humerus vertically up and down across the ribs[105] [Fig. 9]. *479*

One muscle initiates each of these movements [*a* and *b*]. One of the movements [*a*] is initiated by the small surface muscle that I discovered [part of the *panniculus*]. It will be dealt with presently. The other [*b*] is initiated by the biggest muscle [deep part of *pectoralis major*] which I have said produces, along with

480 the muscle at the sternum [*pars sternalis*] the hollow at the armpit. These two muscles are very well developed, particularly in athletes, and clearly visible in them.

In due course I shall speak of the muscle running up from below [*pectoralis abdominis*]. At the moment, however, I shall revert to those that pass from the nipples to the head of the upper arm. Of these the first, I said,* starts from the false ribs near the hypochondria not far from the nipple, and causes the downward movement of the upper arm [thoracic portion of *panniculus*]. Next it is a muscle of considerable size with fibres overlapping each other as though it were twofold, so that one might reasonably think there were two continuous muscles [superficial and deep layers of sternal part of *pectoralis major*]. In succeeding chapters this muscle is to be called 'the largest of the chest muscles'.

A third muscle remains, which becomes visible when this [*pectoralis major*] is removed. It, too, springs from the sternum, [but] at its junction with ribs 2 to 6 [*pectoralis minor*]. It is the
481 highest that adducts the humerus. After it comes the muscle that visibly draws the humerus to the upper ridge [spine] of the scapula [spinodeltoid portion of *deltoid*].

If you choose to separate the scapula from the thorax, as first proposed, you must first dissect the muscle running up from the false ribs to the shoulder-joint [thoracic portion of *panniculus*], then the large one [*pectoralis major*] which arises from the whole sternum, a part of which was the fleshy piece by the armpit [caudal portion of *pectoralis major*], then the third which, I explained, was hidden under the second [*pectoralis minor*]. While the second itself issues from the whole sternum, the third issues from its articulations with all the ribs except the first and seventh.

The third muscle [*pectoralis minor*]† extends over the length of the clavicle, forming a triangle. This, the highest of its sides,

* Here a line perhaps displaced, which may be rendered: 'to make the hollow of the armpit along with the muscle at the sternum'.

† Text says 'second, which is also the largest', and confuses the *pectoralis minor* with the capsular part of *pectoralis major*.

lies at right angles to the sternal origin which is the upright line 482 of the triangle, while the third side joins these. The high muscle over* this is far stronger than the third† muscle and is itself a triangle, but obtuse not right-angled [*pectoralis major*].[105]

These three muscles all terminate in flat tendons inserted into the humerus. But the tendon belonging to the large muscle [*pectoralis major*] has its insertion lower, in the same line along the humerus, below its head, and is double, like the muscle itself. For the first part, from the lower portion of the muscle, is inserted on the humerus on the inside, and the second, which starts from the higher part, on the outside. A tendon from the more sinewy muscle first mentioned [*panniculus*], becoming membranous and delicate, reaches the articulation, where lie the ridges of the hollow [*sulcus bicipitalis*] occupied by the inner head of the anterior muscle of the upper arm [*biceps*]. The tendon of the third [*pectoralis minor*] moves up to the highest part of the head of the upper arm, inserted into the membranous 483 ligament encircling the joint [in the ape but only exceptionally in man].

If you cut away these three muscles from the joint, the scapula will have been loosened from the chest. It is [still] bound, however, to the sides of the thorax by two muscles coming up from below.

One, on the surface, is thin. It is produced from membranes attached to the fascia in the iliac region. These arise primarily from the lumbar vertebrae. Thence the muscle [*latissimus dorsi*] takes its rise, and the fibres, moving round, become gradually fleshy [Fig. 10].

The other muscle that comes from below [lower part of *trapezius*]‡ also arises from the spines of the vertebrae, and especially from those of the false ribs. It is considerably involved with the base of the scapula. It is loosened by excoriation (DARSIS). Before it is laid bare it is attached to the [other] muscles there, so that it is regarded as naturally united to them.

* Reading HYPER for HYPO. † Text reads 'second'.

‡ Here a displaced phrase 'the large one'.

Certain anatomists have cited me in giving this view. The
484 muscle can, however, be separated from these, for the association is a [mere] concrescence (SYMPHYSIS), though since the fibres are delicate the outline of the excoriated structure is preserved without rent. Because of this partnership this large muscle is said to unite naturally with both thorax and base of scapula, though it can be stripped from them.

Its origin from the spine is continuous with the other and lower muscle [*latissimus dorsi*] behind the scapula. For where the former muscle [*trapezius*] stops, the latter has its maximal origin, lying on part of the spinal muscle below it [Fig. 10].

[Here follow eighteen lines concerning severing the thoracic muscles running to the humerus. We attach them to the next chapter, where they properly belong.]

Chapter 2

[*Shoulder Muscles*]

484 Dissect, as I have explained [p. 123], the two muscles that run up to the humerus [*pectoralis major* and *pectoralis abdominis*]. Begin from below [i.e. with *p. abdominis*] and follow to the insertion which the large muscle [*p. major*] makes with the humerus through a flat tendon. Pull it down to its origin to see its action clearly. Inserted a little below the head of the
485 humerus, it draws it down to the ribs. Being so large a muscle, it has a tendon that is strong and large, inserted near the large muscle.*

The small muscle [*pectoralis minor*] has a correspondingly small tendon, mounted on the other tendons in the axilla and inserted on the humerus through a very short handle. Pay attention to its origin in the sternum,† lest you tear the membranes apart, making the same mistake as our predecessors in overlooking the muscle because it is small.

[Here begins Chapter 2 in the Greek text.]

* Text here disturbed and evidently a small hiatus.

† Text reads nonsensically 'ilia'.

When these muscles to the upper arm have been dissected, the scapula remains attached not only by a large muscle [*serratus anterior*] arising from the subcostal arch but also linked with the sternum through the clavicle. Furthermore, it is linked by this [that is, by the clavicle] and another small muscle [*subclavius*] coming down from the clavicle to the first rib. This [small muscle], being hidden under the clavicle, you will overlook and tear, unless you perform the operation thus: *486*

First cut away from the clavicle the muscle of the shoulder [*deltoid*]. It is continuous and united with the largest of the muscles from the sternum [*pectoralis major*] lying along the 'shoulder-vein' [*cephalic*], so that the two muscles seem one. The direction of their fibres indicates the first difference between them; then that of their tendons; and next that the shoulder muscle has an origin in the scapula. Two straight lines (of which one is the length of the clavicle and the other the spine of the scapula) bound the higher [*deltoid*] at an angle that may be compared to the letter lambda Λ, while two other straight lines in the form of the letter gamma Γ, as used* in the contests,[106] form the boundaries of the other [*pectoralis major*]. The insertion of the muscle [*deltoid*] which is higher in the shoulder is set below [on the humerus], whereas the apex where the two muscles† come together is set [higher and] under the acromion. *487*

So in dissecting the other part of the muscle from the clavicle, when you reach the top of the shoulder, change the direction of the cut and dissect the muscle, stretching it up with hooks, and follow the substance of the dissected part, for if you disregard this and cut to the depths of the scapula, you will go wrong. For there another muscle [*spinodeltoid*] lies beneath, with its own outline, which is separable by excoriation (DARSIS) from the muscle of the acromion process [*acromiodeltoid*]. So as you stretch successively each part of the muscle

* Literally 'written'.

† Text says 'ribs' (PLEURŌN) where 'muscles' (MYŌN) is evidently meant. The text of the whole paragraph has needed some rearrangement to give it anatomical meaning.

at the acromion with a hook, as it is being cut, you will observe clearly the defined outlines of the underlying muscle. Once you have lighted on it, you will easily loosen and separate this muscle lying above [*cleidodeltoid*] from the muscle attached to the scapula

488 [*acromiodeltoid*].[107] Moreover, another muscle [*teres major*] extends by the side of the scapula, from which you will separate it without difficulty, if you first loosen it well from the aforesaid muscle. There is yet another muscle [*teres minor*] which runs upon the humerus to its insertion on its front below the articulation.

The attachment of the large thoracic muscle [*pectoralis major*] is also along the humerus, being extended from the median side. This, however, draws the limb inwards whereas the muscle of the acromion [*acromiodeltoid*] pulls it up, not inclining the upper arm in any other direction. [Here two lines of repetition.] This activity belongs to the muscle because it has two heads running round the shoulder, so that if you pull on one, the humerus is drawn either anteriorly to the clavicle or posteriorly to the scapula.

489 Comparable with these are the two muscles extended along the scapula itself [*supraspinatus* and *infraspinatus*], the one above, the other below [the spine of the scapula]. They are visible when the muscle [*deltoid*] over the shoulder has been dissected as I have explained. Proceeding to dissect these muscles, start once more from the base of the scapula [vertebral border] where lies the origin of each. From there proceed to the shoulder-joint, cutting them away as they spring from the scapula, until you see them both expanding into flat tendons by which they move the humerus obliquely, one outward toward the clavicle, the other inward towards the lower part of the scapula. If both are stretched, they produce the same straight tension as between two obliques (as has been said the humerus receives from the deltoid). The higher of the muscles is inserted into the projection of the head of the humerus which the greater head of the anterior

490 muscle [*biceps*] limits externally. The lower muscle produces an APONEURŌSIS continuous with this and also into the head of the humerus, rather more toward the outside.

If you consider the anatomy of the arm as a whole, you may seek to dissect these muscles at once with those next them, following the order of nature. But if you are in haste to reach the thorax, leave them *in situ* and cut away the clavicles from the sternum, severing the capsular ligaments, raising them at the acromion process, bending them back, and successively cutting the other membranes and ligaments by which the clavicles are attached. Do this till you see the muscle, small and oblique, arising from the inner and lower part of the first rib [*subclavius*]. Its head is next the scapula when the clavicle is raised. Its end, through which it is attached to the first rib, is the part of it towards the thorax.

Chapter 3

[*Muscles moving the Thorax*]

When you have cut away this muscle also from the clavicle, *491* take care of one lying close to the first rib [*sternocostalis*]. For when the thorax is presently laid bare, as you pull up [the clavicle] toward its head, you will also draw up the first rib. You should separate the clavicle not only from the sternum, as I have just explained, but also from the acromion, by severing the ligaments attaching it to the spine of the scapula.

You need not seek a third bone in an ape besides the two processes (PERATA = AKRŌMION with KORAKOEIDĒS) already mentioned. For Hippocrates does not say that [a third bone] exists in any other animal but man,[108] and he adds: 'In this respect, man's nature is different from the other animals.' If you cut away the scapula here, you may bend it back again towards the sternum, cutting away the membranes binding it to the neighbouring parts.

Now you will see the muscle of the first rib [*subclavius*]. Cut it away, as I have said, from the clavicle, and either remove the bone completely or bend it back towards the breast and let it lie. If you do this, cut the vessels and nerves at the armpit *492* along with the fascia.

Thus the arm can be separated from the thorax, for nothing remains attaching it thereto except the large muscle [*rhomboideus major*] which I described as attached to the vertebral border* of the scapula. This muscle arises from the first [cervical] vertebra and then passes through the whole neck and [into] that part of the scapula where the superior border meets the base [vertebral border] so that the bone is as a [re-entrant] angle there.

I have said before that a thin muscle [*rhomboideus capitis*, absent in man] reaches this spot, arising from the INION, is inserted into the muscles on either side near the above-mentioned scapular angle. Behind it is the high member of the posterior muscles of the scapula [cervical part of *trapezius*], while in front is the muscle under discussion [rest of *rhomboideus*]. *493* Reaching the beginning of the base [vertebral border] of the scapula, it is inserted throughout its length.†

This part is occupied by another muscle [*serratus anterior*], from which the muscle under discussion is separated by excoriation. It is united only with the base [vertebral border] of the scapula, and it is inserted into the middle parts of the ribs at their maximum convexity. Its action is to draw up the whole thorax except the lower part which is moved by the diaphragm, as I shall show. Sometimes, during violent exertion, it is moved with the parts above, just as some of the parts lying above the diaphragm are moved along with it in a way hard to discern. The sum of the activity [of this muscle] is seen in those ribs wherein it is inserted. It is cleft into digitations which are attached to them. Thus its insertion is neither continuous nor uniform, like that of most muscles. It reaches the false ribs and draws up all those that lie above them.

On either side of it [i.e. of the *serratus anterior*] lie other muscles. One is in the front of the thorax [*scalenus longus*], the other in the back [*serratus posterior superior*], both drawing up

* Text says 'under the hollow parts' as in next paragraph, but describes *rhomboideus*.

† Text adds again: 'itself lying under the concave part'. See previous note. There seems to be some confusion with the *subscapularis*.

the ribs, so that there are these three muscles higher than the thorax. I call them the 'posterior', the 'anterior' and the 'middle'. The middle pair [*serratus anterior*] can by themselves carry on the efficient action of the thorax. You will learn how to handle them in operations on living animals. *494*

The second anterior pair of muscles [*scalenus longus*] begins from the second [*cervical*] vertebra, but springing from all the others in turn it is inserted in the first five ribs by strong ligaments.

So too, the third and last of these membranous muscles [*serratus posterior superior*]—for so they can be called. It begins from the ridge of the last three cervical and the first thoracic vertebrae, each of them having a membranous ligament as its head interwoven with the spinal muscles. When you separate it, first [you will see] fibres attached to the ligament that produces the muscle. These in apes are very weak and delicate, but stronger in other animals. Particularly in pigs, dogs, bears, and all jagged-toothed animals [carnivora], this muscle is more powerful than it is in apes. It is attached to ribs 3 to 7, and if you pull on it from the head you will see them dragged upwards and dilating the thorax. If you do the same with the middle and anterior muscle, you will see the thorax dilate in proportion to the size of the muscles. *495*

These three pairs then of the higher muscles of the thorax are responsible for respiration. There is a fourth [pair] belonging to the first ribs [*scalenus brevis anterior*]. If you stretch them in their original position, you will see the first ribs drawn up and the upper part of the thorax dilate.

If the thorax be laid bare, you will see along it two other pairs of muscles along its length, one pertaining to the spine, the other to the sternum. The pair by the spine is made of nothing but fleshy tissues and lies on all the ribs of the thorax near the spinal muscles [*iliocostalis dorsi spinalis*]. That by the sternum [thoracic part of *rectus abdominis*] is of membranous tissue, except that the upper end is fleshy, but even that, taken all in all, has little flesh. The membranous part of them is not like the other membranes in strength; but it is a sort of ligament *496* or flat tendon, powerful enough, being marked off by a white line. At the point where they rise, separated from the abdominal part of the rectus muscle, this marking off is divided by the transverse lines [*inscriptiones tendineae*] and extends along the ensiform bone to the cartilages of the false ribs there, left and right. I mentioned this before,[109] bidding you spare it in dissecting the muscles from the sternum; for it adheres to them below and is removed with them, so that anatomists are ignorant of it.

This tendon, as I have said, is continuous with the rectus in *497* the region of the abdomen and overlies the ends of all the ribs that approach the sternum. It rises to the first rib in all animals where its fleshy character is obvious and where it gains some breadth. The delicate flesh is buffered by the tendon, and especially at the side parts, where the first rib passes from its diarthrosis with the spine towards the sternum.

The other muscle [*iliocostalis dorsi*] has a similar action. It is independent but extended along the spine so that it could be thought a part of some other muscle, just as that by the sternum is thought to be part of the rectus of the abdomen. Yet it begins and ends with the thorax in accordance with its own outline, which is rather more round than flat. The lower end is inserted into the spinal muscle, turning backwards with a slant so that, when taut, it both protects and pulls in the ribs. Nature seems to want these, to contract the thorax vigorously at need, when the abdominal muscles also visibly act. But I shall speak of them later.

498 There is another pair of muscles [*serratus posterior inferior*] outside the thorax which, inserted along the last ribs, draws down this end of the thorax. The head of this pair too coalesces with one of the muscles in the abdominal region. I shall explain it more clearly when I dissect them. For the time being let this suffice, that it draws down the last rib of the thorax along with the rib next to the last in most animals, especially the carnivores, and it sometimes reaches the third rib. I call the last rib, for the moment, not the small rib that is really false, which is separate from the others and is attached to the fleshy part of the diaphragm, but the rib that comes next to it, under which lies a delicate membrane now plainly visible and continuous with the membrane that undergirds all the ribs. I shall speak more clearly of these muscles a little later.[110]

Chapter 4

[*The Intercostal Muscles*]

It is now time to expound the so-called 'intercostal' muscles. *498* Neither their nature nor function was recognized by the experts in anatomy, any more than those of the muscles mentioned *499* before by which the thorax was said to be moved. They have, however, got as far with the intercostals as to know that their fibres are not extended along from spine to sternum but cross one another. Yet none has written that their position is oblique or that they are twofold, the outer fibres slanting in a direction opposite to the inner.

Ignorant of this, it is obvious that they did not know anything about their function. For the present it will suffice to grasp their nature alone. When I deal with the living animal, however, I shall say a word on their activity, though in my *De causis respirationis*[8] I made clear the function of all the muscles moving the thorax. Now I say only this, that when all the previous muscles are [cut] away, the position of the fibres is clearly seen to be oblique in the mid-part of the ribs.

One must start examining them from the spinal muscles. *500* Observe that the higher of the two ends of each fibre is nearer the spinal muscles and the lower farther away, so that each runs slantwise anteriorly, and does not extend straight up. If you cut out the spinal muscles too, you will see there also the fibres under them slanting in the same way. To observe these at their best, the animal should be thin, large, and old. In sleek young animals the quantity of moisture and flesh conceals them. But given these conditions you will plainly see, springing from the bones and nourishing the flesh, delicate fibrous ligaments.

It is as in the wicker baskets in which they curdle milk [for
501 cheese]. The fibres from the bones that I called ligaments are comparable to the reeds [of the basket], the blood to the milk itself, and the flesh to the cheese, for it originates from blood as cheese from milk.[111]

Beginning then from the spine and following the fibres, examine each one and observe its obliquity. If you do this going forward to the sternum, at one point you will see the direction of the fibres changing as the ribs do. For the rib does not reach the sternum with the same slant as that with which it started from the spine, inclining from above downward, for when it approaches the sternum it becomes [costal] cartilage instead of a bone and takes the reverse direction to before, running obliquely to the sternum, with which it articulates.

Where the [costal] cartilage is first produced, the ribs have a bend [anterior angle] that is curved rather than angular. The cartilages* [there] reverse their direction, running obliquely from
502 below upward. This happens with all the ribs except only those the ends of which do not reach the sternum. The direction of these [floating] ribs, from origin to termination, is uniform, and devoid of such a bend as that of the ribs articulating with the sternum.

They call those ribs 'false' which terminate in a cartilage of considerable size and have the diaphragm attached. [The cartilage of these is] a guard for its attachment, since Nature acts, as ever, with foresight in causing the diaphragm to spring forth not from the outside parts of each rib, nor from the end, but short of it, and from the inside parts. These ribs have their fibres slanting downwards along an oblique line. Those articulated with the sternum accommodate their fibres to the change of direction.

The outer fibres of the intercostal muscles lie, according to their nature, in a reverse direction from the inner, crossing like an X. Try to see them by detaching the ribs from the sternum,
503 for thus the whole expanse of the thorax cavity will be visible and with it the direction of the fibres. To facilitate investiga-

* Text reads 'fibres'.

tion, bend [the ribs] all back to the spine. You will see the false ribs from within, with fibres running in opposite directions within and without, throughout their length. All the other ribs have a division at the cartilages, being like the false ribs throughout their extent, but in the cartilages as far as the breast of the opposite kind.

Chapter 5

[*The Diaphragm*]

There remains one muscle of the thorax, and that not the least important, called PHRENES. Plato thought the PHRENES [or diaphragm] to be merely a partition between two parts of the soul, the appetitive and the irascible [or spirited].[112] But the diaphragm is not only this but—as was shown in my *De causis respirationis*[8]—of all muscles the most useful to the animal in respiration. *503*

This muscle has an origin of such a kind as I have described for the costal muscles, in numerous delicate ligaments springing from the bones with simple flesh coagulated round them. In the middle of the diaphragm, which may itself be likened to a large circle, there is a smaller disk of tendinous nature, in the midst of the first. There the fibres lose their fleshiness. *504*

These parts of the diaphragm can be observed when the sternal ribs are loosened from the upper parts. It is not possible, however, to get a clear grasp of its whole nature without previously severing the eight abdominal muscles. We must therefore proceed to the dissection of these. [See p. 140.]

Chapter 6

[*The Abdominal Muscles*]

Though I know that you remember them, I would remind you of the next steps I take. For it is not likely that this work will remain solely among friends. It will pass through the hands of *504*

many, some ready to cavil at everything, others to extract and
505 learn the best in it. It is for them that I recall what is known to my friends, and repeat what I now say.

I have often dissected the abdominal muscles immediately after the death of the animal by suffocation, and then [dissected] the intestines, stomach, liver, spleen, kidneys, bladder and, in females, the uterus also. To avoid putrefaction I have been accustomed to dissect on the first day these parts only for my friends to see, and then on the next day to turn to the other parts and to dissect them in the order followed here from the start. I shall explain a little later how to handle the parts within the abdomen when one starts from them. Now I shall pass to that part of the teaching which follows on what has been said.

The ribs, detached from the sternum, which I advised you to bend back to see within them [p. 132], you must bring back to their original position. Then strip off any remains of skin on the abdomen and start dissecting the muscles under it.

506 Begin with the largest and outermost of all [*obliquus externus*]. It arises from the thorax, and is spread upon the abdominal muscles. You see its origin clearly when the muscles described [Bk. V, Ch. 1, p. 120] have been dissected. It lies next the largest of the high muscles of the thorax [*pectoralis major*] with its digitated terminals inserted on the ribs. The ends of these processes represent the origin of this muscle, bilaterally symmetrical.

The first of the attachments, situated by the sixth rib, lies under the termination of the anterior [*serratus anterior?*] of those muscles moving the thorax. Next it springs from all the other ribs, near where bone passes into cartilage [*costochondral junctions*]. The first false rib also has something analogous to this bend, for this eighth [rib], counting from above,
507 runs up toward the ensiform cartilage, while the other [false ribs] fall increasingly short of it, the lower being always shorter than the one above.

This first pair of abdominal muscles [*obliqui externi*] arises from all these, and its oblique fibres pass towards the front of the abdomen. They are extended through the length of the abdominal wall, reaching the innominate bone at the pubes, each on its own side, and inserted in front of it through a strong membranous tendon.

The strength of this tendon is sometimes diminished at the groin. This area, thus becoming relaxed with the tendon, admits into itself some parts of the underlying organs—intestines or omentum—and this is now called a 'hernia'. This membranous tendon is set a little above the groin, so that the peritoneum passes through along with the tissues surrounding it, about which I shall speak again. The parts of these muscles, which are extended over the front of the abdomen, end in a *508* delicate tendon, mounting the rectus muscles superficially.

So too the tendon of the second pair of the muscles in the abdomen [*obliqui abdominis interni*] whose fibres have an oblique position at right angles to the first, becoming membranous, lies on the anterior muscles. Each of these [oblique abdominal muscles] begins from the bone of the flank [*ilium*], and has a fleshy origin. From there they are carried up obliquely, riding on the transverse muscles (at right angles), and are inserted fleshily into the ends of the four false ribs. Their tendon, the delicate one, in which they were said to terminate, is between the rectus muscles and the tendon of the muscles we spoke of before. The tendons of the two muscles you will think become one, for it is difficult to separate them, especially when we begin with these parts, in dissecting the animal as a whole. In this operation, when we start it is easier to separate the tendons if we follow up each muscle, for the tendons are continuous with the fleshy part where it ends.

Observing it delimited by its own borders, you will find *509* without difficulty the membranous tendon springing from each muscle. This tendon is produced at the side of the rectus, at the rib. In front, the recti touch each other with their anterior sides. To right and left they have the membranous tendons mounting on them [as the rectus sheath]. Their substance is fleshy above throughout, never true tendon, so that they are even attached fleshily at the pubes. There they adjoin as they do below the animal's navel. The higher part of them, as I said, lies side by side but not united. Regard them as the third pair of the eight abdominal muscles.

The remaining fourth pair [*transversi abdominis*] extend from the straight line of the ilia and the transverse processes of the *510* vertebrae in the loins. The muscle is not produced immediately, but a strong membranous ligament springs from the said bones and as it goes forward it acquires transverse fibres, assuming the appearance of a muscle and extending under the inner sides of the ends of each of the false ribs. Just as they turned into muscles by acquiring fibres, so later discarding them anteriorly, they terminate in a flat tendon.

This tendon, like most of the phenomena I have mentioned, has remained unnoticed by most physicians. Being membranous and light, it is attached to the peritoneum, and the resultant tissue is not thought to be, as it looks and in fact is, composite, but a single membrane. You must try then to examine its unification where first the tendon arises from the flesh and mounts on the peritoneum, since if it be rent there it cannot be separated [from the peritoneum] unless one has practice and knowledge of the nature of each.

In abdominal wounds, in 'suturing' as it is called, they *511* stretch up and sew together the composite tissue formed from both these parts, to wit, the peritoneum proper and the termination of the membranous muscle [*transversus abdominis*]. The peritoneum itself is very like extended webs of spiders, simple and very delicate, not like some tendons which dwindle to membrane and yet show (to those who examine them in a good light) delicate interwoven fibres within; but not so the peritoneum, for it is simple (as has been said), wholly continuous, homoiomerous,[53] and indeed one of the primary tissues. And you see it clearly, as it is by nature, in the lower parts [i.e. below the *linea semicircularis*] where it is alone, the oblique muscles being separated from it. For they mingle and are conjoined with the recti, leaving the peritoneum.

Enough has been said of the eight muscles of the abdomen, at least for a first review of the anatomical operations.

Chapter 7

[*The Abdominal Muscles continued*]

I must next explain how best to conduct the dissection from here. *511*

Remove the skin of the abdomen where there is no danger of cutting or injuring any of the underlying tissues, for the sub- *512* cutaneous tissue here is separated from the muscles. Anyone guided by the nature of the tissues can do this.

In passing laterally to the false ribs, if you are careless you may tear away the head of the small muscle* which, I said, runs into the armpit and was unnoticed by the anatomists [*panniculus carnosus*]. For the membrane continuous with the skin acquires at intervals fleshy fibres, first greater, then less, and then again robust, which extend as far as a muscular strand which is both thin and flat. This runs up to the armpit, where its fibres converge into a narrow fleshy strand. If you strip away its expanded lower origin with the skin, you will find that the fleshy part extended to the armpit is rent. If on the one hand you are dili- *513* gent and seek the point from which it is torn and do not find it, you will be full of doubt, as I was at first. But on the other hand, if you are careless and easy-going (as our anatomical predecessors demonstrably were in many of their operations), holding this fleshy sheet to be of no account, you will cut or tear it away from the underlying tissues and throw it away. As to the need for exercising precision in removing the skin there, enough has now been said [Fig. 8].

When the whole abdominal region has been laid bare, you must dissect the eight muscles as follows. The body is bisected by a straight line from above through the whole thorax. If you obtain clear indications, which I shall now mention, with reference to this line, you will get a useful survey in many places.

* The reference is probably to a passage missing on p. 477 of Greek text.

The first landmark is the end of the ensiform cartilage. Passing 514 upward from there through the middle of the sternum, you will have as your last mark the top of the sternum. This region is hollow, being bounded by the clavicles and the muscles running down from the head, as is clearly visible when the skin is removed. Extend this line downward to end at the junction of the pubic bones as limit. In the middle, between the point of the ensiform [and the pubes] lies the navel. For dissection of the first abdominal muscles, the skin being removed, start from the ensiform, cutting superficially round the navel. You see beneath a line [*linea alba*] whiter than the tissues on either side. This is the surest token of a satisfactory incision, for the fleshy muscles that I called *recti* are bounded thereby. It is whiter because no flesh lies under it.

The membranous tendons surrounding the recti, which are 515 produced from the oblique muscles, meet along this line. So cut it gently, so as not to incise any of the underlying tissues but only to sever the tendons from one another. If you do this well, you will find, as the proverb goes, that 'well begun is half done'. The saying takes every beginning to be half of the job, yet many beginnings are easily made. But the beginning in dissecting the muscles is really and truly half the task; for, unless well performed, there is confusion and disorder in all the subsequent operations. Nevertheless, even when it has been done as I directed, a double operation awaits you.

It is better to practise the easy alternative first, for there is hope that thus when you later undertake the harder you will not miss the mark. It is a simpler and easier operation either to pull up the rectus with a hook or pull it to the side with the left hand 516 and then make the incision gently, separating it from the underlying tissues. (As in this dissection you aided the cutting hand with the left, so it is better to do the same thing in first dissections in general, for in this way you will make the direct incision from the ensiform better.)

The four fingers of the [left] hand should be laid along the muscle and firmly and gently draw it to the side. If this is properly done for the two muscles, the space between them in which I directed you to make the first cut will be plainer to view. When you have separated it correctly, one hand will be enough, drawing the muscle that is being dissected gently to the side.

You must complete the operation as far as the navel region, till you are sure that a large portion of the muscle is bared. The peritoneum lies under it, along with the APONEURŌSEIS of the transverse muscles, from which the large muscles [*recti*] come naturally away, so that I myself separate them with my fingers. You must not do this at the first incision, but in the course of the operation. 517

When they have been clearly separated, the job may be quickly accomplished. Put your fingers beneath and strip off what remains of the underlying muscles. This done, either: [*a*] Cut away their upper end where lie their connexions: displace the muscles a little to make their outlines visible, for on the outside the tendon common to the oblique muscles lying upon them hampers their connexion; or [*b*] if you do not wish to cut their heads but would keep them all uninjured, try to strip off the tendon lying on them, which is thought by those who dissect carelessly to be a sheath peculiar to these muscles, but which is the kind most possess, being their own membranes united. Strip it off first in one piece, so that the outlines of the *recti* appear. Then divide it in two, assigning one part of it to the first and largest of the muscles [*obliquus externus abdominis*] 518 and the part under this to the second [*obliquus internus abdominis*]. Let these then be designated the 'oblique' muscles, and 'first' and 'second' of that kind. Under them is the 'third', stretched out lengthwise [*rectus abdominis*] under which lies the 'fourth', the muscle that runs transversely and adheres to the peritoneum [*transversus abdominis*]. [Here four lines of almost verbal repetition.]

When you have had enough practice in the processes I described, make an attempt, after the first straight incision, to separate from the recti first the superficial tendon of the 'first' muscle, then that which comes from the 'second' muscle.

Having shown that the two are mutually connected [as anterior layer of rectus sheath], begin the dissection of the recti. Thus you will get the whole business clear and avoid confusion when the muscles are separated with their own APONEURŌSEIS.

519 What you did at first with the thorax on the first pair of the muscles, beginning from above, do now in the opposite way, taking in hand the membranous tendon. Stretch it up gradually and try to strip off the first and largest muscle [*obliquus externus*] up to its origin. You will not be able at this attempt to trace its entire length, because of the thoracic muscles overlying it. Dissect it far enough to show its origin. Yet the remaining three muscles you can cut away without removing any of the overlying tissues [except the 'first']. Just as you dissected the first, starting from its tendon to its origin above, following the continuous substance of the fibres, so dissect the second [*obliquus internus*], passing from tendon to fibres and preserving their continuity up to their origin. You had already dissected the third fleshy muscle [*rectus*] to the navel. Somewhat below, you will see the one [second] muscle uniting with the other

520 [first], and intermingled with them there the lower part of the underlying pair of the transverse muscles [the fourth]. For the latter recedes from the peritoneum and leaves it bare [at the *linea semicircularis*].

This is enough for the present about the abdominal muscles.

Chapter 8

[*The Diaphragm again*]

520 Taking up the thread [of discourse] on the diaphragm, let us add what we left unexplained [p. 133] on its nature, since that could not be clear until the abdominal region had been revealed. Obviously—unless we would make many demonstrations on one animal—we can, by cutting through the parts in front, reach the subject of our investigation at each dissection.

What if one wished to demonstrate the nature of the

PHRENES alone, or if some problem arose about their structure requiring a separate anatomical operation? Would it not be reasonable on such occasions to cut right through the abdominal wall, including the peritoneum and, removing the viscera, to show first the origin of the PHRENES from the false ribs (of which I have spoken) and next the junctions into the spine and 521 then display and divide its parts, which differ in substance, position, action, and use?[113]

The muscle produces its APONEURŌSIS as a flat tendon, the mid-point of the diaphragm, which is surrounded on all sides by the fleshy muscles. On both its surfaces, above and below, is a delicate membrane [i.e. *pleura* and *peritoneum*]. These membranes you will display exactly if you attend to the following account.

The higher of them [*pleura*] being twofold lines the cavity of the thorax, right and left. The wide space within the thorax is, however, not continuous but partitioned by these membranes, which run straight up, through the length of the thorax, side by side except for the area containing the heart, where they retreat from each other and are separate. For where they receive in their midst [the heart]—itself girt by a membrane thicker than they—they reach as far as the ensiform cartilage.*

They are simple in their nature and are interwoven, and 522 spoken of as undergirding (HYPEZŌKOTES)[114] the ribs, but, where they run straight up to the throat, as 'partitioning' (DIAPHRATTONTES). They surround and protect the lungs. Their base lies on the upper suface of the diaphragm, corresponding to a similar membrane on its lower surface, which is very justly called the 'apex of the peritoneum'.

This [lower] membrane is continuous, lining the whole undersurface of the diaphragm, and where it is pierced for essential purposes, there it surrounds the structures that pass through it and extends along them. So also the membranes from above that underlie the thorax, extend along and encircle the vessels that pass through them.

* Here three lines of near repetition.

There are two perforations in the PHRENES. The larger, where the PHRENES adhere to the vertebrae, is prepared as a 523 path for the oesophagus (STOMACHOS) and the great artery [*aorta*]. The smaller receives the vena cava [i.e. *v. cava inferior*], which brings blood to the upper parts of the animal, and escorts it safely on its way, surrounding it with a connexion that is quite indissoluble in its passage to the thorax on the right.

None of these organs, vena cava, oesophagus, or artery, can escape the notice of anyone, when the lower part of the diaphragm is laid bare. The vena cava comes to the notice of dissectors first, since it is above and has nothing in front of it, when the [abdominal] muscles have been removed. To examine carefully the other perforation of the PHRENES, set about two operations. Firstly, open up the thorax through its length and follow the oesophagus as it descends to the diaphragm. Secondly pull and draw aside the stomach, and you will see its [cardiac] 524 end lying by the PHRENES. It is not firmly united with them as is the vena cava, but separated from them by slack tendons. This perforation is not quite circular here, but rather triangular, with the apex upward and the base firmly fixed at the back.

Of course Hippocrates is right in saying: 'Thus the PHRENES in this region surround both the ARTĒRIA and the STOMACHOS, as the ARTĒRIA is fixed in the very middle of the RHACHIS and the STOMACHOS lies alongside to the left. And what is more, a certain small PHLEPS and two NEURA pass through along with them'[115]—of which this is not the time to discuss details. For what is said of the artery or the oesophagus is not said so much in reference to them as such, but is incidental to the exposition of the perforation of the diaphragm—a thing that will be more completely expounded in its place.

Because of these parts that traverse it, and even more because of the loin muscles, the diaphragm does not fit naturally to the 525 spinal column as it should. For this circular muscle is active longest of all the muscles in the thorax. Wherefore it needed to be attached strongly by ligaments to firmly fastened bones.

But since the said organs perforce run down from above, and the muscles in the loins had to extend upward above the diaphragm, its muscle was bereft of union with the spine, or rather, deprived of union at this part.

For Nature, with her ready invention, never and nowhere fails in solicitude for the animal creation. Thus in the lower parts she does unite the diaphragm to the vertebrae by two very strong [*arcuate*] ligaments.[116] And the parts of the diaphragm surrounding the artery and the cardia [i.e. *crura*] extend over the succeeding vertebrae, to a greater extent in other animals whose thorax is strong and robust, though it is true that in apes they *526* are there, but connected by weaker ligaments. Later I shall deal with these differences.

Chapter 9

[*The Lumbar Muscles*]

Since our scheme involves an exposition primarily of the ape, *526* you should dissect that form and observe its diaphragm. You will observe also the muscles [*longus colli*] under the oesophagus (STOMACHOS), when you reach them, following the proper order in dissection and moving down to the fourth thoracic vertebra. For while the spine as a whole has muscles on the inner side, you will find only the six middle vertebrae of the thorax to be without them.[117]

Some of the muscles of the vertebrae, beginning above from the head, bend the upper portion of the spine, whereas those of the lumbar [vertebrae] bend only the lower portion. The vertebrae of the part between [i.e. T.4–9] are moved by [the *intrinsic spinal*] muscles on either side.

Since you have laid bare most of what is below the diaphragm, there would be no harm in removing from the lumbar muscles the membrane that lies over* them. This, as I shall explain later, is the peritoneum.

* Text reads 'under'.

When it is stripped off, you will see the psoas muscles; 527 strictly speaking they are single muscles, one on either side along the spine, for the two [parts on either side] are united at their origin above throughout the loin. When they approach the broad bone (called by some, as you know, the sacrum),[118] they separate, and are applied to the inner side of the ilium. At the same time they are joined there by many strands (SARKAI) from the ilium [*iliopsoas*].

Following now from below the strands that we call PSOAI you will find two tendons joining them from the ilia, one for either of the muscles. These tendons anatomists generally call APONEURŌSEIS of the muscles.

One of them, the inner [*psoas minor*], can be better regarded as a ligament than a tendon. It is inserted where the pubic bone joins the ilium. The other [*psoas major*] descends to the small trochanter of the femur. The former arises at the higher portion of the fleshy lumbar mass, and advances through the inner region. The latter arises [somewhat] lower, beside it and on the 528 outside and [lower still] that which comes to it from the ilium. The ligament of the former is longer. The tendon [of the latter], descending to the small trochanter, is shorter but powerful. Preserve it for the dissection of the muscles moving the joint at the hip.

If you examine carefully the other [i.e. the tendon of *psoas minor*], you will find it harder and whiter than tendons [commonly] are, as if of ligamentous substance. You must therefore regard it as a head rather than a termination of the inner parts of the psoas. So each head of the outer parts [of the *iliopsoas*] from the ilium has its head [EKPHYSIS] much smaller than that of the inner [*psoas minor*] but serving the same end. For the said two portions of the psoas, extending downward, bend the spine at the loins, and also the neighbouring METAPHRENON.[119] Similarly the muscles under the oesophagus—and of them I shall speak later—bend the upper part of the spine while involving also the vertebrae of the METAPHRENON.

The psoas provides the head of the tendon that reaches the trochanter of the femur. That which lies on either side of this head is the termination—not a head—of two muscles bending the spine. Thus each psoas muscle-mass has three parts: [*a*] the inner, with origin high up [*psoas minor*]; [*b*] the middle one, starting from a lower origin [*psoas major*]; and [*c*] the outside one, with its fleshy origins lower down [*iliacus*]. However, the ligament below this last starts from the upper parts of the ilium and therefore differs widely from the other two in length, as in thickness. *529*

Chapter 10

[*The Intrinsic Spinal Muscles*]

Examine carefully the origins of all the spinal muscles. They start from the second cervical vertebra [*longissimus intermedius* and/or *iliocostalis*], each having two separate heads. The space between them is fully occupied by the muscles missed by anatomists. (I have already gone through them thoroughly enough [pp. 109–12].) They become progressively more robust. Their origins are delicate, but at each vertebra an additional slip fuses with them and, passing through the neck, they become considerable in size and strength. They coalesce with one another at the end of the neck, becoming muscular there, on either side of the spine, so that the heads of both muscles number four. *529* *530*

Their fibres are oblique, some running from the spine forwards and downwards, and some the opposite way, starting from APOPHYSEIS at the side, but tending backwards and downwards. Give care to them when, in dissecting each muscle, you arrive at last at the loins. For there, from a certain membranous ligament arising in the regions by the spine, muscles spring which run up gently slantwise to the last ribs of the thorax [*iliocostalis lumborum*]. In other animals they are of considerable size, but in apes small, like all the muscles in the thorax.

These muscles draw down the last ribs. In other animals they 531 extend as far as the third and fourth ribs, counting the ribs from below; but in apes they reach [only to] the second and third of the so-called false ribs, sometimes only the latter. Anatomists have overlooked them too, cutting away part of them, I think, with the eight abdominal muscles, and leaving the other part adhering to the spinal muscles.

BOOK VI

On the Alimentary Organs

Chapter I

[*Principles of Comparative Anatomy*]

I decided that it was best to write this work in the same order as my *De usu partium*,[10] wherein the account of the limbs is followed by that of the organs of assimilation. To these we now proceed. 532

Likest man in their arms and legs are those apes which have neither long faces nor large canines; these [parts] increase and decrease in unison. Such [apes] have an upright gait, speed in running, a thumb to the hand, a temporal muscle,[120] and hair variously hard and soft, long and short. If you observe one of these characters, you can be sure about the others, for they always go together. Thus if you see an ape running swiftly upright, you may assume, without close inspection, that it is like a man. And you can predict that it has the other characters, namely round face, small canines, and a relatively fair-sized thumb. On the other hand, [you may predict] that its toes are smaller than those of other apes, that its temporal muscles are small, that the muscles from femur to leg do not reach very far down, and that the so-called 'coccygeal bone' is small.[121] You may assume too that this ape is not shaggy and that its hair is not very bristly or long [pp. 2–4; Figs. 2–4]. 533

So, too, if any of these characteristics are different, all the others will differ. Some such [apes] are very like the dog-faced baboon; they have a long coccyx, and may have a tail. These are also the shaggiest of apes, and have hard, straight hair, and their look is ferocious, while in the true ape it is timid. In the latter, too, the temporal muscle rises very high and stops near the coronal suture, as in men. 534

Again, in all such apes as dog-faced baboons, which have a long jaw and a small thumb, the teeth are large, with conspicuous canines, while the muscles that descend to the leg from the femur go very low, so that the ham is as though flexed. For this reason they cannot extend their legs properly, and so can-

535 not stand well. How could an animal unable to stand well either walk erect or run swiftly [on its hind legs]? Nor in their feet do they resemble man in having one toe large and the others small, but all their toes are large and the largest in man is not so in them. They have the root of a tail in the body, and their whole monkeyhood suggests the dog-faced baboon.

Though it is best practice to dissect the limbs of apes most like man, yet it is better to use one of those unlike than none; better, that is, to take a dog-faced baboon or tailed ape or 'lynx'.[83] In a word, any distinctly pentadactyl animals may be used, for these creatures have a collar-bone and a sternum of some breadth, wherefore they can walk on two legs, like a man, though imperfectly.

After such animals, next best are such as the bear, the lion and carnivores in general (KARCHARODONTA, sawtoothed). If the creeping kind, as weasels, cats, and mice, had not been

536 so small, their limbs too would have been useful for anatomical practice. All these have only four fingers, having lost the 'thumb'. Some indeed have a sort of sketch of one at its base, but note that even this is not far separated from the index as in man. If you have had practice on an ape, you will be able to dissect these animals too, for, among other characteristics, they also have the flat tendon attached under the palm, as also the muscles that move the fingers, wrist, and radius, though obviously not those that move the thumb.

In a word, the activities and appearances of the parts which each of these creatures outwardly displays will give you a hint of its internal structure. For parts that perform the same functions and have the same outward appearance necessarily have

537 the same inner structure.* Nature has created for each a body

* This sentence is repeated.

conformable to the impulses of its psyche. Wherefore they all use their bodily parts from birth as if taught.[122]

I have never tried to dissect ants, gnats, fleas, and other minute animals, but I have frequently dissected such creeping animals as cats and mice, and crawling things, as the snake, and many kinds of birds and fishes. This I did to convince myself that there was a single Mind that fashioned them, and that the body is suited in all ways to the character (ĒTHOS) of the animal. For from such knowledge you can predict, on seeing an animal for the first time, what kind of structure it has under the skin, and oft have I shown the truth of this. Nor did this idea come to me from another source, nor reach me otherwise than from my conviction that each animal has a bodily *538* structure akin to the character and powers of its soul (PSYCHĒ).

There is thus nothing astonishing in predicting the inner structure of each animal from its external appearance, and this the more if you see it in action, as I mentioned with animals that move upright. Nay, more: if you hear an animal's voice, you can make some conjecture about its vocal organs, not alone from the volume of the voice but also from its general character. I shall speak of this more clearly under the vocal organs.

I have enlarged on the point about the limbs because I explained their structure in Books I–IV of this work. So, hoping that those who had gained experience in them beforehand would follow the argument, using them as an example, I gave details on the similarity and identity of the other animals which you can discern from the activities and the shape of the whole and its parts. Thus a finger, wherever it is, has that structure in virtue of which it is a finger. If it be a particular sort *539* of finger, it has such a structure as fits that sort. So too of the ulna and radius and each of the other parts. In so far as it is ulna or radius, it has ever the same general structure, whereas as radius or ulna in any particular animal it will have a like structure in like animals and merely an analogous structure in the unlike.[123]

Whoso then is trained to use his reason and uses his natural ability, easily finds the elements that are identical and those that are different [in each creature]. Even one with neither natural gifts nor training may, by dissecting many animals, come dimly to conceive that it is neither by accident nor by chance that the identical element is present in each species, but by virtue of its own peculiar being; whereas it is by certain accidents that the element of difference is produced in the various particulars in what we call 'individuals' [of the same species].[123]

Wherever you see a limb extended and flexed, and again rotated, there must be in that limb muscles of two kinds, some
540 for extension and flexion, others for rotation. Consider, then, whether there is one bone in the member, as in the upper arm, or two, as in the forearm. If one, seek for straight and oblique muscles, if two (as ulna and radius), be sure that one produces the extension and flexion and the other the rotation. Consider also that among the muscles moving them, those responsible for the oblique movement have a more oblique position, those responsible for the straight movement a straighter. This characteristic is shared by all members with comparable movements. The size of the muscles and their form and position is alike in muscles that are alike in shape, and unlike in the unlike.*

Chapter 2

[*The Three Kinds of Alimentary Organs*]

541 On first hearing you may find unconvincing what I propose to say on the digestive organs, to which all the previous discourse
542 has been leading. Yet if you take pains to observe many animals, like and unlike in kind, it will no longer seem incredible, but marvellous, for they reveal one Art as the maker of all living things. In constructing the parts, He has ever before him their uses for His end.

Now there is one activity common to all animals. All require

* The same point is illustrated again in sixteen confused lines on little finger and thumb which are here omitted.

food. And you will find in each species threefold organs: first, certain organs made by Nature to receive and digest the food and to distribute [it] through the body; second, another kind to receive the 'waste products', which you may so name, or call them with Aristotle 'excreta' (PERITTŌMATA);[124] and third, parts for eliminating these.

The part in which all animals receive the food is called GASTĒR [*stomach* of modern nomenclature]. In it the food undergoes a first minor change. It is thus predigested for the liver which brings about a very great change in the nutriment that reaches it. From the liver veins conduct it, ready digested, *543* throughout the whole body.[125]

That the nutriment may be carried from the liver into the whole body, pure and with no waste-product, Nature has contrived organs fitted for the second kind of purpose. Some of these organs clear away the thin and light part of it, some the earthy and heavy part, some the intermediate, which is watery and serous. The organs that clear away the first are called by physicians 'bile-ducts' (POROI CHOLĒDOCHOI). The gall-bladder (KYSTIS CHOLĒDOCHOS) is named after the ducts. Those of the visceral organs which deal with the earthy and heavy part are the spleen and, of the intestines, the lower part as far as the rectum [lit. 'the part made straight'].[126] The organs of the third or intermediary kind are ureters, kidneys, and urinary bladder. That the elimination of waste products be controlled by the animal's will, Nature has placed muscles surrounding the ends of the passages of those parts of the third class.

It was essential for the regulation of assimilation that these three types of organ should be created by Nature in all animals. *544* Thus common and similar features in all are intestines, stomach, veins, and liver among the first kind; gall-bladder, bile-ducts for separating and evacuating waste products, attached to the liver, and further the spleen, are among the second kind; kidneys and the muscles that subserve [the organs] for elimination of excreta are among the third kind.

Chapter 3

[*The Three Grades of Digestion in Different Animals*]

544 Some animals live on stronger, some on weaker, foods. Nature has looked to this in making the stomach different in different kinds. If you see an animal new to you from India or Libya or Scythia, eating prickly food, be sure it has been given a large and rough stomach. If without upper teeth it certainly has more *545* than one stomach, so that the food swallowed into the first is later regurgitated therefrom, chewed in the mouth, then re-swallowed into a second stomach, and then transferred to another, and then yet again to a further [fourth] one.*[127]

Having learned of the world of Nature from your observations, you must expect her art to be the same in all her creations. Thus much we hold as to the arts of man, for without seeing all the statues by Pheidias and Polycleitus, we conjecture them from those we know. So whoso has experience of the works of Nature from what he has seen, can form an idea of the others. *546* We who have had a more extensive acquaintance with Nature's works are all convinced that the organs which digest food and prepare it are of a size and form that best fit the food to be taken.

I am thus assured that every animal which lacks upper teeth has several stomachs and ruminates. So the animal that possesses the upper row of teeth can neither ruminate nor have several stomachs but must have a single stomach like that of the flesh-eaters (SARKOPHAGOI). Horned animals have no upper teeth because, in them, the earthy excretion in the head is used up for the horns. It is not, however, because they are horned that they have several stomachs and ruminate, but, feeding on herbage (PHRYGANŌDĒ), they have no need of upper teeth. Of course the camel, though hornless, nevertheless ruminates and has several stomachs, because it eats herbage, but for this *547* very reason the inner covering of its mouth is rough, as is that of its entrails.[128]

I would have discoursed longer on the greatness of Nature's

* Here seven lines of repetition.

art as manifested in the animal world, did the plan of this present work allow. Let it suffice to have illustrated it for the argument. You will find the organs of assimilation in whatever animal you examine, as I have described in Books IV and V of my *De usu partium*.[10] For example, you will see coursing to the gate (PYLĒ, *porta*) of the liver all the veins from intestines, stomach, spleen, and EPIPLOON [*omentum*] as it is called. This EPIPLOON is in the first class of organs of assimilation which digest the food, for it is provided as a sort of covering united to them for warmth's sake.

Omitting then, in the present account, any consideration of differences in the intestines and belly, you will find all the features I am going to mention in all the animals on which I advised you to gain anatomical experience. First and foremost *548* observe apes, and among apes, those that most resemble man, and, after them, all to which you can give the name 'animals' (ZŌA). Of these first all that form the ape-like class, and after these bears, and then next the carnivores, then mice and their kind, and then the so-called 'whole-hooved' animals, and sixthly, the ruminants.*

The ancients referred obscurely to these classes when they laid it down that their own anatomical accounts should always be verified only in those 'of a nature near to that of man'. But with the digestive organs, not only do all the animals mentioned in my *De usu partium* possess them, but many others too which are far removed from man: animals which crawl, creep, and swim.† . . . And what shall be said of these things in elephants and camels and Nile horses [hippopotami] and all such *549* animals? For they have all the characteristics in the digestive organs described in that work. Whichever of these animals you have to dissect, make the experiment in two ways, sometimes starting from the muscles of the abdomen.‡

* This sentence in effect repeats the previous sentence.

† Here two irrelevant lines represent a hiatus.

‡ The chapter ends with four corrupt and meaningless lines here omitted.

Chapter 4

[*The Peritoneum*]

549 I shall first state what comes first in the account of their structure. Severing all the muscles of the abdomen from XIPHOEIDĒS cartilage to pubic bones, you encounter a *550* delicate, widespread, web-like tissue, the so-called peritoneum.* This membrane is, in substance, one of the simple primary bodies well named HOMOIOMEREIAI.[53] It has the name peritoneum as stretched round (PERITETASTHAI) all the intestines, viscera, and vessels between the diaphragm and hips. It surrounds all the organs between these, including womb and bladder.

Think of the animal which we are dissecting as lying on its back. You will be told of parts lower in depth, that is, all the parts round and along the spine, those lying along the bone called 'flat' (PLATY) [*sacrum*] as far as the ischium and pubis, and, on the other hand, of the parts that are higher in depth, as those round the navel and the skin continuous with it, and *551* those by the hypochondria.†

Around all these, then, and around the parts which lie between them, this delicate membrane is wrapped. It cannot easily be peeled off without tearing things apart. This is particularly so at the diaphragm and at the two muscles in the EPIGASTRION, one at each side [*transversi abdominis*]. Where these have a flat and tendinous fascia (APONEURŌSIS) the peritoneum is attached to it inseparably. Know, therefore, that the stitching up of belly [wounds] is possible only by including peritoneum with this fascia.

The peritoneum, separated from all the organs in contact with it, is as a container (SPHAIRA), having outgrowths in some places and perforations in others. Proceed then to detach the peritoneum by finding out where it separates from the

* Here five lines of verbiage as to whether the peritoneum be 'coat', 'covering', or 'membrane' are omitted.

† Paragraph somewhat abbreviated in translation.

attached muscles. This is in one place not far from the navel where it is separated from the transverse muscles [*transversi abdominis*] and stands alone [as the arcuate line]. Here you can preserve it without difficulty when you strip it from the surrounding parts, but you will find it difficult when, moving upward, you encounter the transverse muscles. 552

You will realize its nature if you observe it exactly in the parts where it stands alone. You will recognize that they err who [think they] stitch it up alone in abdominal wounds when, in fact, it is with the APONEURŌSIS. It is plainly visible as it rises to the navel, where it is united with the delicate tendon of the transverse muscles from which, I said, it is not easily separable without being torn.

If the animal be large, it is possible for you to attain your object and preserve the continuity of the peritoneum as far as the false ribs. There transverse muscles end and another muscle, the PHRENES [*diaphragm*] succeeds them. The nature [of the diaphragm] is that of a true muscle of circular form, the centre being tendinous surrounded by a circle that is fleshy as far as its attachment, of which I speak at greater length in discourses devoted to it [Bk. V, ch. 5 and 8]. Here it is discussed as far as necessary for explaining the relations of the peritoneum. 553

Where the transverse muscles end, the peritoneal membrane extends under the fleshy part of the diaphragm, from which it can be stripped as you did from the other muscles. But in their case you were moving in the length of the animal towards the thorax; now you will have to move down to the spine, where the diaphragm is attached. The union of peritoneum with the fleshy part of the diaphragm is not so hard to dissolve as it is with the sinewy part. But, with care loosening is possible as far as where the vena cava enters the convex surface of the liver and is attached to the diaphragm, with which we are not concerned.

On the left of this junction there is another lower down, by the starting-place of the stomach (GASTĒR), which they call its 'orifice' (STOMA) where the gullet (STOMACHOS) comes to an end at the diaphragm. The peritoneum extends here to 554 the orifice of the stomach, and its substance becomes thicker there, so that it is not hard to strip it from the expansion (KOILIA). Just as it is thickest there [over the stomach] so it is thinnest over the liver, to the parts of which it is a true protective tunic (CHITŌN). Some call the peritoneum as a whole a CHITŌN since it enwraps stomach, liver, spleen, kidneys, intestines, bladder, and uterus, but what does it matter?

Leave now the liver and follow the peritoneum as it surrounds the stomach until you reach its most convex part. As you strip it you will see a large vein, coursing as though superficially for the length of the stomach [*gastro-epiploic vein*]. From 555 that superficial vein numerous delicate branches extend into the stomach, one after another, in a series along the line of the greater curvature.

The peritoneum, extending over the stomach, meets these veins, clings to them, rises up to the large vein from which they spring, forming a cover, a protection, and a support for them. For it is there double and embraces the stomach completely. In making this circuit, it reaches the anterior and lower part and returns again to the convex part, to meet the same vessels [*gastro-epiploic*] as it met when moving down from above. Thus it surrounds and supports them, coming up from this large vein. In this space between the two layers of the peritoneum lie the vessels of the stomach, and also the large high-placed vessel, with an artery lying beside it, similarly giving branches in its course [right and left *gastric artery* and *vein*].

Chapter 5

[*The Great Omentum and Other Abdominal Structures*]

556 Just as small offshoots of the large vessels move down into the stomach, so also other small branches from the large vessels [*gastro-epiploics*] run down unattached toward the navel, surrounded by the two portions of the peritoneum [*great omentum*]. This body, compounded of two folds of peritoneum and vessels

between them, reaches in some animals only a short distance below the navel, but in others as far as the pubic bones. It was named by the Greeks of old EPIPLOON or EPIPLOUN. It is largest in men and apes. For this reason many men are called 'epiploon carriers' (EPIPLOOKOMISTAI). They give this name to the hernia [*epiplocele*] formed when the omentum breaks into the passage to the testicles of which I will speak later. No animal except the ape suffers from this disorder. This organ has[129] been named EPIPLOON as 'floating on' the intestines without uniting with any, except perhaps by a few 557 strands [adhesions] on the right to the colon. I have explained the origin of the higher portion of the epiploon: its other parts must be next discussed.

Having examined the veins running downwards from the convex part of the stomach, surrounded by a double layer of peritoneum, you must then pursue the vein in the convex part at either end. On the right side of the animal it will bring you to the attachment of the small intestine as it leaves the stomach; on the other side to the sinus of the spleen.

This organ lies on the left. Its convex part is toward the ends of the false ribs and their continuation along the left flank. Its concave part faces toward the right, opposite the liver and the parts there. The [splenic] vein which extends from the convexity (TĒS KOILIAS) of the stomach into the cleft of the 558 spleen, passes into it just as it does to the stomach, that is, high up, supported by the peritoneum where it is double. As in the case of the stomach (GASTĒR) it sends forth many small branches, some into the spleen and others into the omentum. But the vessel is not exhausted at the spleen; for its residue, with the residue of its conjoined artery, passes down through the left flank, serving as a starting-point from which the omentum arises.

The omentum extends with its vessels until they are used up, dividing like branches into twigs and shoots. So too the part of the omentum in the right iliac region can be traced down with the vessels which are continuous there with the convex part of the stomach, so that if you follow them you get a good view of its origin.

These parts [of the omentum] in the flank lie between the upper region characterized by the convexity of the stomach and

559 the lower which I have not yet discussed. Each of them is continuous with the portion in the flanks. They do not differ merely in that one is above, the other beneath, but also in the size of the vessels, for the lower part of the omentum has veins less in number and size.

It [i.e. the omentum] springs from the convexity of the stomach [EK TŌN SIMŌN TĒS KOILIAS), whence also it derives vessels. Certain remnants of these branch there into the stomach and are carried away downwards with it. All these parts are continuous with each other and together form a single body, the omentum, shaped like a purse, pouch, or bag, having for its mouth the attachment to the stomach above, while below, its body is the remaining part extending downward. You will realize more clearly that this is so if, after cutting it away there without perforating it or tearing any other part, you seek to fill it with watery or fatty substance.* For it will be

560 wholly filled with this as long as it remains sound and continuous, like a purse. It is easier to remove it completely from the animal, since short attachments to spleen and colon remain after it has been quite separated from the first attachment. Sometimes, though rarely, it is attached to one or other lobe of the liver, or here and there sporadically to a false rib. In general it is separate from all the other tissues, except stomach, spleen, and colon, to which it is always attached. The nature of the omentum and its origin you will learn easily if you dissect it as I have described.

When all the other tissues have been removed from it, try to strip off the peritoneum, starting again from the convex part of the stomach at the pylorus and the origin of the intestines, or again starting from below (where I said it remains isolated from the fascia of the transverse [abdominal] muscles) and rising

* Reading STEARTAS for the inappropriate STEREAS.

towards the pubic bones. There you will see the peritoneum covers the bladder and uterus. Moving upward over the lower, deeper parts (where lies the MESENTERION, also called MESARAION),[130] you will trace it over the parts in the lumbar region where are the kidneys. You will reach them also if you work down from above, for, as I said at first, the peritoneum, being one continuity, enwraps all the digestive organs in the front parts of the belly (GASTĒR), while at the spine it is both firmly fixed below and widely embracing. *561*

The thickness [of the peritoneum] is not the same on all the organs round which it is wrapped. On the liver, as on the spleen, it is very thin, but not so on the kidneys. It is at its thickest on the stomach, intestines, bladder, and uterus, so that some have been misled into thinking it a special part of these organs. This is not without reason in organs that are sometimes full and distended, since it is then distended along with them, and this, were it thin, would be painful. *562*

That all these parts are covered by the peritoneum you will learn by removing it as described. You will be able to grasp how the mesentery is produced from it if you strip off first the parts of it round the pylorus and beginning of duodenum (EKPHYSIS), then in turn round the empty [*jejunum*] and small intestine, and then that round the large intestine. For the peritoneum encircles all these, but, as they contain many convolutions, of course, there must be a convex and a concave side of the curves.

The vessels running through the mesentery to each of the intestines pass into their concave part and no vessel enters the convex part, nor is there any other junction, either with another organ or with each other. In these regions it is not surprising that all the parts are easily stripped and bared of peritoneum. At the concave region it is necessary to tear it away instead of stripping it from the vessels.* *563*

* Here seven lines on the irrelevant subject of blood-flow, evidently a scribal displacement.

Chapter 6

[*The Peritoneum again*]

563 When you operate as described you must remove all the intestines, but leave in the animal the MESENTERION, so called from its position, MESARAION from its peculiar substance.[130] It is set between the intestines and runs spirally (EN KYKLŌ) round, all the veins coming down to it from the liver, with the arteries and nerves lying beside, [distributed] according to each of the intestinal folds. Where the peritoneum extends over the vessels and intestines it is single; but where it acts as *564* an intermediary it no longer acts as a mere covering but as a twofold ligament.

You can recognize and demonstrate the peritoneum without following the whole sequence of operations that I described, after the division of the parts in the abdomen. Cutting evenly with a sharp knife the most convex part of an intestinal curve, so as to sever the outer membrane or coat (CHITŌN), but keeping the inner intact, try to peel it off on both sides of the incision until you reach the concave part of the curve. Give care here and follow both peeled layers which you will find to meet, so that they become continuous.* Thus they form a double body with the veins that run down into the fold between them.

565 It has been noted that an artery and small nerve lie beside each other here. Just as the intestine is encircled and guarded by the embracing peritoneum, so the triple complex of artery, vein, and nerve is surrounded by peritoneum to form a single body. There are many such groups, one at each turn [of the mesentery], and many spaces between, where the peritoneum is therefore simply doubled. The structure of the MESARAION is formed therefrom, in substance like the omentum which also comprises an artery, vein, and nerve, as one strand. Between these strands is nothing but double peritoneum.

The similarity between omentum and mesentery† is not

* Here three displaced irrelevant lines.

† Text reads PERITONAION.

apparent, because of the quantity of fat with which the omentum is laden in the spaces between the vessels. If the animal be adipose enough, the fat may so increase as to overrun the vessels, *566* and in such creatures fat is seen also in many parts of the peritoneum. This is particularly so in animals with small vessels and viscera. Fat liquefies with heat, and is preserved by cold. It is therefore concentrated round fibrous (NEURŌDĒ) parts and in those subjects that are inactive.

Such then is the nature of the peritoneum and the tissues produced therefrom.

The arteries and veins of the mesentery extend down, like roots,[65] into the concavities of the [intestinal] curves, there meeting one another. Like roots of trees, these can be traced to a single origin. You will easily find the veins gathered into a single stem, namely, that by the fissure (PYLAI, gates)[131] of the liver. The arteries you will not trace so readily, for they are more bloodless and thicker coated, and they are in contact with a bloodless organ [*mesenteric root glands*] which they call the 'mesenteric link' (ARTĒMA MESENTERION) of ligamentous nature, by which the mesentery holds the intestines. This *567* extends upward with the arteries lying by it, into that part of the spine which lies between diaphragm and kidneys. Here is the starting-point of the arteries in the mesentery, sometimes in one root immediately dividing, sometimes twofold from the start. Such details will be set down with greater precision in the anatomy of the vessels.

Chapter 7

[*Coats of Stomach and Intestines*]

All the intestines being removed, consider the nature of the *567* stomach, liver, spleen, kidneys, bladder, and in females, MĒTRA [*uterus*]. Learn the nature of the intestines themselves by handling each. It is easier to consider these by themselves, removing them from the body, for you can then turn them to the light at will, manipulating them to gain accurate knowledge of 568 all their parts. It is well, as they lie before you, to consider the [lymphatic] glands in the mesentery, into which you can clearly see vessels running up from the intestines. Indeed, after the removal of the intestines it is possible to see them with the proper vessels in the mesentery. I shall speak of their nature in considering the glands.

In my *De usu partium*[10] you will find the whole truth as to stomach and intestines and other organs that Nature has created to deal with food. It is said that there are two coats to the stomach (KOILIA) and to each of the intestines, and one to the bladder as to the uterus. (The layers of which they are formed they call 'coats', but not quite rightly, for 'coat' (CHITŌN) means a garment or covering. For what some think the second coat of the uterus and third of the intestines and stomach (KOILIA) is peritoneum, extended over them, as I have said, and really and truly acting as a 'coat'.) The stomach is formed from two flat and delicate layers, lying one on another like the 569 folds of a garment. The inner has straight fibres, the outer circular. The peritoneum has neither but, like other membranes, its whole structure is quite simple and not even like a spider's web nor as though woven. In the intestines most fibres are circular, with a few straight fibres lying on them.

Chapter 8

[*The Liver*]

569 All these parts [hitherto described] pertain to all red-blooded animals and not only to those of the six classes [p. 97]. The liver [also] is found in all, and those that have a liver invariably have a spleen and bile ducts, but they do not all have a gall bladder attached thereto.

Those who have written on animals that, they say, do not have a gall bladder, do not tell the truth. Such is Mnesitheus *De elephanto*, for [that animal] has a gall bladder attached to the liver proportionate in size to the whole organ.[132] And in animals that have [a gall bladder] it is always in the same position, namely, in the largest lobe of the liver.

The lobes in the liver are not the same in all animals in number, kind, or appearance, nor indeed is the size of the organ the same. In gluttonous and timid creatures the liver is large and much divided. It is the reverse in the opposite types. Where large it is divided into more and larger lobes than in man. Herophilus writes of it most accurately and says: *570*

> In man the liver is of a good size, big in comparison with that in certain other animals of equal bulk. Where it is applied to the diaphragm, it is arched and smooth. Below toward the [abdominal] cavity and the vena cava, it is concave (SIMON) and irregular. Here it may be likened to the fissure through which the vein in embryos enters into it from the navel.
>
> The liver is not alike in all, but differs in different animals in breadth, length, thickness, height and number of lobes, and also in the irregularity of the front part at which it is thickest, and the arched top parts where it is thinnest. In some the liver does not have lobes at all but is round and undifferentiated.* In some however it has two, in some more, and in many four and in some more lobes.[133] *571*

Here Herophilus is right. Moreover, in the same Book II of his *De dissectionibus* he said with truth that 'not seldom in many animals and occasionally in man the liver occupies, to some extent, the left parts', specifying only the hare, and leaving us to investigate other animals. These I have decided to discuss in a forthcoming work. For the present, I say only what is useful as commentary on my *De usu partium*.†[10]

Chapter 9

[*The Intestines*]

Everyone knows that the nature of all intestines is the same, the differences being only in size and number of convolutions. The *572*

* Reading ANARTHRON for ANORTHON.

† Here ten lines of repetition.

elephant has the broadest intestine, the horse [one] very like it. The pig has a much convoluted intestine and the longest, with many small differences in the parts. The intestine has the same characters in a man as in an ape.[134]

The first part continued from the pylorus in such creatures is narrow. After this tract, which is twelve fingers' breadth (DŌDEKADAKTYLON) [*duodenum*] long, as Herophilus truly said,[135] comes what they call the 'fasting' (NĒSTIS) intestine [*jejunum*] because it is always found devoid of food. It bends downwards into a spiral in many folds. Next comes the 'slender' (LEPTON) intestine [*ileum*],[136] which in substance is the *573* same as the former, but differs in not being empty and not having so many folds. Next is what is called the 'blind' (TYPHLON) intestine [*caecum*], then the KOLON, on which at the end comes the intestine said to be 'made straight' (APEUTHYSMENON) [*rectum*][137] as far as the fundament [Fig. 22].

Chapter 10

[*The Spleen*]

573 The spleen lies on the left, having its concavity towards the right. From the liver there goes to it a vein [*splenic*], a branch of which goes on to the stomach. After sending branches to all the parts of the spleen, part of the vein continues to the convex part of the stomach and the rest to the left region of the omentum.

These features are common to all the red-blooded animals, but not so with either the size of the spleen or its colour. It is almost black in the lion and the dog, and in all spirited and hot animals. It is of lighter colour in the pig and in aquatic and colder animals. I shall try to describe such differences between animals in the course of the argument, so that whoever studies *574* it may obtain complete knowledge of the works of Nature. But now, as proposed at the beginning, I shall consider the rest of the digestive organs.

When the peritoneum is stripped away, so as to reveal its relation to all the organs below the diaphragm and the relations that they have with each other, cut up each of them, inserting a blade (ELASMA) of bronze, iron, silver, or wood. Anatomists usually call all such things by the common title of blades (ELASMATA), lancets, flat broad probes, two-edged lancets, specilla, oricularia, &c. You can make others like them from hard wood—mine are of box-wood—and such woods ensure that the instruments never break. I employ them, as I said for inserting into the mouths of the vessels in liver and kidneys: into the liver at the 'portal vein' (PYLĒ PHLEPS)—called STELECHIAIA by the younger anatomists[131]—and farther into the double vein in the convex part [of the liver] running up and down; into the kidneys from the large vessels on the spine; into the ureters, and into other parts, as I shall explain. *575*

Chapter 11

[*Vessels of the Liver*]

First I must complete the account of the liver. Into the most concave part run veins from the mesentery. They call this region in which they are all concentrated the PYLĒ [*porta*] of the liver[131] There, in all red-blooded animals, you will find a large mouth of a vein. Have several instruments ready, some narrower, some broader, so as to use the most suitable. Push one of these into each lobe, pressing it gently forward, and cut down on to it with a lancet until you reach the vein in which it is, for the instrument is clearly visible under the thin coat. Anatomists usually call also the tissues of the viscera 'coats', as I said before, for the stomach [p. 162]. I said that it had two 'coats' or layers, one over the other. *575*

Each vein in the liver has a very delicate coat, like that of no other vein. When bared, without cutting it, remove the surrounding substance of the organ between the vessels. You will thus display one large vein entering each lobe. This divides *576* into many small veins, like the trunk of a tree into branches. These again divide into twigs and end in delicate shoots.

The space between the vessels is filled with the fleshy substance of the organ. The disciples of Erasistratus call it PARENCHYMA.[138] This substance—call it flesh or PARENCHYMA—like padding in the intervening regions of the dividing vessels you can remove with your fingers, leaving bare the vessels that cluster in the lobe into which the instrument is inserted. What

577 you observe in this one lobe, you will find in all.

If the animal is of considerable size, you can preserve the biliary ducts and the arteries belonging to it along with the veins, baring them in the liver. If it is small, you cannot do this completely. It is thus better to undertake such operations on the separated liver in animals wherein the artery and biliary vessel are clearly seen beside the portal vein in the liver before removal. In small animals they are not visible at all in the separated liver, but before removal you can at least see the first division of the artery into it, for the artery is whiter than the vein.

Chapter 12

[*The Bile Ducts*]

577 You cannot follow [the bile duct] right to its end as it divides [repeatedly], but if you pay attention to the portal fissure, you

578 will see the duct running from the gall bladder to the beginning of the duodenum a little below the PYLŌROS.[139] In some animals you will see that the point where the small intestine issues is thickened round the PYLŌROS. Some do not think it right to call it 'intestine' until it is curved into spirals. And for this reason some call [the first part] simply 'outgrowth' (EKPHYSIS), others add 'duodenal'. Sometimes at the beginning of the duodenum (EMPHYSIS) the bile duct sends forth a branch a little above the pylorus. And at the same time you will see a small duct* going down with the [*superior pancreatico-*

* Reading PORON for MORION.

duodenal] vein that leads to the viscus [*duodenum*], running down into the membrane, enwrapping and dividing with it deep down.

Having examined carefully all these things, proceed to the convex part of the liver, cutting up that lobe the veins of which you laid bare at the concave part. You will see the veins dividing progressively in the convexity but not the arteries. Far less *579* are the biliary ducts here visible.*

You will see the veins here delicate and devoid of any membranous covering, like all those in the mesentery which some think have two coats. Every vein has fibres twining round it in diverse ways and a single coat, which is always peculiar to it, except where it chances to rise high and unsupported and needs membranes as coverings and supports.

I shall deal with the coats of the arteries in discussing the anatomy of the heart in Book VII.

Chapter 13

[*Kidneys and Ureters*]

Pass now to the kidneys. The right lies higher in all animals, *579* sometimes touching the large lobe of the liver. At the spine it is attached to the [*renal*] artery and vein. These vessels are of *580* considerable size and in apes are single on each side, but in certain other animals, as I shall explain later, are double. The kidneys have their concave parts facing each other, and the convex turned toward the side of the animal. In smaller animals you can introduce the probe as far as the concave part but not into the cavity itself. In very large animals, however, if you insert it immediately after death, you will see it clearly penetrating into the hollow of the kidney. You will see plainly each vessel at the EMPHYSIS (*hilum*) divide into several branches.

Observe the hollow of the kidney. In a small animal it is overlaid by a membranous body [*pelvis of ureter*]. At one part,

* Here four lines on the spelling of CHOLĒDOCHOS which we omit.

near the entry (EMPHYSIS) of the vessels, there is attached to it a hollow and elongated body [*ureter*] which some call by the general appellation common to such bodies, 'vessel' 581 (ANGEION), some 'duct' (POROS), and some 'artery' or 'vein'. But follow Plato[140] and me in taking little account of names and seeking first and foremost facts and next clarity in exposition.

The orifice of this duct [*ureter*] is perceptible unless the animal be too small. And you can insert into it, in two ways, a delicate instrument among those prepared—two-edged lancet or double specillum, call it what you will or, if you need something finer, a probe. [You can insert it] from the hollow of the kidney when you open it, into the duct, or again from the duct via the orifice into the kidney. This duct is called OURĒTĒR. It has a single coat of its own and, like all other organs that run there, it is covered by peritoneum as well. Some anatomists have discussed vainly whether this ureter should be called 'artery' or 'vein'. It has a single coat like the veins, yet not so thin a one as they.

582 If you strip off the outer membrane [*peritoneum*] from the ureter and lay it open to the bladder, you will find it of like substance to the bladder when the covering has been removed. You will also see the nature of the passage which runs obliquely [into the bladder], having a covering in the inside part comparable to the lid (SKYPHŌN) of a dove-cote [*ureteric valve*]. This covering is not something different from the substance of the bladder but a part of it, and so clearly fitted to its form that it is opened only by what passes through the duct [into the bladder].

When you bare the ureters of the peritoneum you will see that the [*testicular*] arteries and veins are both carried obliquely up to the perforations of the peritoneum. They start from below where the peritoneum covers the large vessels [*common iliac*]. They pass towards the testicles, leaving the rectum at the loins, 583 advance and rise to the groin, the peritoneum extending with them, covering and accompanying them as far as where the peritoneum is perforated on either side. For the offshoot that goes forward with its vessels is long, and the large sac of the peritoneum is pierced there. The duct descending to the testicle is a small offshoot of the great peritoneal sac in the lower abdomen [*processus vaginalis*]. That, however, which envelops the arteries and veins to the testicles does not issue from the great peritoneal sac besides the loins, but surrounds, as I have said, the vessels that nourish the testicles, and runs down with them through the duct. So the peritoneal offshoot becomes double there—one part of it forming the duct, just as if no vessel were to go through it, the other enveloping the vessels supplying the testicles, as if they did not come through the duct. I have described these vessels because of their association with the peritoneum, though they do not belong to the present discussion. 584

Chapter 14

[*Muscles which retain or expel Excrement*]

It remains to describe the third class of digestive organs that 584 are muscular and in the region of the abdomen, and that not only eliminate superfluities but also have power to produce efflations and sounds. There are others; at the fundament for binding and closing the end of the passage, drawing it in again when prolapsed during evacuation; and at the bladder for closing only.

When first anatomizing the animals it is preferable to start at once on the muscles in the abdomen, if you intend to dissect them *in situ*. You cannot see plainly those round the fundament unless you first remove the intestines and separate the pubic bones. It is now time for me to explain and for you to learn how to do this.

Since the pubic bones are united by a cartilage anteriorly, seek the exact line of junction. If you cut along that with a 585 large strong lancet, you will easily part them. When separated you will easily remove the skin lying at their base, without cutting through the fundament. Next, seizing each of the iliac bones, bend it backward and outward, until they too are loosened from their junction with the broad bone called the sacrum (HIERON OSTOUN).[118] Thus you display all the parts of the region between the sacrum and the pubic bones.

This procedure is the same for all the organs there. For if you would examine either arteries, veins, nerves, bladder, uterus, or muscles to the great trochanter, you must equally first separate the pubic bones and bend back the two ilia, parting the ligaments uniting them with the sacrum.

But we must get back to business. You will see overlying 586 each of the pubic bones from the inside a sheet of flesh [*m. pubocaudalis*] concealed by a membranous ligament springing in a circle from the bones themselves. The part of it [that corresponds to the *coccygeus* in man] that is continuous with the region by the sacrum has a ligament growing out of the bone which is continuous with the aforementioned ligament. Thus the whole ligament, in part issuing from the sacrum and in part at the groin, ends as one, turning into the head of a muscle that is not thick but completely membranous and flat, reaching the fundament at each side. If you preserve it carefully, you will learn its function from its position [*levator ani*].

Separate the muscle and the rectum from the surrounding tissues, then lay hold of the head [of the muscle] and pull the rectum by it. You will see how it is drawn up. It has no opposing muscle to draw it down, as have most of the parts. The anus is actually pressed down by the muscles of the lower belly which, with the diaphragm, compress the intestine and its 587 contents. It is often so extruded that it is not easily withdrawn by the two muscles [*pubocaudales*] mentioned before. So, when the animal is relieving itself, the eight muscles of the abdominal wall with the diaphragm all contract together when the circular muscle around the anus is relaxed. But at all other times this circular muscle is contracted and closes the anus.

You will easily see this muscle [*sphincter*] if you first cut away the whole skin in this region; and also [you will see] the junction of the coccyx[141] with the membranous tissues [*anococcygeal body*] which unite with the skin extending from the anus outside the circular muscle, Posteriorly this muscle has lying under it the end of the coccyx. Anteriorly it is fastened to the penis by another muscle [*bulbocavernosus*] which you will investigate later in dissecting the genital organs.

Now that you have exposed the muscle at the end of the bladder, at the so-called neck, you will see clearly that, both in function and action it resembles the circular muscle round the anus. It, too, closes the orifice before which it is set; hence some call it, as they do the other, a SPHINKTĒR.[142] *588*

There remain the eight muscles occupying the whole region below the diaphragm designed by Nature rather more for the digestive organs than the respiratory. Of them I need speak no more, as they were described earlier in Book V in the dissection of the outer parts [pp. 133–40].

BOOK VII

[*Heart, Lungs, and Arteries*]

Chapter 1

[*Organs of Respiration*]

589 My task in this book is to explain how to dissect the respiratory organs. I need not repeat the considerations of detail in my preceding book on the digestive organs which apply to these too, but every reader must remember them.

The most important organs for breathing are the lungs, heart, *590* and thorax. Next after these are two kinds of arteries. One kind is distributed from the left ventricle of the heart throughout the body. These beat with the same rhythm as the heart. They all spring, as branches from a trunk, from the greatest artery [*aorta*]. Some call it by that very name 'greatest' (MEGISTĒ), others simply 'the great' (MEGALĒ), others 'the thick' (PACHEIA), and others 'the straight' (ORTHĒ). The second kind of artery is that which they call 'the rough' (TRACHEIA). This is a very large one in the neck [*trachea*] and has many offshoots [*bronchi*] throughout the lungs. At the upper end of this large neck artery lies a sort of head called the LARYNX. This is named by more modern anatomists 'the head of the bronchus', because the trachea is not only 'rough' but also connected with the bronchi.

It was according to basic reason (KATA PRŌTON LOGON) that Nature created all these parts—some to fulfil essential needs of life itself, others as serviceable but not essential for the life of creatures. These have been detailed in my *De usu partium*,[10] Books VI and VII.

Chapter 2

[*The Pleura*]

In addition to these [organs] Nature created another structure of the same substance as the peritoneum and performing like functions for the organs of the pneuma as does the peritoneum for the organs of assimilation. And as that is called the 'embracer' (PERITONAION), for it is extended round (PERI-TETASTHAI) the digestive organs, so this is called the 'under-girder' (HYPEZŌKOS) [*pleura*],[114] since it undergirds the inside of the ribs. Like the peritoneum it has two other desig-nations, being called 'membrane' (HYMĒN) by some and 'coat' (CHITŌN) by others, membrane from its substance, coat from its function. It is woven finely as a spider's web and is 'homoi-omerous'[53] throughout. While lining the ribs it covers all the 'pneumatic' [i.e. respiratory] organs. So also the peritoneum is a membranous coat, as is the delicate MĒNINX [*pia mater*] to the brain, the periosteum to the bones, and those peculiar membranes* covering the heart [*pericardium*]. *591*

In many parts there are other membranous tissues. Some spring from the bones as ligaments, others from the attach-ments of the muscles as tendons. But this undergirding mem-brane [*pleura*] lines and clothes all the organs within the thorax, as does the peritoneum the organs below the dia-phragm. From it are also produced the membranes that partition the thorax, and in this way only does it differ from the peritoneum, in being double, not single. *592*

You will grasp the nature of the pleura exactly if you split at the mid-line the anterior bone of the thorax, which anatomists call STERNON, using specially strong sharp knives. Begin the operation by removing the tissues over the sternum, for when that is bared you can estimate the mid-line more accurately. Pay attention to this and divide the sternum right to the xiphoid cartilage; then work deeply toward the spine, separating the *593*

* Text says 'muscles'.

membranes. This is made easier by gently drawing asunder and bending back the two halves of the sternum.

As you do this the parts readily follow, but less so those about the heart. The pericardial 'membrane' or 'coat' round the heart—for this can be given either name, membrane from its substance and coat from its function—is fastened to the sternum, especially at its apical and adjacent parts [*sternopericardial ligament*]. You encounter this as you sever the sternum and later when you are separating the membranes that partition the thorax as a whole.

It is best to keep the pericardium entire and unimpaired (though even if it be damaged the anatomical objective will not necessarily be frustrated), for if the heart be not seen the open

594 spaces in the thorax will also remain undamaged. Indeed, we often intentionally lay bare the heart without damaging any of the thoracic spaces, while the animal is still livng. Later I shall speak of that operation.

Returning to our procedure—let us restate that any damage to the pericardium is to be avoided, but that, if damaged, at least the membranes that partition the thorax should remain unhurt; it is their preservation that is our aim. You will see each of these membranes continuous with itself, right and left of the thorax, lining the inner aspect of the ribs and the parts above the diaphragm and extending also over the lungs, as we saw the peritoneum covered all the parts below the diaphragm. Further, this membrane surrounds the higher vessels as the peritoneum [does the lower] and, like it, covers those by the spine and the great artery [*aorta*] and the accompanying vein [*vena azygos*] which nourishes the upper parts of the thorax and also

595 the opening of the stomach. Extending upward from there to the sternum the membrane remains double.

Chapter 3

[*Views on the Pericardium*]

The coat proper of the heart, called PERIKARDION, differs *595* from either of the others [i.e. from the *pleurae*]. It lies between them and is enclosed by them on either side. You will see this well in the dissection we are discussing, which is done on the dead animal. Above, extending to the clavicles, you will see the partitioning membranes [*pleurae*] in mutual contact. [Below] at the base of the heart (which some call its 'head') they surround the pericardium, embracing it, and each may be followed to its apex which is conical like that of the heart. The circular base [of the pericardium] surrounds the base of the heart like a crown, while the apex of its cone is in contact with the apex of the heart and united with the lower part of the sternum, at the end of which lies the xiphoid cartilage.

This [outer] layer of pericardium is not united with the body *596* of the heart, for there is throughout an appreciable interval [*pericardial cavity*] to allow for the movement of the heart. It is only at its circular base that it is united with the vessels springing from the heart. Of these you will learn more when you expose the whole [interior of the] thorax or remove the heart for separate dissection.

Chapter 4

[*Views on the Functions of the Lungs*]

That my account may be lucid, I shall now explain the names *596* which we have to employ. As all designate the pulsating organ KARDIA [*heart*], so they call each pulsating vessel ARTĒRIA.

It is easy to discern the arteries throughout the body by their pulsation and by their continuity with the great artery. But it is impossible to discern by the senses the pulsation of those in the lungs [i.e., branches of the 'venous artery', *pulmonary vein*]. In spite of this one might guess at [their nature] from their

597 continuity with the left ventricle (KOILIA) of the heart.[143] Nevertheless, some think they have not only a suspicion, or a well-founded expectation, but exact knowledge of their activity. The two schools claim knowledge in different ways, arising from different opinions.

The one school, following Erasistratus,[144] assumes that the arteries in the lungs [*pulmonary veins*] are empty of blood like the other arteries.[145] They hold that at each diastole of the heart the PNEUMA is drawn through them out of the lungs [into the left ventricle] and by its passage the pulse is produced in all the arteries throughout the body. They are persuaded that the pulse is not produced in these [arteries] by their own action, as is that of the heart, but by their being filled with the PNEUMA passing through them. They say, too, that the heart, when it contracts, sends forth the PNEUMA to the arteries.

The other school thinks that the other arteries [in the body] as well as those in the lungs [i.e. branches of the 'venous artery', *pulmonary vein*] contract and dilate by the same power as the heart. They say that the difference is that the power
598 belongs by nature to the heart and is infused into the arteries from it.

According to the first school, if, on a living animal, you cut through all ribs on both sides and examine the lung [you will find that] so long as the rough arteries [i.e. bronchial tree] convey PNEUMA to the smooth arteries [*pulmonary veins*] that come from the heart, you will find a kind of pulse in them, but when they [i.e. the rough arteries] are empty there will be none.

According to the second school, while the animal lives not only do the arteries in the moving part of the lungs go on pulsating but also those in the exposed part.

As for the received opinions of the experts, I have explained what consequences follow. But since in this work I am not concerned with passing judgement on opinions, but with the phenomena revealed by dissection, I shall try to guide you to the facts. Therefore make a straight incision in a downward direction along the length of the animal where the ribs are cartilaginous. With a single stroke of a large scalpel you can sever all the ribs below the first. Spare that rib for fear of the *599* haemorrhage that might follow your wounding the vessels under it. If you have succeeded so far, strip off the membrane [i.e. visceral layer of *pleura*] from the lungs as fast as possible. Then with your fingers remove the flesh between the [pulmonary] vessels and lay them bare. Try to see and feel if any of the vessels in the lungs has a pulse. Anything you find with a pulse you may regard as an artery. But unless its movement be clearly distinguished you should not call a vessel an artery, whether it spring from the left ventricle or the right, whatever some of the anatomists may say. They differ from one another over this terminology, for some declare that the vessel springing from the left ventricle is an artery or vein, others that springing from the right. A better course is theirs who refuse to call either of these 'artery' or 'vein' simply, but modify this hasty ascription by calling them 'arterial vein' or 'venous artery'. In fact four names have been given to two vessels by anatomical experts. *600*

I follow what I take to be the better view of those who call the vessel springing from the left ventricle of the heart 'venous artery' [*pulmonary vein*][143] and that springing from the right ventricle 'arterial vein' [*pulmonary artery*]. I think it preferable (since we cannot distinguish them clearly by the pulse) to call the vessel containing PNEUMA an 'artery' but, since it has the covering of a vein, to add 'venous.' So to the other I give the name of 'vein' from its function, but since its substance is that of an artery, I add 'arterial'.

It would be best, as I said, to distinguish these vessels by the presence or absence of a pulse. But as that is not clearly discernible by the senses, their names should be given from their communication with the two ventricles, with a qualification from their substance. Those who name them without adding a qualification pay attention to their substance only, or to their function only. By substance, the vessel springing from the right *601* ventricle of the heart is an artery, that from the left a vein.

Conversely, by function, that from the left is an artery, that from the right a vein.

Chapter 5

[*Coats of Veins and Arteries*]

It is now time to detail of what substance the vessels are made.

601 The veins throughout the body have come into being each with a single intrinsic coat, for the membrane that sometimes surrounds them is in contact with them only where they need to be bound to certain tissues or fixed firmly and protected. The arteries have two intrinsic coats, the outer [*tunica adventitia*] like that of the vein, the inner [*tunica media*] about five times as thick and harder. It consists of transverse fibres. The outer coat, like that of the veins, has longitudinal fibres, some slightly oblique, but none transverse. The inner, thick, hard tunic of the arteries has a woven sort of membrane on its inner surface, which can be seen in the large vessels. Some regard it as a 602 third coat [*tunica intima*]. There is no fourth intrinsic coat but, like certain of the veins, some arteries have attached to and round them in places a delicate membrane which guards or fixes them firmly or binds them to the neighbouring parts. The peritoneum does this to the arteries and veins, specially below the diaphragm, as does the membrane [*pleura*] in the region above which underlies the ribs within the thorax, as was told above [pp. 160 and 174].

What the arteries are throughout the body, such is that vessel from the right ventricle of the heart which branches throughout the lungs [*pulmonary artery*]. And what the veins are, such is the vessel from the left ventricle [*pulmonary vein*].[143]

Thus of the three vessels linked with the lungs, the one from the left ventricle is called 'venous artery', that from the right, 'arterial vein', and the third is the 'rough artery' [*trachea*]. The last is made of cartilages shaped like the letter SIGMA.[146] The round cartilages in this large artery are set in the anterior parts, associating in the neck with the gullet, and in the lungs with the 'arterial vein' [*pulmonary artery*]. [This trachea] is like a tree-trunk in relation to the 'arteries' [*bronchi*] in the lungs, and in those 'arteries' that branch from it. *603*

The parts between the vessels in the lungs are filled up by the peculiar substance which disciples of Erasistratus call PARENCHYMA.[138] You can remove [the lungs] from the thorax and dissect them like the heart itself, but it is not possible to realize their association with the membranes if once so removed.*

Chapter 6

[*The Great Vessels*]

To gain accurate knowledge of the membrane round the heart, excise the sternum thus: Force up and bend back the end of the xiphoid cartilage with fingers or hook, then sever all the parts attached to it. When you reach the end of the sternum treat it similarly, cutting freely on either side. Remove the pericardium gently from the subjacent tissues. In doing this, work upwards until you meet with the lower end of the gland called THYMOS[147] and, going yet higher, till you come upon the [great] vessels. *603* *604*

If the animal has been some time dead, and you cut one of the vessels, little blood will flow, especially if it has had its throat cut. If fresly killed or full-blooded, some blood will flow from the severed vessels at the root of the pericardium.

Having sponged this out, you can examine the matter with which we are now concerned. This is best done without blood being shed, for you will see the other parts more clearly, and particularly the root of the pericardium which is not attached to the heart itself but to the vessels arising from it. Of these that on the left is the great artery [*aorta*], that on the right the vein [*inferior vena cava*] arising from the liver, and two others, one of which I called 'venous artery' [*pulmonary vein*], the other 'arterial vein' [*pulmonary artery*]. You will see these clearly even before you bare the heart of its covering, and still more clearly *605*

* Here three lines of repetition.

when you lay it bare. Thus too you will see the arrangement of the bones which is visible when the heart is still in place, but even more plainly when the heart is removed.

Chapter 7

[*The Heart*]

605 In this operation you observe further that the heart is set between the two spaces of the thorax. Its movements reveal that it lies rather toward the left, and that for a double reason. Firstly, because the cavity for the pneuma (PNEUMATIKĒ KOILIA) [*left ventricle*] is there.[148] Secondly, because the whole organ is 606 thus inclined, for though the base is in the middle, the apex is not.*

All this is much clearer if you remove the cartilaginous ribs [*costal cartilages*] with the sternum. For this use a strong large lancet, so that by a single stroke you may cut through all of them in turn, aiming at severing each where the bone ends and the cartilage begins. But first take note of the position of the ribs in another animal, for a correct description of it in words is very difficult.

How one can best operate, guided by what is said, I shall now explain. Each of the ribs runs slantwise, downward and forward, starting at the spine, where it is doubly articulated with each of the [corresponding] vertebrae. When moving 607 aslant along the convex outer surface, having traversed its extreme curvature, it makes a bend thence, ceasing also to run downwards, and now turns upwards obliquely towards the sternum. Here it changes its nature, becoming cartilage instead of bone, and can be cut easily with a sharp, strong lancet. Such there are in the KEPHALIKA [instrument cases] called DELTOI by the ancients.[149] Veterinary surgeons also have such lancets. You should have instruments like these handy for cutting the cartilages, as you see in my own equipment.

* Here two lines of repetition.

Now cut the thorax as I have said, and each of the other parts as I have described for the pubes [pp. 167–70] and shall describe again in the next book. Cut straight down on either side and remove from the thorax the part as defined by the cuts that I mentioned a little earlier [pp. 173–4], telling you to begin from the ensiform cartilage. The position of all the parts within the thorax will, of course, be much clearer if the animal be dead. After excision of the sternum together with the costal cartilages, bend back forcibly the parts of the ribs connected with the vertebrae. You have seen me doing this with such violence that often some of the bones were broken or the ligaments attaching them to the spine were torn. *608*

If you do so, you will be able to see clearly all the parts in the thorax, and still more if the diaphragm be cut from the ribs, and even better if you separate two ribs one from another, cutting all the flesh between them. This will be necessary for you, in any case, when you dissect the parts of the thorax itself. But for the parts round the heart we are discussing there is no need yet of such an incision. It suffices to remove the sternum and the adjoining parts of the ribs. These are cartilaginous and have a direction opposite to that of the bony parts. The former descend obliquely from the spine to the front and lower parts, while the latter, starting in the manner I described, run obliquely to the breast-bone. *609*

Chapter 8

[*Substance and Motion of the Heart*]

You will [now] see the hollow vein [*superior vena cava*], extending straight to the neck, and the appendages of the heart called 'ears' (ŌTA) [*auricles*].[150] These latter are of a kind found nowhere else, though [their nature is] like that of the heart itself. Some of the so-called 'homoiomerous'[53] parts resemble other parts but have some slightly different substance, each having its own peculiarity which can be roughly, though not exactly, *609*

described in words, since what is clearly distinguished only by sight or touch cannot be so communicated. But it is possible to help the reader to a more accurate observation by saying that the heart is composed of fibrous strands, varying in position, a single fold of flesh enveloping each of them, for in this it re-
610 sembles all the muscles as well as the stomach, intestines, bladder, and uterus, but still the fibres do not have equal strength and thickness in all these. Nor has the flesh the same appearance, for that in the muscles is redder and softer than that in the stomach, uterus, bladder, and intestines, while that in the heart is firmer and has more varied fibres.

The muscles have uniform fibres, but not so the heart nor the proper coat of uterus or bladder. A careless glance will suggest that the muscle substance and the heart substance are alike (as are those of nerves, ligaments, and tendons), but the difference in these simple and primary bodies has been already discussed elsewhere [p. 58], and will be again as needed. Nevertheless, that the substance of the heart differs in many respects from that of a muscle, has been well enough demonstrated, and its activity also testifies to this. For the movement of the heart is involuntary and ceaseless, so long as the animal survives, while that of the muscles is often suspended, and springs to activity
611 in obedience to the animal's impulses.

All philosophers and physicians who are experts in natural science (DEINOI PERI PHYSIN) agree that activities accord with the peculiarities of the substance. Therefore all parts of the same substance are active in the same way, even in animals that diverge in other characters, while in the same animals parts of different character have different activities. Thus every heart has the same activity, and so, too, every thorax and every pair of lungs, but the kidneys, bladder, liver, and stomach do not have the same [activity] as any of these or of each other. So the muscles do not have the same activity as the heart, for they do not have the same nature.

If heart and muscle be cooked together and eaten, differences in their taste will be found, just as with spleen, kidneys, lungs, liver, tongue, or any other organ. All differ in taste, touch, *612* appearance, hardness, softness, density, and colour.

Those who maintain that the heart has not the same activity as the muscles because it has no motor nerves but, as they think, only sensory, make several mistakes at once. Firstly, they ignore the nature of the heart. For it is harder than any muscle, and plainly differs in the variety of its fibres, as also in colour and still more so in taste, a most important indication of a difference of nature. I think they can never have eaten a cooked heart or they would surely have known how much it differs from flesh, unless, of course, they do not even know that all kinds of flesh are kinds of muscle. So far they are blundering where they could have learnt by the senses.

Moreover, they err as to the nature of the nerves. They think that the brain is like them in all its parts, except that some are more, and some less, soft. Through some nerves [the brain] transmits the power of sensation to the parts below, through *613* others, voluntary movement. It is intelligible that all the nerves should have both these powers, but the soft are more suited for sensation, the hard for movement. Some of the strands from the same root divide into branches, some of which can be followed into muscles, others into other parts. This happens with the third cranial pair [*trigeminal*] and the sixth [IX+X+XI]. From the latter the heart receives a strand, for from it [*vagus*] not only heart and lungs, liver, stomach, mesentery, and intestines, but also all the muscles of the larynx and certain others receive branches.[151]

Those who say that the heart is a [mere] muscle, notice nothing, not even that, had it lacked motor strands, as they think it does, it could neither move by volition, nor receive its pulsatory activity which must presumably have some cause. This, they must claim, is either a gift from the nerves or is inherent by nature in the organ. Now it does not come from the *614* nerves, for all the organs that receive nerves would have shared in it and when they were severed the heart would not continue beating. But we see neither of these things happen.

Therefore the power of pulsation has its origin in the heart itself. It would not have arisen if the organ had had the same nature as the muscles throughout the whole animal. But the fact that the heart, removed from the thorax, can be seen to move for a considerable time is a definite indication that it does not need the nerves to perform its own function. Those who think the heart a muscle seem ignorant of these things and to have failed to notice that pulsation is of its essence, by the high virtue of some special element in its nature.

Their error then is great who think the heart a muscle, but theirs less who assume the oesophagus (STOMACHOS)* to be of exactly the same substance as the muscles, for its outer layer (CHITŌN) is indeed interwoven with transverse fibres, and yet not even this is exactly a muscle. For if the heart re-

615 ceived its pulsatory activity from the nerves, the gullet would necessarily have had the same movement [being supplied by the same nerves]. As things are, it visibly contracts when animals swallow or regurgitate food in the same way as the stomach and intestines, which contract round their contents but have no pulsatory movement.

Such then is their great error in failing to comprehend the action and power of muscles and heart. On the other hand I have shown in my memoranda *De Hippocratis et Platonis placitis* that the heart is the seat of passion and source of 'innate heat'.[152]

Chapter 9

[*Vessels and Valves of the Heart*]

615 Now let us proceed to the particular parts that are the subject of this work, beginning from the 'auricles' of the heart.[150] They are thus called from their resemblance to ears, for they grow on either side of the heart as ears on the head. They appear more like to sinew or skin than to the heart itself, in so far as they

616 can be described in words; but it is better to trust to visual and

* 'Of the heart' is here inserted in text.

tactile impressions by which alone the hue and structure of a body can be distinguished. Of dark colour and like membranous outgrowths they are intended to provide cavities adjoining the heart; wherefore Nature has made them hollow as providing a cavity, and membranous to subserve the movements of the heart. See what I have said of them in my *De usu partium.*[10]

There are two 'auricles', one by each of the vessels that brings in material—on the right, at the entry (EMPHYSIS) of the vein [*superior vena cava*] into the cavity of the heart; on the left, at that of the 'venous artery' [*pulmonary vein*]. When you lay open the 'auricles' the substance (SŌMA) of the heart will be visible, and each of the above-named orifices and then the valves (HYMENES) attached below the entries (EMPHYSEIS), three to the right cavity [*tricuspid valve*], two to the left [*mitral valve*].

[A passage describing the two ventricles and the origins of the aorta and pulmonary artery from them has dropped from the text here.]

The form [of the cusps] when they are in contact is like arrowheads (GLŌCHINES), wherefore some anatomists call them TRIGLŌCHINES. *617*

These matters you can observe in the heart removed from the thorax, as you can also the other two orifices of the vessels which convey material from the heart, namely the orifice of the right ventricle to the lung [i.e. the 'venous artery', our *pulmonary vein*] and that of the aorta, leading from the left ventricle, to the body as a whole. In these [note] again on each side three membranes in the form of the letter C [Greek capital sigma] opening out of the heart as the tricuspid opens into it.[153]

Before removing the heart from the animal, observe all the offshoots from the vena cava. Of them I shall speak again in the anatomy of the vessels. [Observe] the large gland called THYMOS,[147] and the attachment of the coat of the heart. Observe too how a vein [*azygos*] comes to the spine from the hollow cavity on the right, mounting on the fifth dorsal vertebra,

and how this vein always reaches this region in all those animals
618 on which you were advised to gain anatomical experience. But it does not [arise] from the right auricle in all animals, but in some where the vena cava passes through the auricle it is carried up to the neck. Among such are the apes.[154]

Chapter 10

[*The Coronary Arteries and the Heart-bone*]

618 The veins that nourish the heart spring in all animals from its cavity. People speak of them as 'enwreathing' the heart, since two of them do so surround it, just as two arteries (which arise from the aorta in its first part, immediately after it leaves the [semilunar] valves) come down from the left part into the substance of the heart [*coronary arteries*]. They are best examined in the detached heart, especially in a large animal, but they are the same in all and do not differ according to size, as Aristotle [wrongly] thinks.[155] It is, however, easier to see them clearly in large hearts.

The bone in the heart,[156] which people think is present only in large animals and not in all of them, is there in others too, yet sometimes not quite as a bone but rather as a cartilage.
619 In general, the matter stands as follows in all animals. The [semilunar] valves, which I said are called TRIGLŌCHINES [p. 185], and the root [*aorta*] of the arterial vessels are fastened to a substance which is always hard, but not equally hard in all animals. In smaller animals it is slightly cartilaginous, in larger it is true cartilage, and in yet larger it is a bony cartilage [*os cordis*]. In the degree that the kind of animal is larger, so is the cartilage more bony. In the largest, where the greater part is bony, it is rightly called 'cartilaginous bone' rather than 'bony cartilage', for what is produced in these animals is rather sinewy cartilage [fibro-cartilage] than true [hyaline] cartilage. It is thus not surprising that in small animals it is overlooked by those without experience in dissection, when it often escapes notice even in the larger.

Larger, do I say? Why, an elephant of the largest size was lately killed in Rome. Many physicians crowded to see it dissected and to learn whether the heart has two apexes or one, and two cavities or three. Before it was dissected, I maintained that the same structure of the heart would be found in it as in all the animals that breathe air. This was apparent when the heart was opened. Moreover, I and my pupils easily found the bone in it, by fingering it. But our inexpert [colleagues], expecting in a large animal a like finding to that in others, concluded that the heart contains no bone, even in an elephant. I was going to demonstrate it when my companions, laughing at seeing them unable to perceive it from their ignorance of its position, asked me to forbear. However, when the heart was removed by Caesar's cooks, I sent one of my colleagues, experienced in such things, to beg the cooks to allow him to extract the bone from it. This was done and I have it to this day. It is of considerable size so that those who see it can hardly believe that it could escape observation by physicians. *620*

Thus even very large structures in animals may escape notice by the inexperienced. What wonder that Aristotle, among his many anatomical errors, thinks that the heart in large animals has three cavities? It is not surprising that, lacking anatomical experience, he failed to find the parts, and he deserves to be forgiven.[157] For where those who have given their whole life to this study, as Marinus,[32] have made many mistakes, what are we to think happens to those who approach it without preparation, but deterred by a first failure abandon further attempt? *621*

I call all gods to witness that I have often, on further examination, seen things I had completely missed before. Among them is the bone in the heart, for I learned from my teachers neither its position nor whether it be present in all animals. And yet I tried to find it, cutting up the organ small, as this seemed the surest way. But when I found attached to it the roots of the valves and the origins of the arterial vessels, I concluded that Nature the Artificer must have made this her aim in all animals. Later I became convinced of this by actual experience by *622* following the attachments of the said parts. From yet further experience I learned easily to find it in a moment in any animal for dissection, and now many of our group (HETAIROI) can find the bone very quickly.

Anyone who had not seen us do so, but had learned of it before proceeding to the operation, will easily find it when he has laid bare the left cavity [*ventricle*] and opened the length of the aorta. Let him follow carefully the root of the aorta and the membranes, for this root and that of the 'arterial vein' [*pulmonary artery*], and also of the valves in them, adjoin the bone of the heart.[156]

623 All these, then, can be examined in a heart removed from the animal, and, in addition, the pits that plunge deep into [the walls in] each ventricle. If you make a careful dissection on a freshly-killed animal, you will find them exactly.[158] You can observe the [*coronary*] vessels that wreathe the heart in a manifold series of branches passing over the surface in various ways, all from the junction of the cavities.

Chapter 11

[*Ventricles and Orifices of the Heart*]

623 You will see, if you lay bare the whole heart, the left ventricle extending to the very apex, and the right ending much below it, and often with an outline of its own. This [double apex] is seen in large animals like horses and oxen and camels, and still more in elephants, but sometimes even in small ones. Thus a man who was sacrificing a cock to the gods found a heart with two apexes.[159] Thinking this a portent, he consulted the experts. By chance he met me and said that he had found 624 two hearts in one animal. There were not two, as he thought, but the apex of the right ventricle had an outline of its own. Grasp this, then, thoroughly: that were an animal larger than an elephant or smaller than a lark, the structure of the heart would be similar, nay yet rather in appearance the same.

What sort of heart a fish has and in general all the animals that live under water will be explained later. Meanwhile let us examine the matter, for animals that breathe air. Of all these you will see similar structure in the heart and lungs, as is explained above. (There is still one thing remaining, both with regard to the latter viscera and the heart, which will be dealt with in the anatomy of the nerves. It will also be explained that the auricles of the heart are outside its cavities.)

If anyone were so to regard the auricles[160] as parts of the heart increasing the number of the cardiac orifices, as did Herophilus, he would differ from Erasistratus and me. For we have *625* declared that for the four vessels of the heart there are in all only four orifices. From Book I of my memoir *De dissentione anatomica*[34] he will learn to judge the disagreement among experts as to the appearances of these four and of their opinions about them.

The orifice of the 'venous artery' [*pulmonary vein*] at the left ventricle (KOILIA) is single and on it are the valves opening inwards [*mitral*]. Yet it [i.e. the vessel] hardly remains one, but at once divides into four, each of which reaches a lobe of the lung. The lobes of the lungs are not unbalanced in number* as are those of the liver, but in all the animals we are discussing there are two lobes on each side. It is further agreed, if not by all at least by those who dissect carefully, that there is also a fifth small lobe in the right lung, a mere offshoot of one of the others [*lobus azygos*]. This you will find most easily by paying atten- *626* tion to the vena cava, for it lies under that [lobe] where it first invades the thorax, as it leaves the diaphragm. Sometimes also you can see plainly on the surface [of that lobe] a cavity in which the vein is fixed in life [Fig. 21].[161]

After death the lungs are collapsed and small, there being a considerable space between them and the chest wall contrary to the condition in life. This will be considered after the discussion of the heart, for it remains to describe how to expose it while the animal is alive, without damaging the thoracic cavities [i.e. the *pleurae*].

* Reading ANISOMENOI for ANISOI.

Chapter 12

[*Vivisection of Heart and Lungs*]

626 If you recall what I said of the contact of the pericardium with the sternum, you will understand how to expose the heart. This, which I have already explained, must be done as in the dead animal. But it may be well for clarity to summarize the whole account.

627 Use a young animal so that you do not need large knives. It must be on its back, on a board of the kind that you see I have quantities at hand, both large and small, so that one may always be found to fit the animal. This board should have holes bored in it through which a thin cord or even a rope will easily pass. An assistant should be instructed, when the animal is on its back on the board, to pass cords round it, one round each limb and the ends of the cords through the holes below and tied together there. If the animal has long hair about the breast-bone, that should be removed.

This is the way to prepare the subject for dissection. Make a straight incision with a large lancet along the sternum downwards to the ensiform cartilage. Thence turn the incision at right angles so as to bare the breast-bone—with or without the ensi-*628* form—of the overlying tissues.* Continue to apply the lancet in the same way, moving upwards over the sternum to where in the dead animal you have seen the pericardium attached under it.

In the living the procedure is the same, as far as the incision goes, but there is a complication on which there is no need for long explanations to those who have seen me operating. To those who have not, I would say that from the thorax arteries and veins [*internal mammary*] emerge beside the root of the ensiform cartilage, one of each on each side, and that when severed—as they must be in this operation—haemorrhage results, especially from the arteries.

Nothing upsets any operation like haemorrhage. Bearing this in mind, immediately you see blood spurt from the artery with

* Text reads 'underlying'.

the downward incision, turn the lancet as quickly as possible to the transverse incision. Then with the thumb and index of *629* the left hand, grasp that part of the sternum where the artery is pouring forth blood, so that while the one finger acts as a stopper for the orifice, both grasp the bone.

Next try to do two things at the same time, viz. cut with the lancet as quickly as possible and connect with the end of the downward incision first the transverse cut and after it the upward, and also with your finger keep bending back the breast-bone. When it is bent back properly the cause of the haemorrhage no longer exists, for the incision at either orifice is thus controlled, and the attachment of the pericardium is visible. This guides you to the completion of the incision. For when the sternum is bent back, the lower end is raised and by this position the haemorrhage is stemmed and the position of the vessels is altered as they are kinked above at the sternum and do not run straight down.

On the inside two pairs of large arteries and veins [*internal* *630* *mammary*] lie under the sternum and emerge by the root of the ensiform into the hypochondria. It is they which are cut in this operation. But in the other operation, in which I told you to sever the ribs at the bend where they change from bone to cartilage [p. 132], there is no fear of haemorrhage because of the smallness of the [local] vessels. This second method of incision is useful if you wish to observe the pulmonary vessels in the still living animal. That which I deal with now is useful for purposes of which I shall speak next, because it keeps both the cavities of the thorax undamaged.

There is a third operation on the living animal which differs from the first-mentioned in that a similar incision is made in both the parts of the thorax. You will learn its usefulness a little later; that of the first you have already grasped sufficiently. But it is time for you to learn about the one which is our present subject. You will perform it most successfuly if you expose the heart and keep the [pleural] cavities of the thorax unharmed. *631* Sometimes in this operation the membrane round the heart is severed, but often it remains undamaged. In both those operations it is so far divided that the heart is exposed, but the membranes that partition the thorax are not damaged, for if one be wounded the animal necessarily develops these symptoms which, as will be explained later, arise when the thorax is perforated.

When the heart is exposed, your task is to preserve all its functions unimpaired, as in fact they are, so that you can see the animal breathing and uttering cries and, if loosed from its bonds, running as before. Further, if you continue to compress the wound with ligatures, you will see it taking food if hungry, and drinking if thirsty. And what is strange in that? The slave of Maryllus, the mime-writer, whose heart was once exposed, was cured and still lives [see below]. It is surely more likely that a 632 non-rational brute, being less sensitive than a human being, will suffer nothing from such a wound.

Chapter 13

[*A Slave cured in whom the Sternum was excised*]

632 Since I have mentioned the slave that I treated, there would be no harm in giving details of his case. It is better to consider them because of the usefulness of his history, even if not strictly relevant to the present work.

This slave received a blow on the sternum in the wrestling school. It was neglected and later not carefully looked after. After some four months pus appeared in the injured part. To deal with this, the physician operated and, as he thought, quickly got the wound to cicatrize, but inflammation and suppuration set in again. Another incision was made. This could not be brought to heal.

His master now summoned a number of physicians, of whom I was one, and asked us to hold a consultation. All agreed that the trouble was suppuration of the sternum, but there was visible movement of the heart on the left of it, so that no one dared remove the affected bone, thinking that it would involve a 'perforation' (SYNTRĒSIS) of the thoracic [cavity]. I said that I would excise the bone without making what is technically termed a 'perforation'. As to complete recovery, I made no promise, for it was uncertain whether any of the tissues under the sternum were affected and to what extent. 633

The region being exposed, no more of the sternum seemed affected than had appeared at first. The limits [of the wound] on either side, under which extend the arteries and veins, were seen to be healthy, and I thus gained more confidence in proceeding. When the bone affected had been excised, particularly at the highest level reached by the pericardium, the heart was seen exposed, for the membrane round it had here mortified. We then had little hope for the slave. Yet before long he recovered completely, which would not have been the case if no one had dared to excise the affected bone, and no one would have had the courage to do so without previous anatomical experience.

634 At the same time another physician, operating on a septic state in the arm due to determination of the humours there, severed a large artery through ignorance of the parts. He lost his nerve for the moment because of the haemorrhage, for it was deep and only with difficulty could he compress it with a ligature and thus avert immediate danger. Nevertheless, he killed the man in another way, for gangrene produced by the ligature seized on the artery first and next on the surrounding parts.

More could be said on this, but these few incidental points among many will prove to men of sense the usefulness of this work of mine.

Chapter 14

[*Conclusions from Vivisection of Thorax*]

634 Let us return again to the original suggestion of three similar but not identical operations on the living animal. To observe the arteries of the lungs there suffices either a single incision

635 where the ribs bend, or beside it another in the remaining part of the thorax, the usefulness of which I shall explain later, or a third operation in which the heart is exposed but no 'perforation' is made of the thorax [i.e. *pleura*]. There is nothing extraordinary in this last, for while of course some injury is inflicted on the thorax there is, nevertheless, no 'perforation', for that term is reserved for an incision that enters the pleural cavities. Any other incision of it is spoken of as 'wounding', but not 'perforation'.

What then are the purposes of exposing the heart thus? First, that we may see clearly how it beats and whether it is in diastole or systole that it strikes the chest in the sternal region. Secondly, that, laying bare the great artery, as you have seen me exposing that in the groin, we may observe exactly whether it is contracted while the heart is in diastole and expanded when it is in systole, or if both [heart and artery] are expanded and contracted at the same time. Thirdly, by grasping the heart with
636 the fingers—or with forceps as I habitually do since it readily escapes the fingers—we may see what sort of symptom is produced in the animal. And, moreover, to expose the error of those who say that such and such symptoms seize on the animal if one ligates the large artery or, as some say, the 'venous artery' [*pulmonary vein*] running into the lungs. For on this they do not all say the same. For no such ligation can be made without the thorax being perforated, nor, if it were, could it bind the root of the artery so exactly as to block its aperture.

I found by experience that this was always said by those who could not expose the heart without perforation but who, under pressure, immediately perforated the thorax, saying that the operation was difficult; and that it was for this reason that they had postponed it, for [they said] had they exposed it, they would have put the ligature round it and demonstrated clearly what they promised.

In contrast to them, what I promise I perform. For I expose
637 the heart easily without damage to any of the membranes partitioning the cavity of the thorax. Then I ask them to put the

ligature round the vessels springing from the heart. Under compulsion, without effecting anything, they get so far as to tear apart some of the membranes and make a perforation. At that point they say they ought not to make any further attempt. But again I speedily expose the heart in another animal for them, and present this to them, and force them to make another attempt, until they are put to shame over their impudent pretences.

It is not possible to ligature the course of the vessel. It can be done round the base of the heart, but the animal dies at once. One who said that, if the 'venous artery' [*pulmonary vein*] be ligated when the heart is exposed without perforating the thorax, the lungs remain expanded, had a like experience when he was refuted before many witnesses by one of my colleagues.

Such a combination of pretentious humbug and rash confidence is shown by some in their behaviour to the ignorant, particularly when they come to speak of the 'venous artery' *638* which divides [almost] within the auricle. Others say they have ligatured it, for (they say) it comes forth single, and that then these two things happen: firstly, that all the arteries in the body become motionless, being, of course, deprived of the supply from the lungs that fills them; secondly, that the lungs remain at an equal distance apart, for obviously the heart is drawing nothing from them. Yet others profess to show the lungs moving after a ligation of the ARTĒRIA TRACHEIA [*trachea*] (and some have actually recorded this in writing!) without adding how they observed the lungs, whether without a perforation in the thorax, or with one. Either is unbelievable. For with this perforation the whole process of respiration is destroyed, while if it be not perforated you cannot see within the thorax at all, except by excising a rib and leaving the pleura unharmed.[162] Those who talk such nonsense do not even state this. But something will be said of these things in *639* what follows in the special anatomy of the thorax.

We shall return to what is seen in the heart when exposed.

Chapter 15

[*Movements of the Heart investigated*]

639 There is a third way of operating in which the incisions in the thorax are made about the bend of the ribs. Obviously the animal must quickly die from suffocation, since its power of respiration would be destroyed. But these are the phenomena in the heart. First I shall resume what I have to say about the operation so that not the smallest detail remains obscure.

Ascertain exactly in a dead animal the bending places of the ribs and recall them before you start. Arrange the animal on its back as explained [p. 190]. Then, having removed the hair from the site of the incisions, make two longitudinal cuts dividing the flexures of the ribs. Next make a transverse incision at *640* right angles across the xiphoid process, where, of course, you will encounter the arteries and veins. Disregard haemorrhage from them, for you no longer aim at keeping the animal alive. Now bend back the sternum and make another incision under it, separating the pericardium from it. If you wound the pericardium without wounding the heart, pay no heed, for your aim is to see if both the ventricles beat, and that together, or only, as some say, the left. You will see still more clearly now than before and have more abundant evidence as to whether the arteries throughout the whole animal expand and contract alternately [with the heart] or at the same time and with the same rhythm.

All this will be clear to you at once when [the heart] is exposed. As time goes on, the movements of each ventricle become brief, long pauses intervening, and also there becomes apparent the diastole of the right ventricle, accomplishing [its function] *641* according to its own nature, as you will see particularly when those [parts] approach immobility. For in each [ventricle] the apex stops moving first and then the part next to it, and so on until the bases only are left still moving. When even these have stopped, an ill-defined and short movement at long intervals is still seen in the 'auricles'. The cause of this phenomenon we must investigate at leisure, for it would not seem natural (EULOGON) that its appendages should move longer than the heart itself. But here it is not our aim to examine causes but observed anatomical phenomena only.

Chapter 16

[*Against the View that Arteries are Empty*]

For those who vivisect almost all that is necessary and useful has been said concerning the heart. It would be better now to turn to the phenomena of the thorax and lungs. But since some, talking impudent nonsense, openly promise to show that the arteries are empty of blood, one giving the lie to the other on actual observations, I too must spend time on this topic. *641* *642*

One of them was always promising to exhibit the great artery empty of blood, but never did so. When some ardent youths brought animals to him and challenged him to the test, he declared he would not make it without a fee. They laid down at once a thousand drachmae for him to pocket should he succeed. In his embarrassment he made many twists and turns, but, under pressure from all present, mustered courage to take a lancet and cut along the left side of the thorax especially at the point where, he thought, the aorta should become visible. He proved so little practised in dissection that he cut on to the bone!

Another of the same gang (CHOROS) made his cut onto the bone across the intercostal region, and straightaway severed artery and vein. Thus the fellow incurred the ridicule of the youths who had deposited the stakes with the assembled spectators. *643* The youths themselves now carried out what the last had promised, making their incision as they had seen me, without damaging any vessels. Moreover, they quickly applied two ligatures, one immediately beyond the point where the aorta rises from the heart, the other where it reaches the spine. Thus, as the impudent fellow had promised, after the death of the animal it might be seen whether this stretch of the artery between the ligatures were empty of blood. When it was found far from empty, they said that an irruption had taken place into it when the ligatures were applied, as if someone else and not they themselves had undertaken to do the operation, though they were without the necessary experience and were incapable of applying the ligatures faster than others. For they did not even know that an artery and vein follow the lower border of each rib.

Of the same ilk again was the man who invented the four-edged hatchet but did not make nor even try it, though he inso- *644* lently promised to demonstrate with it an artery empty of blood! His dream was something like this. He wanted to get made a four-edged axe, square and coming to a single point whereat a handle was to be attached. Then an animal was to be stretched out on its belly and struck violently on the spine with the axe, so as to cut out a rectangular piece with one blow. With this peculiar outline, he said, the part of the great artery would be included and found empty of blood. This device may be left to the comic writers.

We may recall yet another effort, that of a pompous septuagenarian who claimed that he would demonstrate an artery empty of blood. The animal must be one that can be readily skinned, as a sheep, ox, or goat. The incision must be made at some point where a large artery lies just beneath the skin. The artery must have the skin removed all round and bared of the *645* surrounding tissues so that it stand free. The cut in the skin must be protected and, after six or seven days, its edges opened and two ligatures put round the artery, as far apart as possible. When the part between were cut out it would then, he said, be found empty. This old fellow never dared to make his experiment himself, but we did so for him as soon as we heard of it. We tried it on a goat, on kine, and on sheep, as the old man had directed. We then invited him to wake up and see for himself, once and for all, and be convicted of the error of what had appeared to him in a mere dream.

Moreover, not long since another fellow gave a totally false account of an experiment described by me in my book *An in arteriis natura sanguis contineatur*.[145] Those who had observed my experiment were astonished at his temerity and asked him if he had ever performed it himself or merely relied on hearsay. He replied that he had performed it often. So they brought a goat and tried to force him to demonstrate it. He declined because, of course, he did not know how. They then demonstrated to the onlookers that the actual phenomenon was different [from what he said] and thus ended his absurd claims. *646*

The method of experiment is as follows. Of the large arteries near the skin, expose one, such as that by the groin, which is the one that I habitually use for the operation. Ligature it above and compress the artery itself with the fingers of the left hand, choosing as great a length as possible from the ligature devoid of a large branch. Then make in its wall a straight incision long enough for you to insert a tube between the ligature and the fingers. (Have ready a tube of a finger's length, such as a writing quill, or bronze pipe made for the purpose.) Obviously there will be no haemorrhage from the severed artery since the upper part, whence comes the blood, is stopped by the ligature, while the lower part no longer pulsates because of the ligature and because it is compressed by the fingers. Hence you can at your leisure insert the tube into the artery through the incision in its wall, and then ligate artery and quill with fine linen thread. (Take care that no part of the tube go [too far] beyond the incision of the artery, and that the quill be of a calibre that the arterial coat does not lie slack on it, for we want it to remain in place, neither running up beyond the division in the artery, nor down it.) This done, loosen the ligature [first made] and, as a precaution, alter the position of the fingers with which you were compressing the artery, to the part round the quill. If the quill be tight and well ligated, there is no need to control it, and you can observe the uninterrupted part of the artery above the tube still pulsating as before and the lower part quite pulseless. *647*

This then is what is actually observed. Erasistratus, however, gave an opposite account, saying that the part below the quill *648* is seen moving. So great is the temerity of those who make rash assertions without observing.

During the experiment if you want no effusion of blood when the artery is cut, you can put a ligature not only above but around the lower part too, which, of course, you will loosen later when you insert the tube. I do not put one around because I wish to keep the main body of the artery unpressed and uncrushed.

Some describe further experiments, promising to demonstrate an artery empty of blood, claiming to be more clever and skilled than Erasistratus. For he certainly would have discovered it if there were any way of dissection by which an artery could be shown to be empty, like the method he described in the case of

649 new-born goats. But if you test it you will find that it is no true method. Make the test not only with kids but with any other sort of animal which has liquid in its stomach. For in proportion as the liquid is more subtle, it will be the more easily absorbed into the arteries.*

They say then that at first when the mesentery is exposed the arteries appear full of air. Later they are seen to be filled with milk. Whether then they appear full of air need not detain us, though many vainly maintain inconsistent views on this, but as to the consistent falsity of their being full of milk, you can test for yourself on any animal. [It may be that] by its liquidity milk does enter the orifices of the arteries to the stomach and

650 tends to flow towards the empty part, as Erasistratus says. But we never saw it absorbed in any case, nor will anyone who chooses to make the experiment.[163]

* Several repetitions are omitted in this paragraph.

BOOK VIII

The Remaining Thoracic Organs

Chapter I

[*The Ribs and Boundaries of the Thorax*]

This book records operations on the organs of respiration which *651* you have often observed. Since my aim is to reach, not only you, to whom the treatise serves as memoranda, but all seriously interested in anatomy, I must write it as clearly as possible for those who have never seen the operations. In Book *652* VII almost everything has been said that is to be observed in the heart and lungs, both in the dead and living, and all the membranes in the respiratory organs are described. Our next task is to expound first the structure of the thorax as a whole, and then all that is observed in the thorax during vivisectional operations.

As those who describe a country set forth its boundaries before its parts, so shall I with the thorax. It is the region bounded by the ribs. All animals hitherto mentioned have twelve ribs. Thirteen is a very rare condition and eleven even rarer. Either is so rare that you would not find one in a thousand. In animals with clavicles these form the upper limit of the *653* thorax, while the diaphragm is the lower. All the ribs have two attachments; in front to the sternum and behind to the [*thoracic*] vertebrae. The latter are obviously equal in number to the ribs, but the breast-bone appears as single through fusion of its parts. Yet if the membranes all round it are scraped off, the sternum is seen to be of more [than one bone], in fact formed of as many as are the ribs articulated with it [in the monkey but not in man].

The anterior end of each rib is articulated with the lower [part] of the corresponding bone which makes up the sternum [*sternebra*]. The end of the rib, growing thinner, is fused with the mid part of the bony sternal mass (HARMONIA), so that in some animals the ribs articulate no more with the bone above 654 than with that below, but rather with both. The first seven ribs of the thorax thus articulate. The eighth reaches the root of the xiphoid cartilage. The remaining four end in the lateral parts of the thorax, falling short [of the sternum] in front in proportion as they diminish. The last is the smallest and each of the others, in order, exceeds in length the one below as much as it falls short of that above.

Each rib articulates behind with a thoracic vertebra by a double joint, above with the body of the vertebra [*costovertebral joint*], below with the apophyses at the sides in a vertical row [*costotransverse joint*]. Thence the ribs slant forward and downward for most of the way, changing [their direction] towards the front. There they cease to be bony and, in small animals, the remaining part becomes cartilage in the strict sense, in larger, bony cartilage. These [costal] cartilages have not the same direction as the ribs (which from the start run down 655 together slantwise) but, turning the opposite way, run up to the sternum, making, in some animals a curved turn, in others [notably artiodactyla] an angular.

Those ribs that do not reach the sternum are called 'false'. They have a cartilaginous tendency, but at the ends are actual cartilages. From the inner parts of these arises the diaphragm (PHRENES), its higher front part from the xiphoid, its lower back part from the spine. At the middle part it rides on the front of the vertebral column through two very strong ligaments inserted into the lower vertebrae [*crura diaphragmi*]. These, when the animal is loud-voiced or has naturally sinewy muscles, are very strong and long, extending to about the 656 twenty-second vertebra [L.4], counting from above. In a weak-voiced animal with muscles of the thorax no more powerful than those of the ape they [i.e. the *crura*] are neither thick nor powerful.

The upper end of the sternum always articulates with the

first rib, as in other animals. (In those which have collar-bones, it articulates with them also.) Yet this joint contributes nothing to the motion of the thorax,[164] for at the front ends of the ribs, where they are joined to the sternum, its movements are indistinct, while they are plain to see in the back parts where, I said, the ribs articulate with the vertebrae by freely moving joints [i.e. by diarthrosis].

As was stated in Book V, not all the muscles attached to the thorax exist to move it. Some run up from the chest and the regions by the false ribs to help move the shoulder joint. Others run down to the epigastric region and, for purposes of their own, draw down the thorax somewhat. Yet others laid upon the ends of the ribs outside, at the sternum in front and at the vertebrae behind, bind the articulations and contract the thorax a little. 657

Chapter 2

[*Some Errors as to the Movement of the Chest*]

The whole movement [of breathing] is obviously initiated below by the diaphragm, expanding and contracting alternately on its attachments, according to its own tension and relaxation. This [contraction] draws down the sternum by the xiphoid cartilage, while the false ribs move gently upwards and forwards. Respiration—which is thought to be a physical and not a psychic act, in which the lower parts of the thorax and hypochondria are plainly seen to move while the upper may move little or not at all—is produced by the diaphragm, which is a muscle both in substance and function. 657

But our teachers were wrong in thinking that only the diaphragm moves the thorax when the breath is drawn in, expanding it when it is taut and allowing it to sink down into itself being relaxed. How we exhale or phonate at all they did not even try to explain. They thought that the wide movements of the thorax, seen in racing or after any violent exercise, were 658 produced by the diaphragm. They passed over the intercostal muscles altogether, as though these had come into being purposelessly. Similarly they forgot the six muscles running down from the neck, of which those attached in the concavities of the scapulae [*atlantoscapularis anterior*] are the largest, the anterior muscles [*scaleni*, very different in ape and man] are next in size, and those that grow out of the vertebrae of the spine [*rhomboidei*] the smallest. They omitted the muscles that elevate the ribs and those that depress the last ribs. (It was explained in Book V how best to examine these muscles. Something was also said of the posterior muscles of the scapulae, which link them with the thorax, as with the thoracic vertebrae, but impart no movement to it [that is, to the thorax].) Nor did they mention those spinal muscles attached under and beside the thoracic vertebrae, and those set under the upper orifice of the stomach, and the muscles in the loins below; for *659* the spine is bent by these but they contribute no part to the act of respiration as do muscles that distend and contract the thorax.

I have spoken of the last among the factors of respiration. At present I do not aim to demonstrate what has already been properly demonstrated in those books, but only to remind you how rightly to demonstrate what we said there of what is seen to happen in the thorax. Indeed even in my *De thoracis et pulmonis motu*[11] I have mentioned a number of anatomical observations. It is fitting now, too, to say something about how to make them.

It has been stated also in my *De causis respirationis*[8] that my three books *De thoracis et pulmonis motu* were compiled before I had made any considerable discoveries of my own. Being given to a colleague they became public property, contrary to my judgement, like many other works. Right from boyhood I thought it right that any who made a discovery should put it and it only into writing, for I had no wish to publish as mine *660* the work of my predecessors. But I think it not only an unexceptionable, but a most useful practice, that each compose exercises of his own, as for example to gratify a friend who has asked for them.

My teachers—they were the foremost among the pupils of Quintus[14] and Numisianus[15]—demonstrated and proved to me that the lungs are moved by the thorax as Erasistratus had described. Proofs of this are set down in the first two books of my *De thoracis et pulmonis motu*[11] with the observations which provided the evidence for this. The third book of that work explains the nature of thoracic movement. It, too, is in accord with the view of my teachers. But what I myself discovered on the movement of the thorax, I explained in another work of mine *De causis respirationis*,[8] wherein I made clear the double character of the intercostal muscles, their nature, and the number of all the muscles that move the thorax and the origins of the nerves distributed to them.

Chapter 3

[*Results of cutting the Intercostal Muscles*]

I must now explain how to demonstrate the phenomena mentioned in my *De causis respirationis*,[8] starting with the intercostal muscles, whose superficial fibres you will see pass slightly obliquely and anteriorly from the rib above to that below. Dissecting them little by little in the dead animal (for it is best to get practice on a carcase), you will reach to where the fibres within cross them in the opposite direction, so that their relation is like [the limbs of] the letter X. This you will see maintained as far as the [bend at the] cartilaginous portion of each rib, but there the fibres of the two interchange, and you can see the outer taking the place of the inner and vice versa. In the muscles of the false ribs the fibres have the same nature throughout, for these have no bend. The fibres in these muscles are mostly clearly seen in an old thin animal. *661*

When you have practised separating the superficial fibres from the deeper on a dead animal, try the same on a live one. *662*

You will then admit that I am right in my exposition of the situation when the fibres are cut. I discussed these in my *De causis respirationis*, but I shall do so again now. It will do no harm thus to start afresh, so as to be clear. I want you first then to practise on a dead animal, noting accurately the position of each part, so that in the living you may expose it as quickly and with as little loss of blood as possible.

In the intercostal muscles, then, close to and below the rib, you will see artery, vein, and nerve, the nerve being nearest [the intercostal space]. In dissecting the superficial muscles in a dead animal, practice beginning from the lower rib. Breaking up the *663* conjunction of the fibres, cut gradually to the rib above without fear of severing vessel, muscle, or nerve, until you approach the rib above. There you must pay careful attention to the tissues beneath the fibres, for you will see artery, vein, and nerve in contact, the nerve in the space between the superficial and deep fibres, if you follow them exactly. The superficial fibres will look to you more numerous than the deep, both because they really are more numerous and because the deep fibres are fined away.

In the living animal, that you may dissect either the outer fibres without the inner, or the inner along with the outer, and without the membrane [*pleura*] lining the ribs, it is better for you to practise on a pig, for the animal with the loudest cry is the most suitable for anatomical experiments in which the voice is liable to injury. This was naturally unknown to my teachers, since they had never attempted the operation to be discussed.

That when both the layers of fibres are cut, the animal's *664* voice is destroyed as well as what I call 'expiration' (EKPHYSĒSIS), if you attempt to cut them, the facts themselves will convince you. For this operation it is best to use a large pig, for then the membrane lining the ribs [*pleura*] is strong. Take care not to cut it, for if you do the thorax is distended, much air from without is drawn into the region between thoracic wall and lung, and as it is contracted this is emptied out again through the wound. Obviously the quantity of air breathed in through the mouth which is lost via the wound corresponds to the excess that flows into the thorax from outside.*

It is superfluous to expound here the causes of what happens to animals in anatomical operations, for they have been stated in works devoted to them. My present aim is not to demonstrate *665* the action of the nerves but to explain verbally the operations illustrating the phenomena that I revealed by dissection in those treatises—experiments often seen by many, but within the capacity of few. Let us do this then in what follows, and again first state what was known to our predecessors in anatomy.

When a considerable incision is made anywhere between the ribs and through the [pleural] membrane lining them, the animal at once loses half its power of respiration and phonation. If a similar cut be made on the other side of the thorax, it ceases to breathe or cry. But, when the thorax is contracted and the air that has got in through the incisions has been emptied out, if you then block [the incisions], the animal will at once breathe and utter a cry. It is easy to block them by drawing together the lips of the incisions, using the hand that is drawing them together as a cover for the part that is not blocked.

These observations were known to all those who were seri- *666* ously interested in anatomy. But it was my discovery that, when the fibres are cut in all the intercostal muscles of both sides, not only is the power of utterance lost but also that of expiration is destroyed; just as when the nerves are cut short of the spinal cord, the action of the intact muscles is destroyed. This experiment is more refined [than the cutting of the fibres] for it shows resulting conditions more clearly. But the cutting of the muscular fibres, which must be along the whole length of the ribs in all the ribs below the high muscles of the thorax (which, I said, come down into them from the neck), is easily carried out and does not impair the activity of any of the muscles moving the thorax except those actually cut. (To make the incision in the intercostal regions above, it would be necessary to remove the shoulder-blades.)

* Four lines of repetition here.

Chapter 4

[*Results of injuring the Intercostal Nerves*]

667 A better experiment is the cutting of the [intercostal] nerves. It paralyses the intercostal muscles. It should be done where the spinal muscles are first distinguishable at the side of the vertebrae. You can cut these, but owing to the thick flesh you cannot easily insert the hook under the exposed nerve. Because of the depth of the flesh, you cannot easily insert the kind of hook that we use in operations on varices. You must use one with a very short bend to get beneath the exposed nerve, without perforating the pleura. Too sharp an instrument might wound it, and one too blunt could be passed only with difficulty through the tissues beneath the nerve. It must so taper at the end that when passed under the nerve it is not checked by the underlying muscle fibres but passes through them all readily.

Having raised the intact nerve with such a hook, straightway let the hook be thrust carefully under it as though you were using *668* a probe or something of the kind.* Now grasp it and, along the neighbouring rib, pull upon its origin in the spinal marrow. If you pull too hard it may happen that the nerve breaks away from the spinal marrow. So far as this involves paralysis of the intercostal muscle this matters little, but harm is done in another respect as I shall state shortly. Therefore do not stretch it to breaking-point.

After the stretching, put under it a curved needle with a thread; push it through beneath the nerve, and you will have the thread lying under it. Grasp it and put a loop of it round the nerve as near as possible to the spinal marrow. You aim to paralyse the whole muscle. This is easily done if you paralyse the nerve first by inserting the loop near the root. The operation can be done without a needle by a pierced hook, as is usually *669* done for the nerve adjoining the carotid arteries.

You can do the same thing if you examine by yourself what happens to the animal when the nerves are tied, but for a

* A line of text here is so corrupt as to be unintelligible.

demonstration it is better to put threads under all the nerves without tying them. Then you can show that the animal cries out when struck, but that it suddenly becomes silent after the nerves have been tied. The spectators are astonished. They think it wonderful that phonation is destroyed when small nerves in the back are tied. Have several assistants to help you in such demonstrations so that the loops may be put round all the nerves quickly. If you do not want to loosen them, it does not matter how you bind, but if you want to loosen them again to show how the animal recovers its voice—for this surprises the spectators even more—do not bind the loops too tightly, so that it is easy for you to loosen them quickly. What is called the 'blind knot' is quite hard to undo. If you tie it moderately *670* tight, the animal will be able to cry out at once. Nerves too tightly bound are liable to be crushed when the cord is thick, and cut through when it is thin. If this happens, the nerves will not be able to function again. Being on my guard against this, as you know, I often used strong woven threads of yarn or wool.*

You must know two things here. (*a*) In the upper ribs the nerve extends higher along them, but retreats a little towards the region below in the lower, so that it is easier to slip the hook *671* under the nerve in them. (*b*) The extent of the damage is not exactly the same for all the intercostal [nerves], for those to the false ribs it is less in that their muscles are smaller than those to the higher. Thus injury to the first intercostal muscle causes least damage, that to the second greater, and paralysis of the other muscles in ascending series produces yet more injury, that is of the third, fourth, and on to the sixth and seventh [from the bottom].† So that in demonstrating, as you know, I usually pass it [that is the last nerve] over, so as to complete the experiment the quicker. The last intercostal nerve is very easily extracted, that in the first [interspace] with the greatest difficulty, because *672* many structures lie in front of it and because the nerve itself is very small, as is the whole [of its] intercostal region.

* Here eight lines of repetition.

† Here four lines of almost verbal repetition.

The last intercostal region of all is the smallest, yet not its nerve,* for in the false ribs the size of the nerves is greater than what you would expect, for they are not distributed there only but pass out of the thorax into the hypochondria. On the other hand, the nerve of the first intercostal region is distributed only to its own muscle, which is very small. So nine intercostal regions are left, which need dissection as described.

As you have seen me make the demonstration whenever the thorax was the subject for dissection, it is possible for you to do it yourselves, giving the explanation of the phenomena that are to be shown, and directing others to extract the nerves in order to make separate demonstrations to the audience. If we give a demonstration single-handed to a few diligent students, *673* it is obvious, I think, without my saying it, that we must first choose a light room and scalpels as sharp as possible. It has been remarked already that such a scalpel is needed for perfect exactitude in the incisions. Use especially the convex part of the double-edged scalpel with both cutting edges curved, but concave on one side, convex on the other. I want you particularly to make the incision first when practising by yourself in the way I explained, but later in the opposite way, as I shall explain next, after I have reminded you of the method described before.

According to it, I desired you to make the incision in the mid part of the intercostal region, away from the rib above but along the upper part of the rib below. Loosening the fibres attached to it, you can strip them off little by little as far as the rib above, until you encounter the vein lying on the surface, and then the artery and the nerve, all alongside the rib, the nerve lying a little nearer [i.e. lower].

674 When you have practised observing their position in the carcase, turn again to those at the very bottom of the [next] higher rib. Lay the part bare with one stroke of the scalpel, severing the overlying fibres but keeping the nerve undamaged, for which purpose a convex 'myrtle' scalpel is best. At least I use it, as

* Here text inserts by dittography TO MESOPLEURION POLON from two lines above.

you know, for severing the fibres of the lower rib, and then of the others one by one. Sometimes I bare the nerve with a single stroke of the scalpel and, if I fail to hit the exact distance, I do the job with the second. You must not give up hope of improvement, if at first you need three or four strokes to expose it. Hear Hippocrates on the matter: 'You should accustom yourself beforehand to the operations you have to carry out and keep your hand in.'[165] For sooner or later you will attain your aim and expose the nerve with a single stroke.

In practising this do not neglect to slip the hook under it [i.e. the nerve] in the right way and try not to wound or tear apart the artery or vein. With the nerves damaged, the animal becomes dumb, but with two other consequences that I have shown to follow injury of the voice. Firstly, as cause of the next two symptoms, immobility of the intercostal muscles. Secondly, loss of the power of 'rapid expiration' without which no cry can be uttered, as I proved. From this a third consequence is dumbness. And in this experiment there is a fourth consequence that requires explanation. You will recognize it clearly in the actual experiments with the aid of the following exposition. *675*

Chapter 5

[*Control of Thoracic Movements*]

The nerves [*recurrent laryngeal*] that accompany those arteries that people call KARŌTIDES were known to my teachers. When these nerves receive one of the injuries I mentioned not long since, the animal becomes dumb, but not to such a degree as from injury to the intercostal nerves, for it can still produce a hoarse sound like that of a man snoring in sleep. This power is lost when the intercostal muscles are paralysed; and they are quickly paralysed when either their fibres are cut, or the ribs removed, or the nerve destroyed at the root, or the spinal cord severed at the top of the thoracic vertebrae (METAPHRENON). *675* *676*

In this last operation the hoarse sound is lost, since all the parts below, i.e. the intercostal and abdominal muscles, are also paralysed. (These operations have been discussed in Book V, where I described how best to distinguish the eight of them.) Along with them the muscles in fundament, penis, bladder, and legs, are also paralysed. The diaphragm, however, though lower than the intercostals, is not paralysed, because the origin of its nerves is above the thorax. Nor is there damage to the six muscles descending from the neck which dilate the thorax [p. 128], and particularly its upper part, for they too have their nerves from the spinal cord (NŌTIAIOS) in the neck.

677 You have seen all this publicly demonstrated when the thorax was the subject for dissection. I had to explain and demonstrate its nature during many consecutive days. When the spinal cord was severed at the beginning of the thorax, which is between the seventh and eighth vertebrae, the animal fell and lay on its side, the lower parts of the thorax being moved by the diaphragm alone, which an animal uses for shallow breathing only. When, however, it needs to fetch deeper breaths, whether by reason of exhaustion, or fever, or because of the heat, or for some bodily distress, it must invoke the intercostals to the aid of the diaphragm and, at need, the higher muscles as well.

You observed the animal, when the spinal cord was severed at the beginning of the back, falling down at once, lying on its 678 side, remaining dumb, and its thorax devoid of movement except below where it is moved by the action of the diaphragm. Also you observed that the movement of the parts of the thorax is more clearly seen when all the surrounding skin has been removed. All the intercostal muscles became completely motionless, while the lower parts of the thorax were dilating, some faint movement passing to the upper parts. So with the animal in this condition, as you know, I again cut the origins of the nerves descending into the diaphragm. Immediately the movement of the lower thorax ceased and the high muscles were forced into action, and the upper region of the thorax was clearly seen being dilated by them.

Taking a second animal and cutting the cervical nerve-roots to the diaphragm, I immobilized the lower thorax at once while the intercostals remained active.

When the cord was cut at the beginning of the back, [you will remember that] the animal at once lay on its side, moving both parts of the thorax, the higher and lower [but not the middle] for, because of the need to inhale more deeply, the diaphragm alone did not suffice.[166] When, however, the animal inhales with the aid of the upper muscles, the movement is plainly visible along the entire shoulder-blades as far as the top of the shoulder. But when it breathes with the diaphragm alone, the hypochondria swell at each inhalation, and contract at each exhalation, the parts at the shoulder-blades remaining motionless. When only the intercostals are called into play, the shoulder-blades are motionless, but the hypochondria contract as the animals inhale and swell as they exhale—the reverse of what happens when the diaphragm is active. *679*

If you choose to paralyse the muscles of the shoulder-blades you can do so in two ways, either severing them transversely or damaging their nerves. For you must know that this is true of all muscles, that whether you damage their nerves or cut their fibres, you render them motionless. So it is essential for you to know of the muscles, not only the origins of their nerves, but also the lie of their fibres. Some [fibres] run down from above, like those of the anterior and middle muscles of the thorax, some pass transversely like those of the posterior muscles. In nearly all the muscles the fibres run parallel to the length, though in some they behave in the opposite way, as in the intercostal muscles. *680*

Thus when, as I have said, you paralyse the higher muscles only, as need arises the animal invokes the activity of the intercostal muscles. I have mentioned almost all the conditions in which the animal needs to breathe deeply, but sometimes there is added, not a bodily condition, but a strong impulse, as when the animal desires to utter a cry. As a herald about to make an announcement inhales as deeply as possible to have ample breath (HYLĒ) for his voice, so sometimes do some animals when being dissected. You must remember these facts and all their consequences, some of which I think I had better 681 enumerate, and particularly those that belong to the experi- ments already described.

Chapter 6

[*Operations on the Spinal Cord*]

681 In dissection of the intercostal muscles you must begin to expose the bone, as I said, at the lowest part of the edge of each rib, but when the nerve comes to light examine with it the vein and the artery, lying nearer the surface than the nerve and a little higher.* Insert then from below† the small hook beside the edge of the rib, extract the nerve as far as you can without the vessels by it, and particularly avoiding the artery, since by pro- fuse bleeding it conceals the nerve. Should you wound it, cut it right across immediately. This is the one way to check such haemorrhage in all vessels, since each severed end is retracted to contiguous parts. These, if fleshy, may serve as a covering, 682 but if bare little can be gained by this cutting. The intercostal vessels themselves are not bare of flesh, so bleeding stops when they are cut. Neither this point, germane to what was said before, nor the severing of the spinal marrow, was previously discussed.

I perform this [experiment on the spinal cord], as you know, in larger animals by excising first the [arches of the] vertebrae, but in small animals, like young pigs of a few days old, by an instrument of my own devising, like the so-called sharp-pointed bistoury.[167] It should be made of the finest steel, like the Nori- can,[168] that it be not blunted, bent, or broken. It must be thicker than a common bistoury, so that, as you press on the junction of the vertebrae, the operation is accomplished with ease. Sometimes, as you know, after piercing the skin and under-

* Text says 'lower'. † Text says 'from higher parts'.

lying tissues with the scalpel, I insert the 'elongated knife', for so I call it (with its sharp edges meeting at the end in a single point), as far as the joints of the vertebrae. Sometimes too I excise beforehand the posterior apophyses or the whole convex part at the back of the vertebrae themselves. Often also I remove as much of the spinal muscles as lies between the middle of the spine and the ends of these oblique apophyses [*transverse processes*] to get an accurate view of the vertebral joints. I think it right to notice particularly the processes of the spine. They run slightly downwards, so that the first stroke of the scalpel should be made rather slantwise down from above, and the second precisely at right angles. *683*

Sever the spinal marrow transversely and completely, unless you wish to half-paralyse it. That operation is indeed most useful for learning its whole nature, about which I shall speak in Book XIV. But for displaying that on which we are embarked, it is enough for you to know as follows:

When the spinal marrow is cut in the middle, straight downward, it does not paralyse either [set] of the intercostal muscles, or those in the loins or legs. When cut transversely, if only the half is severed, all the nerves on that side are paralysed in series. So if you wish to make the animal half-vocal you must cut it so; if you want it voiceless you must sever the whole cord. *684*

Chapter 7

[*Operations involving Loss of Voice*]

I have said that when the ribs are excised the animal suffers in its power of expiration and of phonation, as when the muscles and nerves are cut. It must now be explained how you are to excise the ribs. I want you to pay attention to the position of the ribs when the animal cries. For as the intercostal muscles are drawn in tightly by this act, the convexities of the ribs become apparent. As this is the case specially in thin animals, I wish you to make these experiments on such. *684*

685 While the animal is phonating observe accurately the position of the rib you are going to excise. Cut down through the skin and fleshy substance that lies under the main part of the rib, using a 'cutting-block' (EPIKOPON) as it is called by anatomists and surgeons. If not enough is cut at the first stroke, it may need a second or even a third. The first incision must be made carefully, for sometimes the inexperienced tail the incision over the length of the rib, and the scalpel slips from the convex part to the intercostal region and touches a nerve, artery, or vein by the lower edge of the rib. If you practise in the first incision, by making the longest cut you can along the rib down to the periosteum, you get the job done best and quickest.

686 Each rib is enveloped by a membrane like the other periosteal membranes. So when you cut along the rib, scrape this from the bone, using a 'myrtle' scalpel curved on each side. When the periosteum is stripped so that the bone is seen high up, slip a delicate MĒNINGOPHYLAX or a flat spatulary probe between periosteum and rib, taking care not to tear or perforate the pleura.

This done, excise the rib by two chisels opposing each other in the usual fashion. If the animal is new-born, there suffices a single transverse cut, made through the cartilaginous part of the rib. If the periosteal membrane has been carefully removed, it is easy to grasp with your fingers and gradually to bend up the divided parts of the rib, each toward the part continuous with it, at the back to the vertebral joint, at the front to the junction with the sternum.

687 Avoid the excision of the ribs under the scapulae, for they would need to be removed as well; for, hampered by them and by the high intercostal muscles, as I said before, the excision of the ribs in this region is very difficult. For this reason the experiment involving the destruction of the nerves is better.

To be truly convinced that the power of both expiration and phonation is injured by the paralysis of the intercostal muscles, it suffices to destroy those below the shoulder-blades, by severing their fibres, or by excising one of the bones. The proportion that those paralysed bear to all the intercostal muscles seems to determine how much of the whole natural power of expiration and of utterance is lost.

The same thing happens to them in all the experiments causing paralysis, which are four: one by excision of the ribs, another by severing the spinal marrow, a third by severing the nerves, and a fourth by severing the fibres. If then the muscles are paralysed on one side, half the power of expiration and of *688* phonation is lost; if in half of either, then the fourth part of both these activities is destroyed: for the damage done to the voice is in proportion to the number of muscles paralysed, of course taking into account the size of the muscles. For if you paralyse on either side the largest only or the smallest only, the damage you will do to the power of utterance will not be the same, though you injure the same number of muscles, for there is a difference between the larger and the smaller in respect of the damage.

It has been remarked [p. 215] that the power of utterance and expiration is more completely lost when the spinal marrow is severed. But if you cut the fibres of the intercostal muscles, or excise the ribs, there remain of the muscles moving the thorax those set upon the ends of the ribs, and, among the muscles in the abdomen, the first and third pairs. Since the movement of *689* the thorax that they effect is small, the power of expiration becomes small, and the voice also. Hence in the experiments I have described, the animal sometimes makes a feeble and indistinct muttering. However, the cutting of the nerves produces almost equal injury to, or only little less than, that caused by the cutting of the spinal marrow, because* the said muscles [? of abdomen, &c.] do not receive offshoots from the intercostal nerves. Indeed if the parts of the first and second pair of muscles after the hypochondria have nerves from either side, the part of them by the thorax must necessarily lose its activity, so that, being itself moved along with the lower parts, it produces no perceptible damage either in the power of expiration or of utterance.

* Reading DIA TO MĒ instead of DIATOMĒ.

It has been stated in the books on the voice that the power of utterance is lost according to circumstances in such cases, but first that of expiration. But since once more expiration is a kind of complete and violent exhalation, it was necessary to mention such experiments now, in the account of the respira-
690 tory organs. I shall speak of them again in the anatomy of the vocal organs.

Chapter 8

[*Further Experiments to illustrate Thoracic Movements*]

690 Logically the next step would be to make the whole thorax motionless by ligating the nerves that move its muscles. This you have often seen me demonstrate not only to you privately, but in public. You can immobilize the intercostal muscles through the nerves that reach them from the spinal marrow, as I have described, and then the diaphragm by destroying the origins of its nerves. You have seen me demonstrate all these things both privately and publicly, using pigs because there is no advantage in having an ape in such experiments and the spectacle is hideous. It is not possible to indicate in words the place where it is necessary to make a clear demonstration. But my statement will be useful both in reminding those who have already observed these things, and for inducing those who have never seen anything of the kind to make the experiment.

691 When the animal is in position on its back, held on the board by cords, not only by its four limbs but also by its head and neck, you will find the nerves lying underneath at the origin of the forelimbs. It is better to remove the whole skin there to observe two large veins, one running up to the neck slantwise [*external jugular*], the other, at a right angle to it, to the origin of the front limbs [*subclavian*].

When you have stripped off with your fingers the membrane between these, you will see the [*phrenic*] nerves in the side of the neck running down slantwise to the thorax, attached to the underlying muscle [*scalenus anterior*] and almost touching the first rib where these [i.e. muscle and rib] conjoin.

Once you visualize the region exactly, you can proceed to strip the skin of the neck by a single incision to the site of the [*phrenic*] nerves. And if you practise this you will succeed in exposing them with one stroke. *692*

In pigs there are generally three on each side, in apes usually two, and occasionally three, as there is occasionally a fourth in pigs. The spinal cord in the neck is the origin of them all. The first pair springs from between the fourth and fifth vertebrae, the second from between the fifth and sixth, and the third from beyond the sixth. The last is quite small. If a fourth be present it is a minute offshoot of the pair after the seventh vertebra. When all these nerves have been cut, the diaphragm becomes motionless. In the same way, if you were to destroy each of the six muscles coming from the neck into the thorax, you would injure their nerves and destroy their activity.*

There are two methods of destruction, cutting or interrupting. But since neither the muscles nor (even less) the nerves are visible when only the skin is removed you must dissect the muscles first that run up to the shoulder-joint† from the breast. *693* This seems difficult to the inexperienced, and perhaps one might think that one animal is not enough for all the experiments which you must perform, apart from the destruction of the nerves which make the whole thorax motionless. But anyone who has seen me often doing this can be persuaded of the possibility of the experiment described, for it seems troublesome and discourages the inexperienced through the impression it makes on the mind rather than by its actual practice. So let no one be cast down, but take heart for the attempt; first removing the skin from the breast, for this is done without losing blood; secondly removing the muscles entering the joint at the shoulder, which also involves no loss of blood; and thirdly separating the scapulae from the muscles underlying

* Slight disturbance of text here.

† Reading KAT' ŌMON for the senseless KATŌ MONON.

694 them, as well as the muscles running up to the shoulder joint, namely the large one that forms the armpit [*pectoralis major*] and the small one [*pectoralis minor*] found towards the shoulder.

This having been done, there will then appear the two pairs of the high muscles of the thorax [*scaleni dorsalis et ventralis* traversed by the brachial plexus in pigs]. Thus you will see clearly the nerves of the one, the larger, mounted on the muscles, while those of the other, the lesser, which has an anterior position, too, are harder to discern; but if you have practised beforehand on a dead animal, even they are not difficult to find. Also, without stripping off the shoulder-blades along with the aforesaid muscle, it is possible to find the starting-points of the nerves of the muscles moving the thorax, which nerves enter the heads of each pair. I shall speak of them in the anatomy of the muscles so clearly as to enable any diligent student working by himself to do perfectly the experiment just described.

There is a third pair of the muscles moving the thorax, thin and small, arising from a delicate membranous ligament behind the shoulder-blades [? *m. rhomboideus thoracis* of pig]. It is not seen when the skin has been removed until the muscles peculiar

695 to the scapula have been dissected. Therefore you must grasp this fact about these muscles, too, that when you cut its own peculiar muscles at each shoulder-blade and lay bare the pair of membranous muscles, even so it is not open to you as with the former muscles to make them motionless by destroying the nerves. This is because the nerves moving them are at once hidden and very delicate. But you can readily paralyse the muscles by cutting their heads which are membranous ligaments.

You must grasp this fact in general about all muscles, that if their heads be severed, they no longer act. If then the muscle have one single head, it is easier by cutting that to deprive the muscle of motion; if it have several, you must cut them all. In some muscles the number of heads is not easy to discover when they start from several bony processes, as happens with these two pairs belonging to the thorax that I mentioned before and more so with the anterior pair. It is safer then, to cut them at that point where their heads first gather together. For I am in the habit of doing this with the anterior muscles as well whenever I want to produce paralysis, not by destroying the nerves but by severing the muscles themselves. In these a deep incision is required, since they reach a considerable depth when their heads are gathered together. The division is easiest in the posterior muscles, so that it can be made with the nails. *696*

Enough has been said of the muscles peculiar to the thorax.

Chapter 9

[*Transverse Sections of Spinal Cord*]

Of course, the incision in the spinal marrow will be discussed later when I reach that topic. For the present it will suffice to say no more than is useful for our immediate problems. *696*

If you sever it completely between the third and fourth vertebrae, the animal at once ceases to breathe. Not only does the thorax become motionless, but also the whole body below the section. (It is clear that if the section be above the second or first vertebra or at the very starting-point of the spinal marrow, the animal immediately perishes.) If beyond the sixth vertebra, all the muscles of the thorax become motionless immediately and the animal breathes in only by means of the diaphragm. Transverse sections below this vertebra permit other parts of the thorax to move. For the largest pair of the higher muscles [*pectoralis major*], which has two origins for each of its nerves [*lateral* and *medial pectoral nerves*], receives the branch of the greater one as a rule beyond the sixth vertebra [namely from C.7 in ape but from C.6 in man]. For this reason sections of the spinal marrow after the seventh vertebra leave both pairs of muscles working, and even more those after the eighth or ninth. For the muscles receive the other starting-points of the nerves also and take over the activity at the back of the membranous muscles as well, and the animal is seen inhaling with both parts *697*

698 of the thorax, the upper and lower, unless it needs to breathe only slightly, for then the diaphragm alone suffices for it. The further you advance towards the lower vertebrae the more muscles of the thorax you will leave active. Yet the sixth pair of nerves from the brain is not seen contributing to the work of respiration, because no part of it enters any muscle of the thorax. For this reason, when the origins of the other nerves are all cut and this alone is preserved, the animal ceases to breathe immediately, as it gets no help from it. However, this does not happen to the pair of nerves entering the PHRENES [*diaphragm*]; when all the other nerves are destroyed the animal breathes with diaphragm alone, the movement in these parts of the thorax being plainly visible.

Chapter 10

[*How to see the Site and Movement of the Pleura*]

698 Since anatomists have made investigations about the way in which the breath filters through into the region between the thoracic wall and the lungs, it is now time to mention the experiments in dissection useful for this. The removal of the rib by excision is an old-fashioned device, affording no clear means
699 of deciding the question, for some say they see the lungs joined to the thoracic wall and some that it is separated from it. This is because of the density of the membranes under the ribs that are cut out. I, however, obtained a clearer view by not stopping at excising the rib, but removing along with it one of the surrounding membranes [*periosteum*] before excision; for when this is removed the pleura is left single and alone. This allows a clear view through it, so that all admit they see plainly the lung in contact with the thorax. A still better view is obtainable through the diaphragm, when it is exposed after the cap of peritoneum has been removed.

The operation must be carried out as follows: with the animal lying on its back, sever all the muscles in the abdomen by the end of the false ribs, keeping the peritoneum uncut. It has been remarked [p. 136] that the aponeuroses from the fourth pair of muscles there [*transversi abdominis*] are united with the peritoneum. When you have stopped cutting, leaving the *700* aponeuroses uncut, the peritoneum should be stripped off below from the PHRENES [*diaphragm*], the aponeuroses being no longer stretched out along with these.

This is easily accomplished by using both hands without a scalpel, and the job is much more easily done with the animal alive than dead. For the tissues that can be separated from one another by excoriation are chilled at death and become more difficult to separate. In that case when you strip off the peritoneum from the sinewy part of the PHRENES, you will pull the stomach down and draw away the parts on either hand to the side towards the fleshy part of the diaphragm. If in addition you draw upwards the parts by the ensiform cartilage, and stretch the parts by the last rib broadways (if necessary making transverse incisions in the muscles of the abdomen at each flank) you will render the sinewy part of the diaphragm easy to examine.

All are in full agreement that the lungs are moulded here to the shape of the thorax at this point, that they never leave it, *701* and that they always cling to it in both phases of the act of respiration, inhaling and exhaling. These observations support the view of Erasistratus[56] (who thinks no air issues from the lungs) but it conflicts with what I am now going to say. For when the diaphragm is thus exposed, if you kill the animal at once, the lungs are seen to be at a distance from the PHRENES.[169] And while there are many ways in which an animal may die, you will observe the lungs very far separated from the PHRENES however you kill it. So having choked the animal, sometimes by drowning, sometimes by strangling, or by an incision made in the spinal cord at the first vertebra, or by cutting through large arteries or veins, I have observed the lungs gradually withdrawing from the diaphragm while the animal was dying.[169]

When a rib is excised the same thing is visible, especially to

one who has observed beforehand that in a living animal the
702 lungs are applied to the thoracic wall but that after death they are withdrawn therefrom. The appearance of the lungs shows that the air in them has emptied into the space between them and the thorax [i.e. the pleural cavity]. Moreover, while the animal is still alive, when the bone of the rib has been excised, an empty space is seen between both organs at the ends of the lobes and specially when the animal inhales more deeply, for with slight inhalations it is sometimes not perceptible at all, and in other cases seems quite small. If you want the space to appear larger, make the animal run before dissecting it, so that the rib is cut out while it is panting, for the size of the empty space always increases along with the extent of the inhalation. It would appear even larger after the animal has run rapidly, if you paralyse its diaphragm by cutting the nerves that belong to it, for then it is compelled to inhale with the aid of the intercostal muscles and the thorax is clearly seen moving at a greater distance.[169]

There is another experiment which is thought to show that
703 some of the air filters through to the thorax [i.e. pleural cavity] from the lungs. Prepare in advance a bladder with a mouth of suitable size. Then cut the skin over the ribs in a circle, so that the area of the cut is the same size as the mouth of the bladder. Then excise the rib in the way described. Next sew the bladder to the lip of the wound, putting the mouth of the bladder underneath all round, so that the skin is outside. Now seal the holes made in it with a needle and thread and some plastic substance like that called 'moist plaster',[170] or a liquid preparation of wax. There is now no perceptible gap between thread and skin, for what escapes the eye is safely closed with the wax preparation so that no air can pass in from the surrounding atmosphere, nor from the inside out. Now perforate the bladder at its end and
704 insert through the hole a scalpel with a round handle, so that, when a suture is put round the bladder outside, its membrane is tied round the handle of the scalpel so that nothing can escape between it and the bladder and handle. For this purpose again

use the preparation of wax. Then incise the pleura with the scalpel and observe how through the incision air percolates from the thorax into the bladder during exhalation. During inhalation, when the thorax is distended you will see this air once more drawn into the thorax through the incision, and then again passing into the bladder as the animal exhales, and from it again entering the thorax. And you will see the air increasing in quantity at each breath and the bladder becoming completely filled by it.[169]

Objections may be raised respecting this phenomenon on two grounds. It may be said either that some air filters through along the thread, a larger quantity coming in from outside with *705* inhalation, and less passing out from within during exhalation. Or again that the membrane surrounding the lungs is severed along with the pleura. This does sometimes happen, for it is difficult, when the lungs are always joined to the thorax, to perforate the one organ while keeping the other intact. You will discover this after the death of the animal by exposing the lungs. As to the possibility that something filters between thread and skin into the bladder from the surrounding air, it raises a tiresome controversy and needs to be refuted at greater length.

It is unnecessary to have recourse to such arguments when the matter is proved by other concrete evidence. To settle the question before us we must not make any use of such a method of handling, when what has been described a little before plainly proves that some air escapes from the lungs. For invariably with animals that have been killed in any way, if, as I have said, you excise a rib and expose the diaphragm, the lungs are seen at a *706* distance from the thorax, while this could not be so unless some breath filtered through from the lungs into the open space of the thorax.

BOOK IX

On the Brain

Chapter 1

[*Dissecting the Brain*]

707 How the phenomena revealed in the brain and cord can best be observed in the dead and the living respectively will be made clear in this book. The anatomy of the dead teaches the position, number, proper substance, size, and construction of the parts. That of the living may reveal the functions at a glance or *708* provide premisses for deducing them. Obviously, then, operation on the dead should precede that on the living, for it can be performed on an organ either detached or still an integral part of the body.

The first dissectional operation on the brain that I shall explain will be that made when the bones of the skull have been removed, leaving intact its covering meninx. Whether you call [this membrane] 'thick' (as I do now) or 'hard', or 'cuticular', and that under it 'delicate', or 'soft', or 'membranous', will neither help nor hinder the science of anatomy. For the gain from dissection is knowledge of the nature of the parts, not the names by which they are called.

Ox brains, ready prepared and stripped of most of the cranial parts, are generally on sale in the large cities. If you think more bone than necessary adheres to them, order its removal by the butcher who sells them. If he be not there, do so yourself, using strong knives for excision or carpenters' adzes, such as you see *709* I keep ready. The instruments of this kind are best made of hard iron, for those made of soft will become useless after repeated strokes. But I would not that the skull be violently and repeatedly hit, for such blows shake the soft brain, shattering and disintegrating it. You must prepare it for examination without any accident of the kind, so that all the origins of nerves be observed with precision, as well as the arteries and veins and the partition between the front cavities and parts round the so-called PYELOS (trough) or CHŌNĒ (funnel) [*infundibulum*] and suchlike structures.[171]

When the part is suitably prepared, you will see the dura mater appearing much thicker in the middle line than in general, and dipping a little way just where lies the median suture. So also under the lambdoid suture you will see the dura *710* mater doubling itself and penetrating some distance into the brain. You will see veins coming up through it, along the lambdoid suture, one on either side. Where these meet at a point is roughly the most prominent region.

The front and back parts of the brain differ, the front being much greater.* [A sentence missing here to the effect that the dura is twice as thick near the highest part of the sagittal sinus as elsewhere on the convex surface.] Towards this highest point the second doubling of the dura mater is formed, so that in thickness it appears four times as thick as all the other parts of the membrane that gird the brain.

In addition to the two already mentioned [at the lambdoid suture], there extends along the brain moving forward a third 'vein', for what other name can you call such a vessel seen to contain blood? For when the brain is exposed by trephining (as we usually do for a cranial fracture) you will observe blood in these cavities in the living, and in the dead a clot. Moreover, *711* these cavities do not have the coat of the veins which join them through the bones of the head; for when the veins reach the skull the dura mater is doubled, while the space within [the skull] becomes merely tubular, being a vessel for keeping the blood in the same state as it was received.

To observe this properly, have ready a long slender instrument like that called DIPYRĒNON (double probe) of wood—either of box or something as solid. Insert this into the cavities of the membrane, pushing it where there is no resistance and

* Reading MEIZON for MEGETHEI.

cutting through the meninx over it to meet the wood. If this be not possible, insert into the cavity of the meninx a DIPYRĒNON, a SMILĒ, or a SPATHOMĒLĒ by the end that has no rounded knob.[172] Thrust it forward into the cavity and cut slantwise, sloping the instrument inserted on each side towards 712 the other part so that you may not break the scalpel by running up against it and may reach the cavity.

In stripping the surrounding bones from the folds of the meninx some part [of the meninx] is often torn and pulled away. This will be the spot for the insertion of an instrument into the blood-containing cavity [*sinus*]. But, if it be not torn then, with a sharp scalpel, cut each side of the fold of membrane in the parts beneath where it first reaches (EMPIPTEI) the skull and then, introducing the scalpel through the incision, force it up to the junction where the two veins meet the region that Herophilus [is said to] call the torcular (LĒNOS) [Fig. 25]. The part to which he really gives this name is deeper, but on the surface there is another complex of small veins, lying along the 'torcular'.[173] Its narrow calibre no longer admits the olive of the probe, and therefore in small brains it is either 713 indistinct or invisible. Try then to introduce one of the other olivary probes or ear-probes and make an incision along it.

The delicate superficial process of the meninx already mentioned arises where the lambdoid suture meets the squamous [part of the temporal] bone. So first cut these superficial veins as far as the torcular, that is on the surface. Having cut this, empty out any clot in these [vessels] and then observe how very like the inner surface of the membrane is to the substance of the veins, except for its delicacy. No wonder that Nature does not need to extend the coat of the vein bringing blood up to the cavities of the dura, since the two trunks (SŌMATA) are of like substance.

Chapter 2

[*Membranes and Veins of Brain*]

Next you must observe the delicate veins issuing on either side of the torculars. Some are quite small and admit no more than a hair, but some are larger. You will see those from the smaller [superficial] torcular dispersing on the surface to the neighbouring parts of the surface of the brain. Those veins from the greater [torcular] in the depths[173] disperse into the whole back part of the brain, called by some ENKRANION, and also into the front part. (It makes no difference whether you call the back part of the brain ENKRANION (*cerebellum*) or PARENKEPHALIS.) Into it veins extend from those that pass into the [deep] torcular along the sides and from the lambdoid suture and from the [superficial] torcular itself; they have the coat that is proper to a vein, like the veins throughout the animal. Even before they plunge into the main mass of the brain you will see them plainly springing from the veins at the meninx, unless you happen to have torn them apart.* 713 714

The blood reaches the brain itself, which some call 'anterior brain', through the dura mater that cleaves the brain into two equal divisions in the middle line [*falx cerebri*]. Thence veins in numbers are distributed through its whole length into both halves of the brain.

All [these vessels] are small except two. One of these is from the torcular, branching into the front part deep down along the whole head [*inferior sagittal sinus*]. How you are to find it I shall explain a little later. 715

The second [*vein of Galen, great cerebral vein*] is much larger and not very near the torcular, nor very distant either, roughly in the middle of the 'brain' (ENKEPHALON. I give this name to the compound formed from both the back and front parts). This vein plunges vertically into the depths, where it breaks up into many branches. However, this does not happen to

* In the text this sentence is displaced and precedes that which in the translation precedes it.

it at its origin from the meninx but when it has passed forward to a certain point not far off.

You will observe all these things before dividing the brain and with the dura mater only laid bare. You can expose it at three places, since it divides the whole brain into three with its folds [i.e. *falx* and *tentorium*]. Pull it by the incisions, separating with your finger the left and right parts, which cover the brain in front, and also the remaining part, with which it covers the back part of the brain. You will thus see the origins of the veins dis-
716 persed into the three parts of the brain. Some are on the surface so that their divisions are visible. Some descend into the depths.

The delicate membrane binding together the veins surrounding the brain on the outside descends with them to the cavity within. People call this the 'delicate meninx' [*pia mater*] from old habit, the name meninx being somehow now reserved for the membranes round the brain. For our predecessors used to call all membranes MĒNINGES, not only these brain membranes, as you may learn from many treatises written by them, and not least from those of Hippocrates[174] and Diocles.[42] These Marinus[32] also mentioned in his work *De anatomia*. The pia mater can always be observed to embrace the brain and to accompany it in the depths, but the dura mater you will see at quite a distance from it. How great that distance is you will be able to gauge if you make a small opening at one of the three
717 parts into which it cleaves the brain, and introduce therein the point of a tube like those for 'goldsmiths' bellows' that you see I keep ready. (This is the name they give, as you know, to the instruments with which they blow in kindling the fire.) If you introduce the point of the tube into the incision and bind the meninx tightly round it and blow through it, you will see the region beneath fill with air. This meninx, the dura mater, undergirds the skull, but the brain, expanding and contracting, approaches and withdraws from [the skull] in the empty space between. But about this I shall speak shortly in the experiment on living animals. In the present discourse let us keep to the natural order of things.

Chapter 3

[*Chorioid Plexus and Pineal Gland*]

After the surrounding parts have been examined it is now time *717* to dissect the brain itself. Start from the membrane that bisects the front part [*falx cerebri*]. Cut or tear away from it the branches of the veins towards the side, beginning from the *718* front and raise it with your fingers until you reach the large vein springing from it, which, we said, runs vertically down to the depth [*great cerebral vein*].[175] Raise this too and give it to someone else to hold. Then yourself separate the two parts of the brain, sundering them gently with your fingers till you reach a previously mentioned vein of considerable size extended lengthwise [*inferior longitudinal sinus*].

With the sight of this vein its function is revealed, for it obviously sends forth on either side delicate branches dispersed into the brain. Remove the vein from the underlying tissues, and either cut it out as far as the torcular, or isolate it to the point where it issues therefrom and lay it down on these parts.

Examine the region exposed. It is like a callus, so that there appears to be a natural hollow there which receives from the *719* overlying and surrounding tissues incompletely concocted nutriment (which has the special name 'residues', PERIT-TŌMATA, and there is nothing against this term [p. 151]). Gently continuing the dissection you will find what look like slender passages reaching as far as the middle ventricle of the brain. The dissection here must, I say, be gentle because of the top of the septum which rises to this point and partitions the ventricles. It is time to examine it.

Slice straight cuts on both sides of the mid-line down to the ventricles. You will recognize them because the corpus callosum differs very plainly from the severed brain substance. You will see in the ventricles what is called the 'chorioid plexuses' (CHOROEIDĒ PLEGMATA). The followers of Herophilus call it a 'chorioid concatenation' (CHOROEIDĒ SUSTREMMATA), of course taking the name from the outer

membrane of the foetus. It is a plexus of veins and arteries held
720 together by delicate membranes. (So too the component parts of the brain itself are a complex of veins and arteries, bound together by the pia mater which is of the same substance as the other delicate membranes, namely those in the embryo, the pleura, the peritoneum and all such membranes.) Extend [the gap] gently with your hands, so as not to break the plexus, and observe the veins that move downward from above and divide and the arteries from below that correspondingly move upwards and divide.

Try to preserve the plexus unharmed here so that later you may follow it when you expose the parts and may observe clearly the veins in the ventricles. These all branch from the vessel [*vena magna cerebri*] that we said moved downwards[175] and reached the brain, while the arteries run up from the two others out of the lower parts [*carotids*]. You will make a more accurate examination of these as the operation proceeds.

The corpus callosum and chorioid plexus serve as landmarks
721 for the first cut into each ventricle. Try immediately to examine the membrane that divides right from left ventricle [*septum lucidum*]. It has a nature like that of the brain as a whole and is thus easily broken if stretched too vigorously. For it is so delicate that if the dissection be made in a good light, the light will shine through as with those translucent stones cut in thin layers and put in windows. Hence you must not elevate it roughly lest it be rent, and yet it cannot be plainly seen without raising it.

The upper border [of the *septum*] is naturally joined to the severed tissues—perhaps I should say united thereto. You must therefore grasp the severed parts with care and bend them towards the other ventricle, laying them on the top of the septum. Thus the exposed ventricle will be easier to see, and the septum raised but moderately, as is necessary.*

722 Before the septum is fully raised it is slack and wrinkled, and neither transmits light nor displays its relations. But when raised to tautness, and yet not torn, it will be clearly evident. If you

* Reading DEOMETHA for DOMETHA.

now remove it with the parts united with it as far as the incisions, you will see the ventricles more clearly. Also the vein running vertically downwards [*vena magna cerebri*] can be seen dividing round a body like a pine cone (KŌNOEIDĒS) [*pineal*]. A delicate membrane [*tela chorioidea*], like in substance and continuous with the pia mater, binds the branching veins, as well as all the others. It conceals the pineal body which cannot be seen till you have torn it apart a little, for this membrane lies as a support to the veins split off from the great vein [*vena magna* 723 *cerebri*] which runs downwards.* How to lay bare this body I shall explain a little later. I add only that anatomists call the cone-like body (KŌNOEIDES SŌMA) also KŌNARION.

[This body] rests in the cleft of the vein and is hidden until the membrane is severed. Sever it [the membrane] gently without raising the conarium forcibly along with it. For if it be torn away from the underlying tissues the operation will suffer in an important respect which I shall later explain.

As the heart is bared of the coat surrounding it, so you must lay bare the conarium. Sever the surrounding membrane [*tela chorioidea*] with a straight cut from the base toward the apex. Then strip off the membrane along with the [*internal cerebral*] veins on either side of the pineal gland. Bend it [the conarium] towards the incision (DIAIRESIS), so that it may be at once laid bare as it approaches the part opposite the slit cover. This done it is now possible, before exposing the region between 724 pineal and ventricles, for you to perceive that both veins come from the division of the vein to the chorioid plexus, not but what you will realize clearly that they proceed from there if you lay bare the body lying between.

Chapter 4

[*The Fornix*]

Give me your attention while I explain how you must expose 724 it. The part covered by this tissue is no indifferent part of the

* Here two lines of repetition.

brain but a third ventricle. It is over and above those already mentioned earlier which the septal membrane parts and separates. Expose it at the very spot where the veins issue as if from holes [*interventricular foramina*] and enter the anterior ventricles; for at these same holes the middle region is perforated to communicate with the anterior ventricles.

You must put the knob of a probe or flat part of a spathion or of a spatulary probe gently underneath at both holes and raise the body [*anterior column of fornix*] resting on the veins high up. For if you do this at each hole the instruments will meet and 725 this body will be visible which lies on the veins passing through in concealment like a kind of arch [*fornix*] in a domed (SPHAIROEIDĒS) building. Such things are popularly called not arches (PSALIDES) but domes (KAMARAI). Accordingly this body has been called 'arch-like' (PSALIDOEIDĒS) by those who have observed it. But some who have not, deny that this arch-like body exists, and some, under misapprehension, think that this is the name of the structure above the septum [that is, the *corpus callosum*]. But whereas the latter [*corpus callosum*] is not called arch-like, this is really worthy of that name.

If you cut it [*fornix*], you will see a callus (TYLON) here like that in the anterior ventricles at the base. Moreover, the veins which go through the cavity [of the ventricle] are supported at the base and in the curvature of the fornix itself. The convex part is on the outside and the concave—like the ceiling of an arch—on the inside. [It can be seen] only when the overlying structures—by which it is supported up to the fold in the meninx—have been removed.

726 If you notice how, while the animal is still alive, all parts of the dura are attached to the skull but to the brain only those parts at the folds, you will readily believe that the top of the fornix is kept raised, producing a large hollow beneath. So too, the anterior ventricles being still larger, the whole top of the septum lucidum (DIAPHRAGMA) is necessarily raised high with the tissues continuous with it.

The septum [lucidum] cannot be a support and buttress of the tissues above it, for it is extremely soft and delicate. Even if it had but one of these qualities, it could not have borne the weight of the least part of the brain lying above. Its function, however, accords with its name, for it separates the anterior ventricles; it does not support the overlying tissues. These ventricles have no supporting prop (nor has that which is to follow), but by hanging suspended the overlying structures maintain the empty space of the three ventricles. This space is necessarily destroyed in dissection, because the structures above fall down as I said earlier.

There is a large duct (POROS) below in the base of this third ventricle which receives the waste products from the anterior ventricles by the holes [*interventricular foramina*] already mentioned and there is another [duct] from the tissues above also.[176] These [ducts] conjoin in the ventricles where the veins from the conarium enter it. Those ignorant of this ventricle are naturally unaware also of the duct extending backwards [*aqueduct*] whereby the conarium is supported, and if it is bared of the surrounding veins and broken off at the base, a hole is seen there high up. This, to put it plainly, is like a chimney, though the brain has no exhalation of its own to be sent through such an elevated passage. Its orifice can transmit no surrounding air, since the great mass of the cerebrum lies on it and over that the dura which is itself double and over that again the skull. Thus Nature would have made this hole purposely forsooth, though she never does aught in vain![177] *727*

Those who set about dissection in the wrong spirit introduce such errors not only into the actual process, but into the theory of Nature. It necessarily follows that just as the uses of parts really observed in dissection are marvellous, so if they be wrongly observed, it is impossible to give a [consistent] account of their action. *728*

But with you, when you have exposed properly all the parts under discussion, you will observe the third ventricle between the two anterior ventricles with the fourth behind it. You will see the duct on which the pineal gland is mounted passing to the ventricle in the middle, so that at the hole there are two [ducts] of some size. One leads back to the cerebellum. If through this you introduce a double olivary probe or spatula probe, you will find that it ends in the ventricle behind. The other, that at the bottom of the ventricle, leads downward [to the *infundibulum*]. But the pineal gland, when freed of sur-rounding tissues and left resting on the duct, usually falls down 729 instead of standing up, as when it was enveloped by the mem-branes and vessels. Generally it sinks backwards as it falls.

Chapter 5

[*Corpora Quadrigemina and Vermis*]

729 The pineal gland is received, as it falls, by gently rounded tissues which have outlines of their own, though they are parts of the brain and have the same substance as it. Some call them from their shape nates (GLOUTA [buttocks]), and they call others 'twins' (DIDYMIA), for so they call the testicles (ORCHEIS) DIDYMOI to be seemly.

This duct [*aqueductus cerebri*] then, which passes through from the middle into the posterior [fourth] ventricle and lies between the nates, is covered by its proper coat of the same sort of substance as the meninx linking together all the vessels in the brain. Wherefore carefully seek to remove from it the tissues lying above; realizing that it will be torn asunder if you are careless. There lies on it a part of the brain shaped like the worm that grows in wood. Thence the name 'vermiform pro-cess' by which name anatomists call this structure covering the 730 duct. You will observe that it has two ends, the anterior near the pineal gland, while the posterior is not visible, because there rests on it the whole upper substance of the back of the cere-brum. Take hold of the hind end of this, near the origin of the spinal marrow, and try to bring it forward, rolling it, as it were, until you see another worm-like body. When you find it, remove gradually the greater part of the tissues lying above so that only those on the duct are left. These end doubly on each side in a form resembling the worms mentioned before. Here you will see delicate strands binding the vermiform process at the front to the parts of the brain lying beside the nates on either side. Some anatomists call them 'tendons'.

When you have finished handling each end of the vermiform process in turn, move the whole body forward and backward. I mean by 'whole' what I said a little earlier lies on the duct *731* with a vermiform end at either side. Then notice how, when it is bent towards the front, the posterior ventricle, the fourth, is exposed, and when it is moved backwards the larger part of the ventricle is covered and only that part is visible which Herophilus likened to the groove of a pen for writing. It is really like a pen, with a hollow like an incision [*posterior median sulcus*] in the middle, and on either side of this each of the side parts [*eminentia facialis*] stretching as far up as they rise in pens from the line in the middle. The pens we write with are grooved in this way particularly in Alexandria. Herophilus lived there, so it is natural, of course, that when he was operating he applied the name, being induced to do so by the likeness in the image [Fig. 26].

NOTES

The letter K *refers to* C. G. *Kühn's edition of the works of Galen. It is followed by the number of the volume in roman with that of the page in arabic figures.*

(1) Marcus Aurelius Antoninus, born at Rome, A.D. 121, was the adopted son of the Emperor Antoninus Pius whose daughter Faustina he married. He succeeded his adoptive father in 161, and died in Pannonia in 180. Galen's *De anatomicis administrationibus libri duo* (note 3), written between 164 and 165, was a different work from that here translated.

(2) Flavius Boëthus was an adherent of the Peripatetic philosophy. He is mentioned several times by Galen whose demonstrations to him may be dated March 164. Boëthus, with his wife and son, were Galen's patients. He became governor of Palestine in 165, and died in or before A.D. 169.

(3) Galen's *De anatomicis administrationibus libri duo* has not survived. See note 1.

(4) 'Now' is about A.D. 177, the approximate date at which Galen gave the lectures of which the present work is the expanded shorthand report.

(5) Galen's *De Hippocratis et Erasistrati anatomice* in three books was written in Rome when he was 34, *c.* A.D. 164. It has not survived. It is quoted in Galen's *De libris propriis.*

(6) Galen's *De vivorum dissectione* has not survived. It is mentioned frequently in his works. A spurious medieval work with that title appears in some collected editions of Galen.

(7) Galen's *De mortuorum dissectione* has not survived.

(8) Galen's *De causis respirationis* is printed in K. iv. 465–9.

(9) Galen's *De voce* has not survived, unless it be represented by the fragment printed by Chartier (vol. iv, pp. 219–22), but not reprinted by Kühn.

(10) Galen's *De usu partium corporis humani libri XVII* is his best known and most complete anatomical work. It was written between A.D. 169 and 175. A Latin abridgement of it was made late in the thirteenth century, and a full Latin translation direct from the Greek by Nicholas of Reggio was made *c.* 1310. It became the standard source of anatomical knowledge from the thirteenth until the sixteenth century. It was then amplified by the publication of the newly discovered *De anatomicis administrationibus* and soon after displaced by the work of

Vesalius (1543), who based his own researches on these two treatises of Galen. The text of *De usu* is printed in K. iii and K. iv. 1–366. There is a French translation by Charles Daremberg, and the Greek work is now being rendered into English by Mrs. May of Cornell University.

(11) Galen's *De thoracis et pulmonis motu* has not survived.

(12) This was in A.D. 159. Pelops was a Dogmatist and exponent of the humoral pathology. He had a controversy with Philippus the Empiric. See R. Walzer, *Galen On Medical Experience*, Oxford, 1944. Pelops wrote several books on anatomy which, as we learn from Galen, were burned. Later, other works were passed off as his. He held at one time that nerves, arteries, and veins all arise from the brain.

(13) Satyrus, the first anatomical teacher of Galen, worked at Pergamum. His works have disappeared. He is known to have written commentaries on Hippocrates.

(14) Of Quintus we learn here and elsewhere from Galen that he was the pupil of Marinus, and the teacher of Satyrus and Numisianus, that he wrote nothing, that he did not follow 'Hippocrates' exactly, and that for some reason he was expelled from Rome.

(15) Numisianus, anatomist and exponent of Hippocrates, wrote anatomical works, now lost, setting forth the theories of Satyrus. There survives a fragment of a commentary by him on the 'Hippocratic' *Epidemics*, from which it has been inferred that, like Pelops (note 12), he belonged to the Dogmatist School. Among his pupils in anatomy were Galen and Pelops.

(16) Eudemus the Peripatetic was, as we learn from Galen, K. xiv. 605, 615–18, author of a work *On prognosis*. Nothing else is known of him.

(17) Alexander of Damascus—to be distinguished from Alexander of Aphrodisias—became Professor of Peripatetic Philosophy in Athens about 176. He was the teacher in philosophy of Boëthus (note 2). Later Galen seems to have quarrelled with him and regarded him as malevolent, K. xiv. 627–9.

(18) Sergius Paulus became Governor of Rome in or about 165. He remained in office till about 178. He can hardly be the same as the rhaetor, a patient of Galen mentioned in his commentary *Hippocratis de acutorum morborum victu*, K. xv. 565.

(19) In fact the sterna of apes are not the flattest of the animals that Galen had dissected. The sternum of the pig, for example, is relatively much flatter, but the misstatement illustrates the point that Galen's knowledge of bones was based mainly on human material.

(20) Galen's *De ossibus ad tirones*, printed in K. ii. 732–778, is the only surviving anatomical work of antiquity based directly on human material. As its title implies, it is elementary. The translator has published an English version of this work in *Proc. Roy. Soc. Med.*, 1952, xlv (Sect. Hist. Med.), pp. 25–34.

(21) Evidence that some human material at least was still systematically used for instruction in the last third of the second century.

(22) Galen does not make clear here what species of ape he dissected. He certainly used more than one. He preferred the Barbary ape (*Macaca inuus*) but it is probable that he relied chiefly on the Rhesus monkey (*Macaca mulatta*).

(23) In the Barbary ape the neck of the femur is more transverse than in the Rhesus and forms with the shaft an angle of about 100°. In the adult human male this angle is about 125°, but varies in inverse proportion to the width of the pelvis and the height of the individual. It is less in females than in males. The angle, in human beings at least, is widest in infancy and decreases during growth. See Fig. 7.

(24) This is notably the case with the outer hamstring tendon, that of the biceps femoris. The crural insertion of this muscle in *Macaca mulatta* extends about half-way down the shaft of the tibia. On the inner side the insertion of the gracilis, which is a robust muscle in apes, extends a considerable distance below the tibial collateral ligament [Figs. 16 and 17].

(25) The Empiric anatomists, against whom Galen constantly tilts, were content to gain their anatomical knowledge in the course of surgical practice. They regarded dissection of apes as useless.

(26) A hint that human dissection was still being occasionally practised.

(27) It is impossible to identify the disease here called ANTHRAX. It was certainly not what we now call by that name. The word means primarily 'charcoal': hence 'dark substances' or 'dark patches'; compare Latin *carbunculus* from *carbo*, charcoal.

(28) Costunius Rufinus is not mentioned elsewhere in classical writings. The name KOSTOUNIOS is perhaps a scribal misreading for the abbreviation of K[OINT]OS IOUNIOS. Another possible identification is with a ROUPHINOS often mentioned on dedicatory inscriptions at Pergamum.

(29) Galen's *De musculorum dissectione ad tirones*, K. xviii, pt. ii. 926–1026.

(30) Lycus of Macedon (died *c.* A.D. 170, see pp. 6, 111, 127 of translation), a pupil of Quintus (note 14), was an Empiric. Galen had an especial dislike for him. He wrote extensively and composed a book on muscles. In it he missed the pterygoid and also certain neck muscles. See pp. 107–8 of translation. He had his own theory of renal secretion. None of his works survives. See note 98.

(31) In apes the plantaris muscle is relatively stronger and more fleshy than in man, extending in the Rhesus to the lowest quarter of the leg. Its tendon passes through a groove in the tendo Achillis, over the tuber calcanei, to be continued as the plantar aponeurosis. The belly of the plantaris in apes is with difficulty separated from the fleshy part of the gastrocnemius lateralis.

(32) Marinus (*fl. c.* A.D. 100) taught anatomy at Alexandria. Galen mentions him several times. He wrote (*a*) a practical manual of dissections; (*b*) a general anatomy in twenty books, the source of much of Galen's knowledge, see page 230; (*c*) a work on the series of nerve roots; (*d*) an account of the muscles. He treated the foramina of the skull in detail and discovered the nerves of voice. Quintus was his pupil. None of the works of Marinus survives but there is a good account of them in Galen's *De libris propriis*, K. xix. 25–30.

(33) There is no such reference in the recognized text of *De usu partium* Galen may be referring to another version of that work, as he did in *De semine*, Book II, ch. 6; K. iv. 643.

(34) This work cannot be identified.

(35) Galen throughout describes as 'inner' or 'inside' what we call the anterior or flexor aspect, and as 'outer' or 'outside' what we call the posterior or extensor aspect.

(36) In the Rhesus and allied forms the pisiform bone is elongated and tipped with cartilage.

(37) In the Rhesus the extensor digitorum communis sends tendons to all four fingers and there is, in addition, a separate extensor for each finger. Galen is clearly here describing the hand of an ape and not that of a man.

(38) In the Rhesus and allied forms the external surface of the lower end of the radius is very deeply cleft for the tendon of the abductor pollicis longus. See Fig. 6.

(39) It may be noted that in the Rhesus an extensor pollicis brevis is absent.

(40) Galen's view that there was a class or sect the children of which were initiated into anatomical practice is fanciful. It is unsupported by evidence and is probably part of a legend of the Asclepiadae current at Pergamum. Yearning for a 'golden age' of anatomy under such disciples of Aesculapius is patent in the paragraphs that follow.

(41) The idea that general philosophers studied anatomy is probably a version of a well-known legend of Democritus (*c.* 460–*c.* 370 B.C.), a contemporary of Hippocrates.

(42) Diocles (4th cent. B.C.), son of Archidamus of Carystos in Euboea, is quoted by Theophrastus (died 287 B.C.). He was regarded as the most

important representative of the 'Dogmatist' School and was known in Athens, where he lived, as 'the second Hippocrates'. None of his works has survived, though it is believed that passages from them are to be found in a Latin work bearing the name *Vindicianus*. There is an extensive account of Diocles by M. Wellmann in Pauly-Wissowa.

(43) This was indeed precisely what did happen. Galen was the last to practise anatomy for many centuries.

(44) The gracilis muscle, in both ape and man, is in fact a flexor of the knee-joint and a medial rotator of the thigh when the knee is fixed in flexion. This passage, however, suggests that Galen had some access to human anatomy, for the gracilis is a relatively feeble muscle in man, as its name implies, but is very much stronger and more robust in the Rhesus.

(45) The anterior superior spine of the ilium is obvious in the human skeleton but hardly if at all discernible in that of the ape. The anterior border of the ilium of the ape is relatively much longer than in man and almost straight. Galen knew the bones of both species and momentarily confuses them (Fig. 5).

(46) 'Changing legs', that is pulling up the opponent's leg by bringing one's own into the 'tailor's position' behind his knee.

(47) These sesamoids are always present in both *Macaca mulatta* and *Semnopithecus entellus*. They are rare in human subjects and when present occur usually in the lateral head only.

(48) The flexor digitorum fibularis (in man, flexor hallucis) and the flexor digitorum tibialis (in man, flexor digitorum longus) in the Rhesus are relatively larger than in man. Their insertions in the ape are variable but differ from those in man.

(49) The 'rings' were to change the direction of pull of the reins as the terrets in modern harness. The main insertion of the tibialis anterior, after passing through the transverse crural ligament, is into the medial and plantar aspects of the first cuneiform. A smaller tendon from the same muscle is inserted into the plantar aspect of the hallucial metacarpal.

(50) This passage draws a distinction between the ape's foot and the human foot and might be expected to reveal some of Galen's experience of human anatomy. It is thus particularly unfortunate that the text is here disturbed. It would be worth a special attempt to restore it by appeal to the Greek manuscripts and to the Arabic translation.

(51) I cannot attach anatomical meaning to this paragraph except that it refers to the quadratus plantae.

(52) There are only three contrahentes in *Macaca* but four in *Semnopithecus*.

(53) HOMOIOMERIA literally 'of similar parts'. The term is said to have been invented by Anaxagoras (*c.* 500–428 B.C.) who held that all matter was composed of similar particles. Galen doubtless derives it from Aristotle who uses it for those parts of the living body that were uniform. He thus means much what Bichat (who neglected the microscope) meant by *tissu*. The HOMOIO-MERIA of Aristotle must be distinguished from organs or members, and approximate to what we mean by 'tissues', if we try to forget all knowledge brought to us by the microscope.

(54) From the beginning of the chapter to this point is a rough summary of certain passages in Aristotle's *Historia animalium* and *De partibus animalium*.

(55) Erasistratus who flourished as an anatomist at Alexandria about 270 B.C. held that each organ contained a nexus of minute divisions of artery, vein, and nerve.

(56) It is probably *De Hippocratis et Erasistrati anatomice*, for which see note 5. The physiology of Erasistratus can be gathered from Galen's *De venae sectione adversus Erasistratum*, K. xi. 147–249.

(57) Galen uses the same word NEURON for both 'nerve' and 'tendon'. This is not due to confusion on his part but is based on a definite physiological theory. See Introduction, p. xix.

(58) This passage is an expression of Aristotle's doctrine of 'mixture' of elements. See his *De generatione et corruptione*, 334^{a}22, and his *Meteorologica*, 386^{a}18.

(59) The use of the word APOSKĒMMA as equivalent to 'abscess' is peculiar to Galen and seems to have escaped the lexicographers.

(60) The idea of foretelling as a means by which the physician may escape blame permeates Greek medicine. See notably the opening passage of the work in the Hippocratic Collection *Praenotiones* which is of about 400 B.C. PRO-GNOSIS has to be distinguished from PRONOIA which is knowing about things before one is told—'spot diagnosis' in modern medical parlance.

(61) Owing to the practice of blood-letting, physicians before modern times attached more importance to the anatomy of veins than to that of arteries. Thus it was natural to speak of the 'companion artery' to a vein, where we reverse the relationship.

(62) On the Methodist School, see Introduction, p. xvi.

(63) The injury was clearly in the neighbourhood of the last cervical vertebra.

(64) The quotation is from the work in the Hippocratic Collection *De fractis*, opening of chapter 9.

(65) Galen here, as often, uses 'roots' when we would say 'branches'. He thinks of sensory nerves as carrying something to the brain, as do roots to the stems of plants.

(66) Assuming that this work was taken down in shorthand from the spoken word—as I believe to be the case—such a passage as this must have been added by Galen to the manuscript.

(67) Quotation from the work in the Hippocratic Collection *De articulis*, ch. 1.

(68) Galen here as always describes the course of the veins as though blood flows through them towards the periphery.

(69) Either the present chapter order is disturbed or an earlier reference to the six animal types is missing from the Greek text.

(70) The superficial veins were highly important for ancient physicians and are always stressed by them. The regular scheme ascribed to these vessels by Galen can hardly be established by observation.

(71) Galen is always on the look-out for differences and resemblances between simian and human anatomy. Nevertheless, the superficial veins are as variable in the one as in the other.

(72) This and the previous paragraph suggest that occasional human dissection was normal.

(73) Phlebotomists in all ages have been warned against the common accident of piercing the artery in this region.

(74) An early trace of the traditional system of phlebotomy in which special veins are let for special pathological states. This passage may provide an explanation of the term *cephalic vein*, which, however, reached Western anatomy not, as might be expected, from Greek but from or through Arabic sources.

(75) I have not been able to trace this phrase of Hippocrates.

(76) The pelvic nerve-plexus and distribution of nerves in the leg are very different in man and in the Rhesus.

(77) The sartorius in the Rhesus is a relatively slender muscle, especially in contrast with the robust gracilis. It is not innervated by the femoral nerve.

(78) In apes the gluteus medius is much larger than the gluteus maximus.

(79) Galen always allows his admiration for the hand, expressed in very great detail in his *De usu partium*, to mislead him into suggesting that the human hand is structurally further from the ape's than is the human foot from the ape's. The reverse is the case.

(80) The correct form is MASĒTERES and is found in the 'Hippocratic' *De articulis*, xxx. There they are distinguished from the KROTAPHITAI or temporal muscles.

(81) This odd statement concerning the crocodile is made by Herodotus (ii. 68): 'He does not move his lower jaw, but brings the upper toward the lower, unlike all other creatures.' Basking crocodiles rest the lower jaw on the ground, raising the huge upper jaw (together with the small skull) and occasionally snapping it down. The statement of Herodotus is repeated by Aristotle in the *Historia animalium* ($492^{b}23$; $516^{a}24$) and *De partibus animalium* ($660^{b}27$; $691^{b}5$). In the latter work Aristotle comes near to the explanation of what seems an anatomical absurdity.

(82) The extent and development of the platysma varies greatly in different species of ape and even in individuals of the same species (Figs. 8, 11, 12).

(83) I am uneasy as to the rendering by *lynxes* of the word LYGKES used here and elsewhere by Galen but can suggest no alternative.

(84) The mental foramina in apes are less regular than in man. See next note.

(85) 'Near the end' (KAT' AKRAN, literally 'at the tip') suggests that there may be some confusion of the mental foramen with the *foramen symphyseosum* present in most apes but absent in man.

(86) Galen is here speaking of sensory nerves, branches of the trigeminal, that emerge through the multiple mental foramina of the ape. They have no motor action such as he supposes. The muscles of the lower lip and chin are supplied by the slender mandibular branches of VII which pass forward across the masseter muscle.

(87) *De motibus dubiis*. No book of this title by Galen is known.

(88) Galen here makes an error as to the innervation of the lower lip similar to that which he has made for the upper lip. See note 86.

(89) Galen, in discussing HOMOGENĒ and HOMOEIDĒ, has in mind the opening chapter of Aristotle's *De generatione animalium*, $715^{a}23$; compare $747^{b}30$.

(90) Galen here describes the medial and lateral pterygoids as one muscle but omits the attachment of the lateral pterygoid to the neck of the mandible.

(91) The Hippocratic *De articulis*, ch. 34, describes fracture at the symphysis. This, if it occurs at all, must be one of the rarest of injuries. I have found no statement in the Hippocratic Collection that the lower jaw is formed of two bones.

(92) In some species of ape the fusion of the two rami takes place later and less firmly than in others, but in all it is less firm than in man.

(93) This refers to the insertion of the medial pterygoid between the angle and the mylohyoid groove of the mandible.

(94) The description of the eye-muscles is lost from the Greek text. Galen's advice to anatomize the eyes of 'larger animals', notably of the ox, led to many misunderstandings, since the eyes of these animals have a very deep anterior chamber and thus the lens came to be regarded as in the centre of the eye.

(95) In the Rhesus and allied species the auricular muscles have retained a close and primitive connexion with the platysma. In man, and in some other animals, this connexion has been broken.

(96) This passage is interpretable if by *base* of his right-angled triangle Galen means not the hypotenuse but the lowest side of the triangle representing the trapezius muscle, and that he does not include in the trapezius the part below the level of the scapular spine. The reader should be warned that my interpretation of Galen's meaning here differs from that of Guenther of Andernach, Vesalius, and other anatomists of the Renaissance who worked over the text. See Fig. on p. 105. They were seeking analogies in the trapezius of man and did not know that in apes the muscle is divisible into a cervical and thoracic part. If the acromion of the ape be depressed and/or the scapula rotated till its spine be nearly at right angles to the middle line, the geometrical comparison becomes clear. See Fig. on p. 105 and passage on p. 116.

(97) 'Nature makes naught in vain' is an Aristotelian catchphrase (*De partibus animalium*, 661^{b}24 and elsewhere). It fits well Galen's intense teleological view.

(98) Galen's book *Adversus Lycum* survives, K. xviii, pt. i. 196–245. See Note 30.

(99) Galen makes some confusion here, assuming that he was dissecting a macaque. In these animals the rhomboideus consists of three parts: (*a*) pars capitis inserted on vertebral border of scapula; (*b*) pars cervicis running between ligamentum nuchae and scapula; (*c*) pars dorsi from dorsal spines 1–7 to scapula.

(100) Galen's book *De motu musculorum* survives, K. iv. 367–421.

(101) See note 20.

(102) The atlantoscapularis anterior in the Rhesus is a stout muscle arising

from the posterior surface of the transverse process of the atlas and inserted on the lateral half of scapular spine and acromion as far as the clavicle. It adjoins the trapezius.

(103) This refers doubtless to the atlantoscapularis posterior, a much smaller muscle than the former (note 102). There is, however, no reference to it in Book V.

(104) This is, of course, an error of Galen.

(105) This paragraph and the next are confusiug. The pectoralis major in the ape may reasonably be described as one, two, three, or even four muscles.

(106) I cannot trace the meaning of this allusion to the Greek capital letters lambda and gamma, describing some flag-like signal used in games. But umpires did use a forked wand resembling a lower-case gamma (E. Norman Gardiner, *Athletics of the Ancient World*, Oxford, 1930, figs. 52, 173, 174).

(107) The deltoid in the ape is separable to a variable degree of distinctness into cleidodeltoid, acromiodeltoid, and spinodeltoid portions.

(108) The quotation is from the Hippocratic *De articulis*, ch. xiii. The suggestion of Galen seems to be that some anatomists have claimed that Hippocrates described an extra bone in the human shoulder.

(109) This mention is not to be found in the Greek text. It was perhaps in a passage now missing at the foot of our page 120.

(110) In the Greek text in its present state there is no further reference to these muscles.

(111) The analogy may seem strange but was not in antiquity; compare

> Hast thou not poured me out as milk,
> And curdled me like cheese?
> Thou hast clothed me with skin and flesh,
> And knit me together with bones and sinews.
>
> Job, x. 10–11.

Compare also Aristotle, *Meteorologica*, 384ª22–31.

(112) Galen is here referring to a passage in Plato's *Timaeus*. The 'immortal soul' was situated in the head but the 'mortal soul' was divided into two parts by the diaphragm or PHRENES; an upper, where is seated the 'irascible soul' which assists reason against desire, and a lower, where the 'appetitive soul', that is the soul that desires, is chained below the diaphragm, far from the council chamber of the immortal soul. Should the barrier break down the sufferer would become PHRENĒTIKOS, or *frantic*, being in a state of *frenzy*.

(113) A difficulty of translation arises from the fact that our word *diaphragm* is singular but Galen's normal equivalent PHRENES is plural.

(114) HYPEZŌKOS. The same word is used in Acts xxvii. 17 and is rendered 'undergird' in the Authorized Version.

(115) I cannot trace this passage but one somewhat resembling it is in the Hippocratic *De carnibus*, ch. 5, Littré viii. 591. This work is probably of early Alexandrian date, say 200 B.C. STOMACHOS is the Greek term for oesophagus. The PHLEPS is the inferior phrenic vein and the two NEURA are the great splanchnic nerves. The RHACHIS is the spine.

(116) The reference is to the attachment of the diaphragm at the back, not directly to the vertebral column but through the lateral and medial arcuate ligaments connected with the quadratus lumborum and psoas major.

(117) To the bodies of the upper 3 (4) thoracic vertebrae the longus colli is attached, while to the lower three the crura of the diaphragm are attached, thus leaving the middle six free.

(118) Despite many suggestions, no light has been thrown on the origin of the well-established term HIERON OSTOUN, *os sacrum*, 'sacred bone'.

(119) METAPHRENON literally 'behind the diaphragm'. In practice the term became restricted to the lower thoracic vertebrae.

(120) The temporal muscle, though it differs greatly in size in different forms, is present in all mammals.

(121) The coccygeal bone is, of course, small only in tailless forms such as the Barbary ape.

(122) This is Aristotelian teaching. See Aristotle's *De anima*, ii. 1 and 2.

(123) This passage is a compression of Aristotle's *Historia animalium*, iii, ch. 7. In terms of modern morphology it contrasts 'homology' and 'analogy'.

(124) The word PERITTŌMA is thus used by Aristotle who, however, also uses it in other senses.

(125) In Galen's physiology nourishment is conveyed by the veins which take their rise in the liver. See pp. xviii–xix.

(126) The rectum is in fact straight in the ape (Fig. 22) though not in man, an illustration of how the anatomical tradition of nomenclature is derived from simian material and ultimately from Galen. See note 137.

(127) See Aristotle, *De partibus animalium*, iii. 14.

(128) The passages at the opening of this chapter bear close resemblance to passages in the opening chapter of Aristotle's *De partibus animalium*.

(129) The text adds here PROSPHATOS, 'lately'. This must be a scribal insertion because the omentum is called EPIPLOON by Homer, Herodotus,

Hippocrates, and Aristotle, all known to Galen. It therefore had this name at least a thousand years before Galen used it.

(130) MESENTERION, '[membrane] intermediary to intestine', is an Aristotelian term. MESARAION, 'thin intermediary [membrane]', is a term, probably of Alexandrian origin, used by Galen and Rufus.

(131) PYLĒ, *porta*, gate, i.e. 'fissure of the liver'. *Vena portae* (less properly *vena porta*), vein of the gate. STELECHIAIA is an adjective from STELECHOS, 'shaft', 'trunk'; hence PHLEPS STELECHIAIA, 'trunk vein'. The last, a neologism in Galen's time, did not catch on.

(132) Mnesitheus, *De elephanto*. Nothing is known of this Mnesitheus except through Galen who treats him with respect in several places. But Galen is wrong and Mnesitheus right in saying that the elephant has no gall bladder. The fact was known also to Aristotle, *Historia animalium*, ii. 16. The common bile duct of the elephant expands in the wall of the duodenum into a vesicle which seems to serve the purpose of a gall bladder.

(133) This is one of the longest of the surviving fragments of Herophilus, founder of the anatomical school at Alexandria (300 B.C.). None of his works survives. His anatomical fragments are collected and translated by J. F. Dobson, *Proc. Roy. Soc. Med.*, 1924–5, xviii (Sect. Hist. Med.), p. 19.

(134) There is, however, no vermiform appendix in any ape that Galen is likely to have dissected.

(135) DŌDEKADAKTYLON, '[a space of] twelve fingers', Latin *duodenum* '[a space of] twelve'. Thus the word comes to us as a Latin version of a term of Herophilus.

(136) Our word 'ileum' is of medieval origin, without classical justification. It involved a confusion between Latin *ilium*, lower belly, and Greek EILEOS, abdominal pain. Thus our modern terms 'ileum' and 'ilium' are really connected and both with the term 'iliac disease' or 'iliac passion'.

(137) Rectum. This tract of intestine is quite straight in the ape and many mammals, but not in man. The first known application of the word *rectum* to the viscus is by Celsus (first century A.D.), who doubtless translates APEUTHYSMENON ENTERON 'the gut that is made straight' of some earlier Greek writer, from whom also Galen doubtless took it.

(138) PARENCHYMA, 'poured in beside'. This passage is the origin of our modern term which did not come into use until the seventeenth century.

(139) PYLŌROS, literally 'gate-keeper'. The word is first used in its medical sense by Celsus, first century A.D.

(140) The allusion to Plato is either to the *Republic* 7, 533E, *Sophist* 244, or *Statesman* 261E.

(141) The mention of a coccyx shows that Galen was here dissecting a tailless monkey such as the Barbary ape.

(142) SPHINKTĒR means 'that which binds tight'.

(143) Galen usually ignores the atria, regarding the 'venous artery' (our pulmonary vein) and the vena cava as attached directly to the left and right ventricles respectively. Thus our 'pulmonary vein' is for him a vessel proceeding *from* the left ventricle.

(144) Erasistratus of Ceos (*fl. c.* 280 B.C.) was one of the earliest and greatest Alexandrian anatomists. He laid emphasis on fullness or emptiness of the vessels. His works have not survived, but his anatomical fragments have been collected and translated by J. F. Dobson, *Proc. Roy. Soc. Med.*, 1926–7, xx (Sect. Hist. Med.), pp. 21–28.

(145) Erasistratus held that the arteries in general contain only pneuma, a view in refutation of which Galen wrote his *An in arteriis natura sanguis contineatur*, K. iv. 703–36. This famous tract records one of Galen's most remarkable experiments. See pp. 198–200. The next three sentences summarize the Erasistratean theory of the pneuma.

(146) The form of the Greek letter sigma to which reference is here made is the capital shaped like our C.

(147) For Galen the thymus is the gland *par excellence*. This seems remarkable, but it must be remembered that the thymus is relatively larger in apes than in man and that, moreover, Galen was inclined to dissect young specimens and had dissected human foetuses. He knew that the thymus decreases as the animal becomes adult, *De alimentorum facultatibus*, K. vi. 674.

(148) In Galenic physiology the left ventricle is called the pneumatic ventricle because the World-pneuma is brought thither from the air in the lungs by the 'venous artery' (our pulmonary vein).

(149) A DELTOS is a writing tablet and was perhaps used for a case of writing instruments. I do not understand why it should be called a KEPHALIKON.

(150). Galen used the word ŌTA (sing, OUS), 'ears', to mean the 'auricles' or 'auricular appendages' of the heart. Until the recent Birmingham revision (1933) the word 'auricle' meant one of the two upper chambers of the heart, into the atrium of which the large vessels entered. At the revision the word 'atrium' was applied to the chamber as a whole, and the term 'auricle of the atrium' is now used for the ear-shaped projection on which Galen's attention was focused. That his 'auricle' implied more than this is shown by the passage on p. 185. See also note (160).

(151) Galen numbers cranial nerves quite differently from modern anatomists. His system is brought out in the following table.

Modern notation	*Galen's notation*
I. Olfactory	Not regarded as nerves
II. Optic	First pair 'Soft nerves of the eye'
III. Oculomotor	Second pair 'Nerves moving the eye'
IV. Trochlear	Not described
V. Trigeminal	Third pair Fourth pair
VI. Abducent	United with second
VII. Facial VIII. Auditory	Fifth pair
IX. Glossopharyngeal X. Vagus XI. Spinal accessory	Sixth pair
XII. Hypoglossal	Seventh pair

(152) *De Hippocratis et Platonis placitis*, K. v. 181–805. The discussion in question is on pp. 702 ff. The THERMON EMPHYTON (*calor innatus*, 'innate heat') as an indwelling sign of life is a conception that goes back to the Hippocratic writings (*Aphorisms* i. 14, &c.). It was accepted by Plato (*Timaeus* 62A, &c.) and Aristotle (*De partibus animalium*, &c., *passim*), was transmitted by Galen to later ages, became current at the scientific revival, was familiar to Descartes and Harvey, and hardly disappeared from the scientific vocabulary till the nineteenth century. It is an essential part of Galen's physiology though rather obscurely linked by him with the three bodily PNEUMATA.

(153) The chapter on the heart has been disturbed. There is scribal confusion between the tricuspid and semilunar valves.

(154) The azygos vein varies much in its course but never empties into—Galen would say 'arises from'—the right atrium. In apes, however, the vena cava superior has the curious appearance of being embraced by the atrium near the azygos. See Charles Singer and C. Rabin, *A Prelude to Modern Science, being . . . the Sources of the Tabulae Sex of Vesalius*, Cambridge, 1946, p. liv.

(155) Galen here interprets Aristotle erroneously. Aristotle denies the presence of any vessels in the heart (*De partibus animalium*, 665^{b}30 and 666^{a}5). He uses their absence as an argument for the heart itself being a vessel.

(156) Attention to the heart-bone was drawn by Aristotle in the *Historia animalium*, 506^{a}9; ii. 15, and in *De partibus animalium*, 666^b; iii. 4, where this structure is described in oxen and horses. Heart-bones have been found in many large mammals both in relation to the semilunar and to the mitral valves. The heart-bone is represented in man by the tracts known as the right and left trigonum fibrosum.

(157) This curious mistake of Aristotle has led to endless discussion. We believe that no solution is attainable.

(158) The pits in the ventricular septum Galen believed connected the two ventricular cavities and so allowed the pneuma from the lung to pass from the right ventricle to the left.

(159) A double apex of the heart is an embryonic feature found, in a greater or lesser degree, in the adults of species of several mammalian groups. It is not normally seen in birds.

(160) The translation of Galen's ŌTA as 'auricles' is here literally correct, since he refers to the auricular appendages and not to the atria. See also note (150).

(161) In most apes the vena cava inferior lies in a fossa of the lung almost surrounded by the azygos lobe and lying on the lobus inferior of the right lung (Fig. 21). It is untrue that the number of lung lobes is equal on the two sides in most animals.

(162) The pleura would then be almost opaque and no movement visible through it.

(163) There is apparently confusion here between lacteals and blood vessels but the Greek text is itself disordered. It may also be that there was such confusion in the original passages of Erasistratus.

(164) A physiological error and contradictory to what Galen stated on pp. 128–9.

(165) The phrase is perhaps a paraphrase of Hippocrates, *De officina medici*, iv.

(166) The movement of the lower part of the thorax is due to the action of the diaphragm.

(167) The word here translated is SKOLOPOCHAIRIOS, literally 'pointed knife'.

(168) Noricum, a Roman province, corresponds roughly to the modern Styria. The iron-ore of Noricum produced an excellent steel. It was in high repute in antiquity.

(169) If the text here is correct, these observations of Galen can be explained only by his having accidentally perforated the pleura and/or the lung.

(170) PARYGRON, 'moist [plaster]', is a preparation mentioned by Galen in his *De compositione medicamentorum per genera*, K. xiii. 952, 953. There he ascribes its invention to one Heras, not otherwise known. He gives its composition as: Fresh lard 44 parts by weight, wax 24, white lead 6, and litharge 6.

(171) PYELOS is a term that Galen uses for the infundibulum, as is also CHŌNĒ, an abbreviated form of CHOANĒ.

(172) The exact form of these instruments can hardly be recovered.

(173) The deep *torcular*, LĒNOS, 'winepress', of Herophilus is the anterior end of the sigmoid sinus at its junction with the jugular. Here is an enlargement of the sinus which is, perhaps, inadequately stressed by modern anatomists (Fig. 25). The superficial *torcular* is the junction of the sigmoid sinuses and the sagittal sinus.

(174) The work in the Hippocratic Collection *De carnibus*, 3, Littré viii, p. 586 (middle) uses the word MĒNINX in a way that can be translated only as 'membrane' in general. This usage is supported by the Greek lexicographer Hesychius. Galen is, however, wrong in suggesting that 'Hippocrates' normally gives MĒNINX this general application.

(175) The rather unexpected epithet of the great cerebral as 'the vein which runs down' recurs in a confused passage at the end of this chapter.

(176) The first duct is the groove in the floor of the third ventricle leading to the infundibulum. The second duct is the aqueduct.

(177) Galen seems here to be refuting some unnamed colleague.

ILLUSTRATIONS

Except where otherwise indicated all the figures are by Mr. Benjamin Kopel and are taken from *The Anatomy of the Rhesus Monkey*, edited by Professors C. G. Hartman and W. L. Straus, Jr., Baltimore, 1933, by kind permission of the editors and publishers.

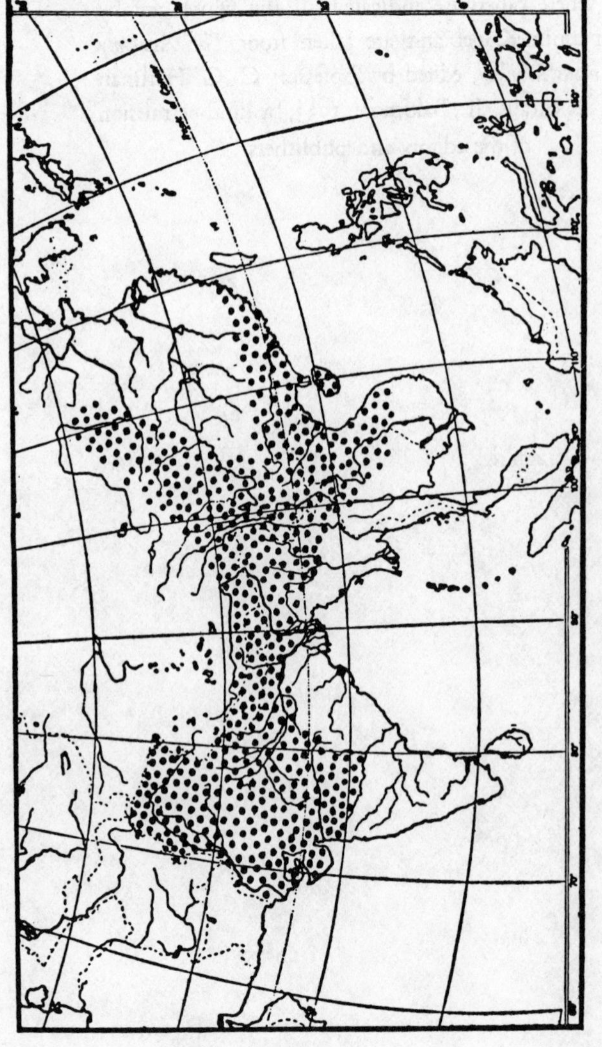

FIG. 1. Distribution of *Macaca mulatta*, the Rhesus monkey.

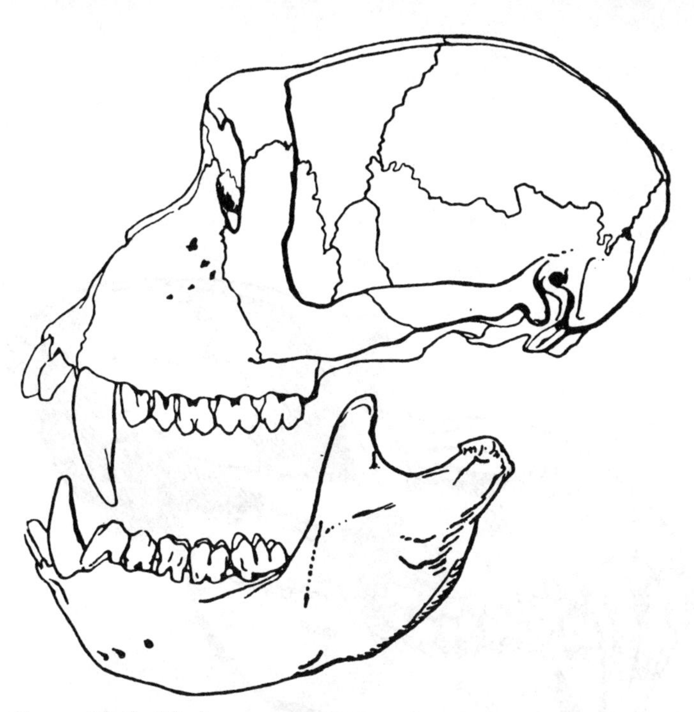

Fig. 2. Skull of Barbary ape, *Macaca inuus*, from Paul Rode, *Les Primates de l'Afrique*, Paris, 1937.

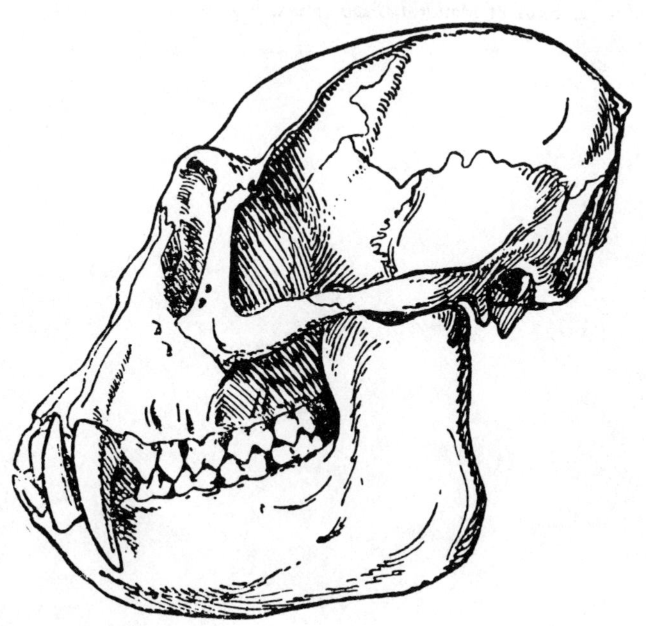

Fig. 3. Skull of Colobus monkey, *Colobus polykomos*, from Rode, loc. cit.

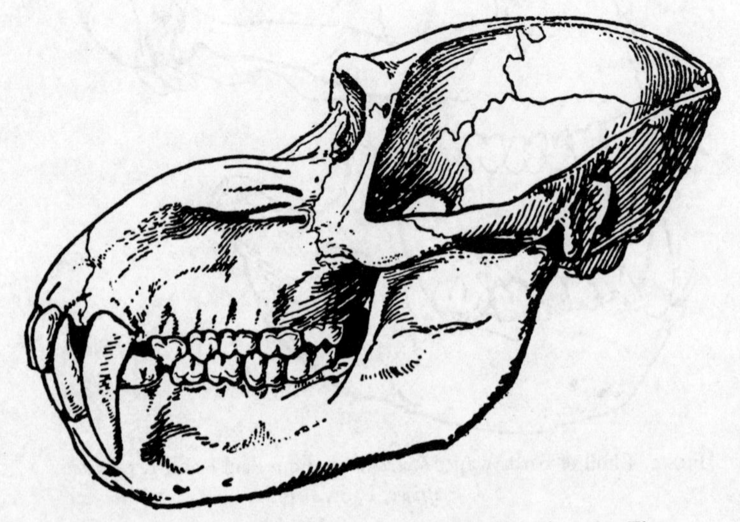

FIG. 4. Skull of Mandrill, *Papio sphinx*, from Rode, loc. cit., Fig. 2.

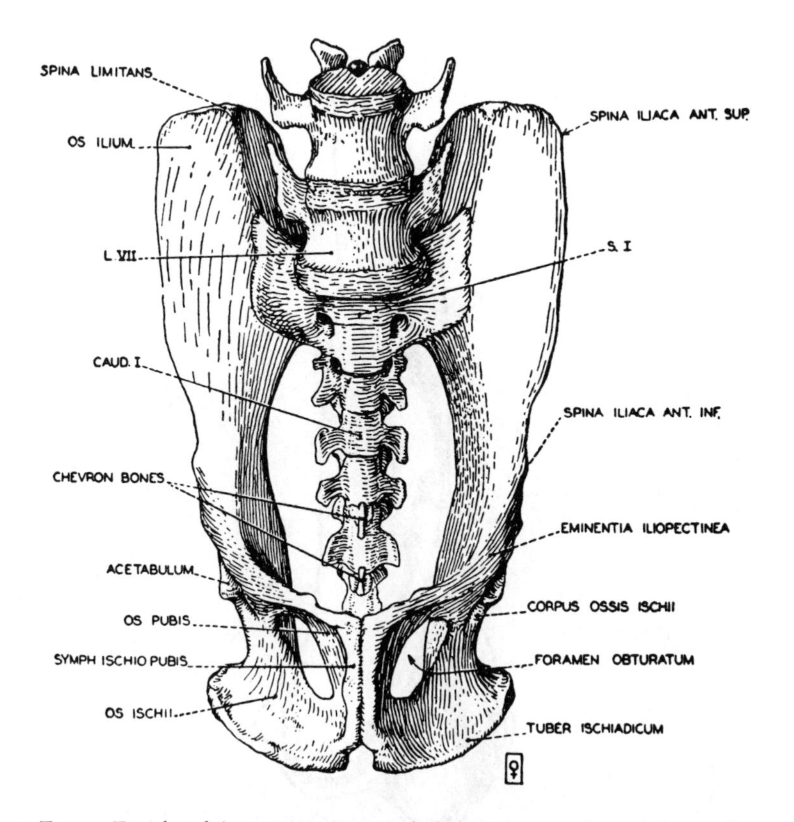

FIG. 5. Female pelvis, anterior view. Both the anterior superior and the anterior inferior spines of the ilium are inconspicuous.

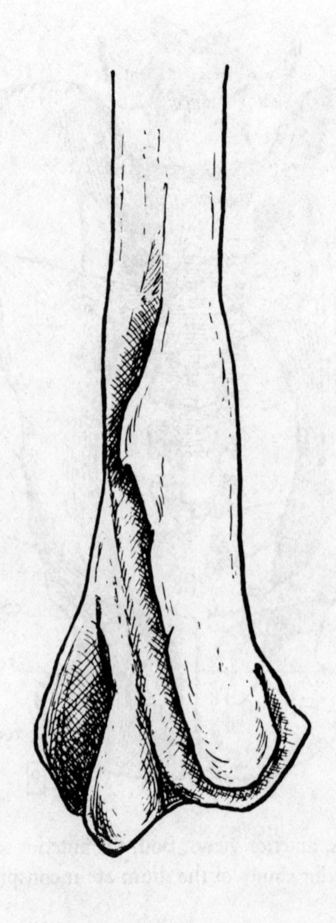

FIG. 6. Dorsal aspect of distal end of right radius of *Macaca mulatta*, showing the deep grooves for the extensor muscles. Drawing by Professor A. J. E. Cave.

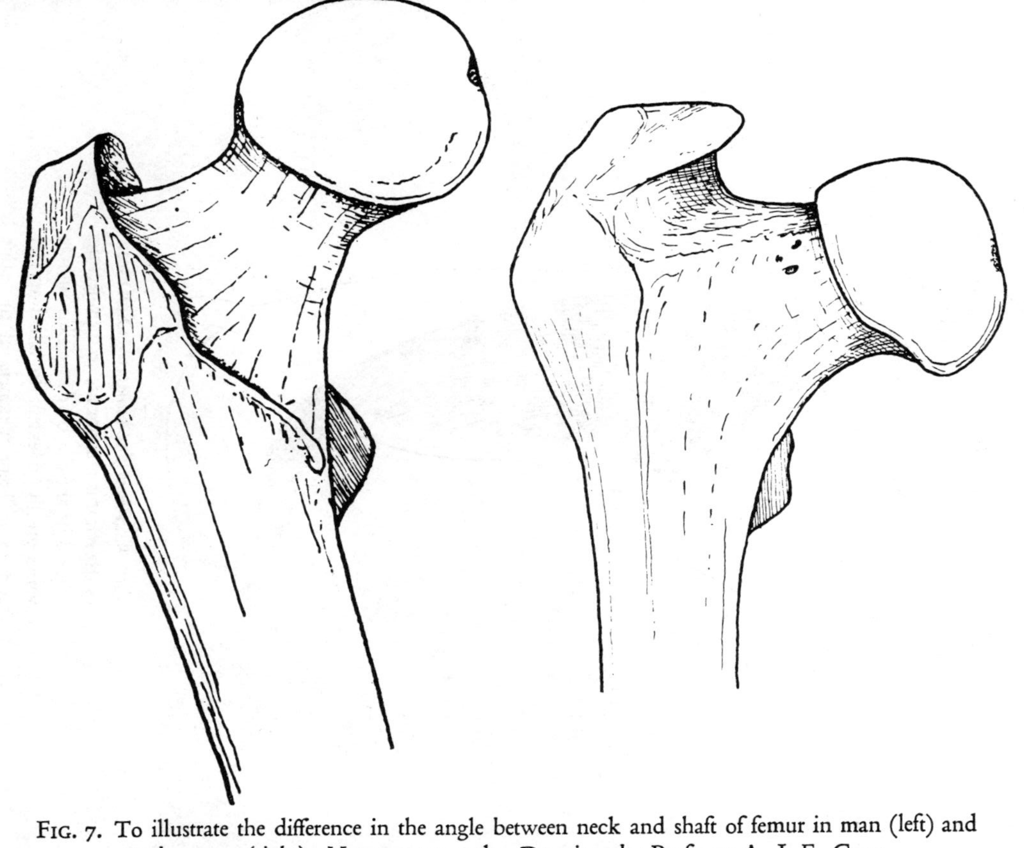

FIG. 7. To illustrate the difference in the angle between neck and shaft of femur in man (left) and Barbary ape (right). Not to same scale. Drawings by Professor A. J. E. Cave.

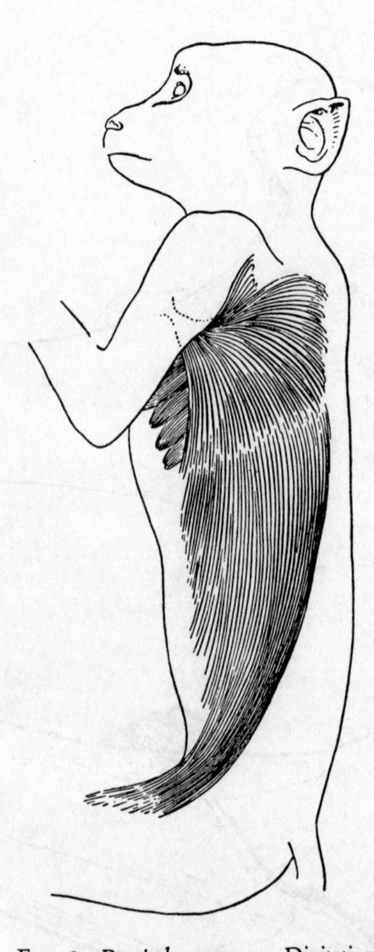

FIG. 8. *Panniculus carnosus.* Digitations of the serratus anterior are seen projecting beyond its anterior border. This muscle varies greatly in extent in allied species and in different members of the same species. It has caudal and thoracic parts, the division between which can be seen extending from the lowest part of the serratus anterior.

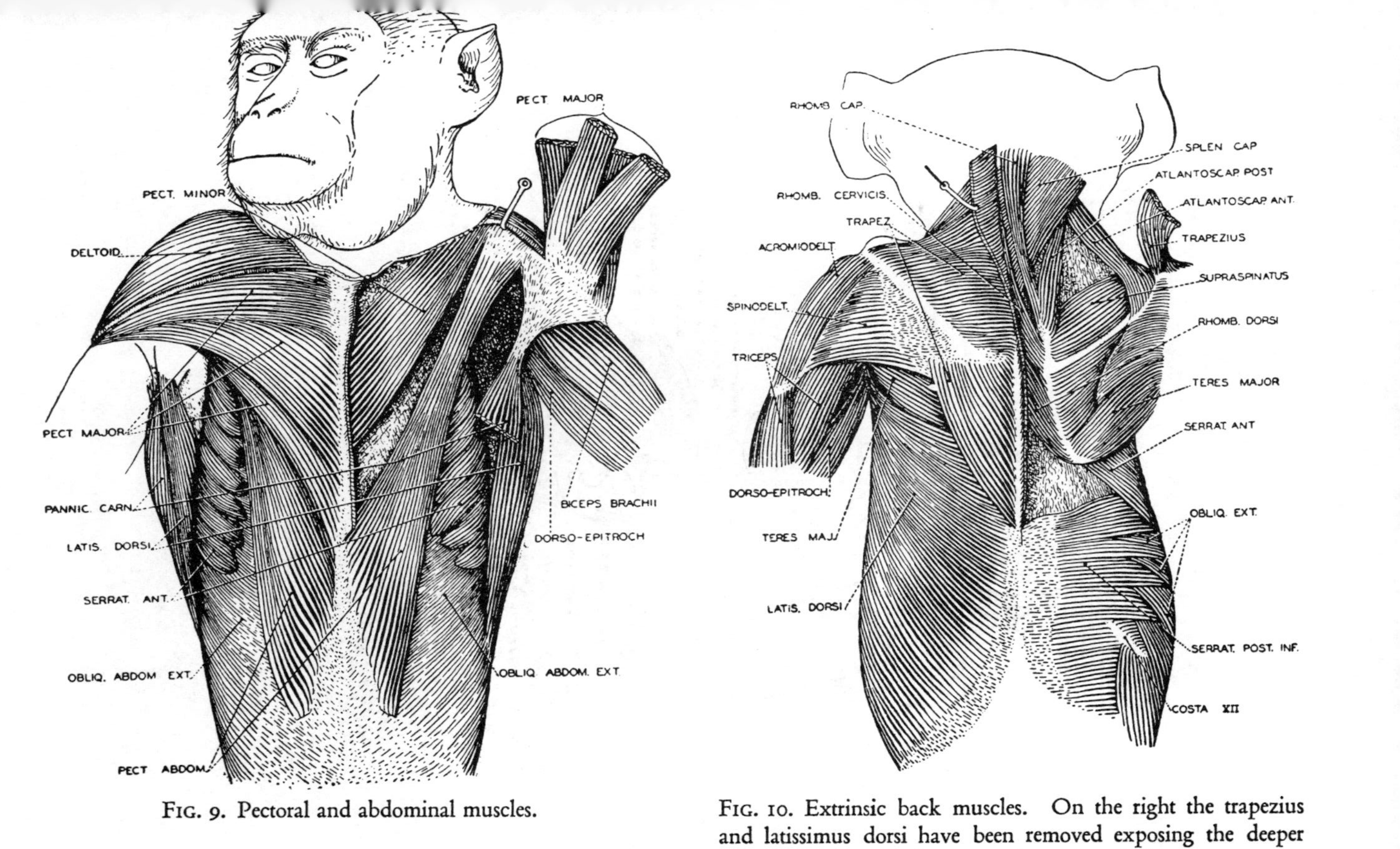

FIG. 9. Pectoral and abdominal muscles.

FIG. 10. Extrinsic back muscles. On the right the trapezius and latissimus dorsi have been removed exposing the deeper extrinsic back muscles. Note division.

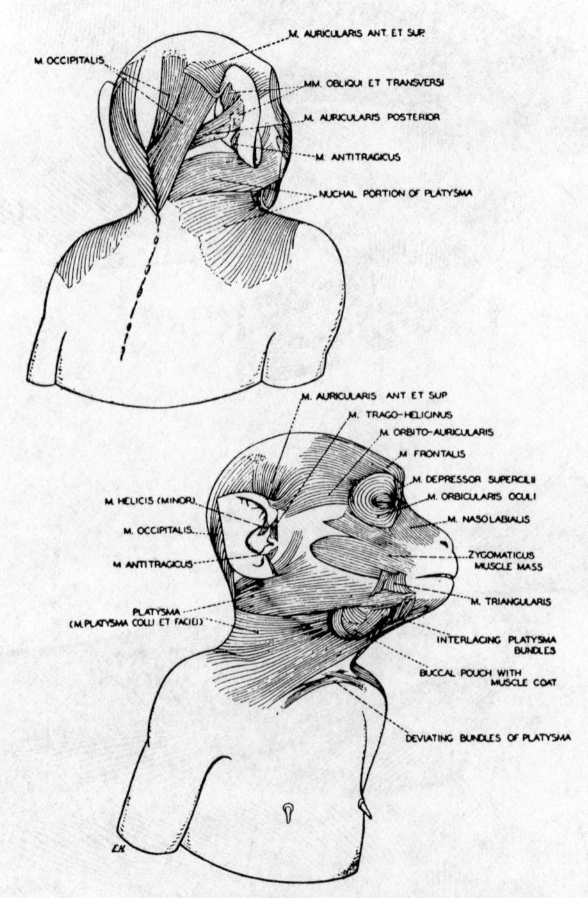

FIG. 11. Superficial facial muscles.

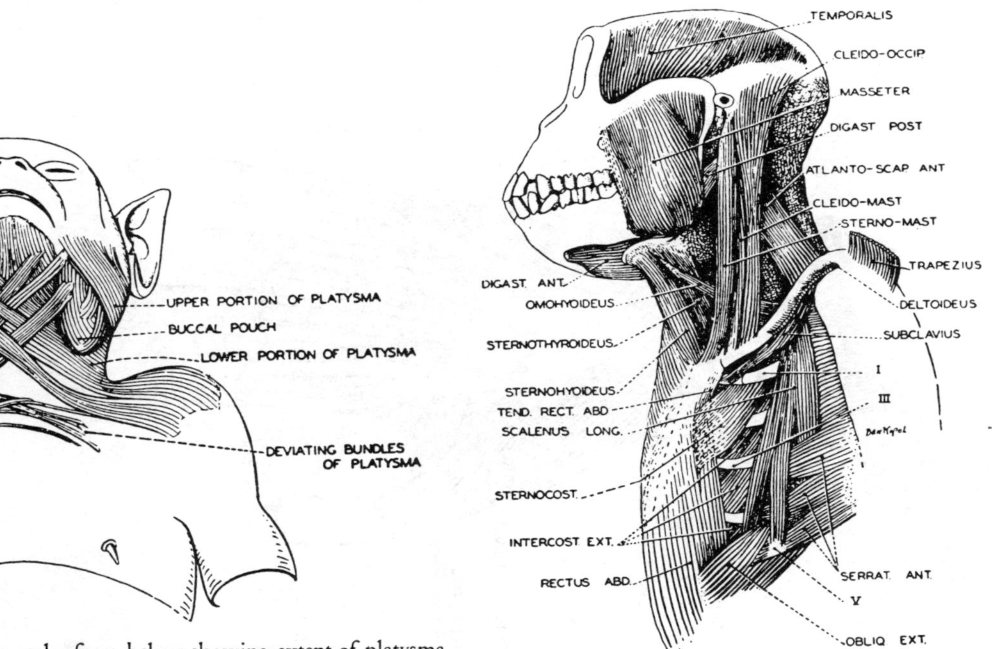

FIG. 12. Superficial facial muscles from below showing extent of platysma plates of the two sides and their extension into the buccal pouches.

FIG. 13. Muscles of head, neck, and thorax.

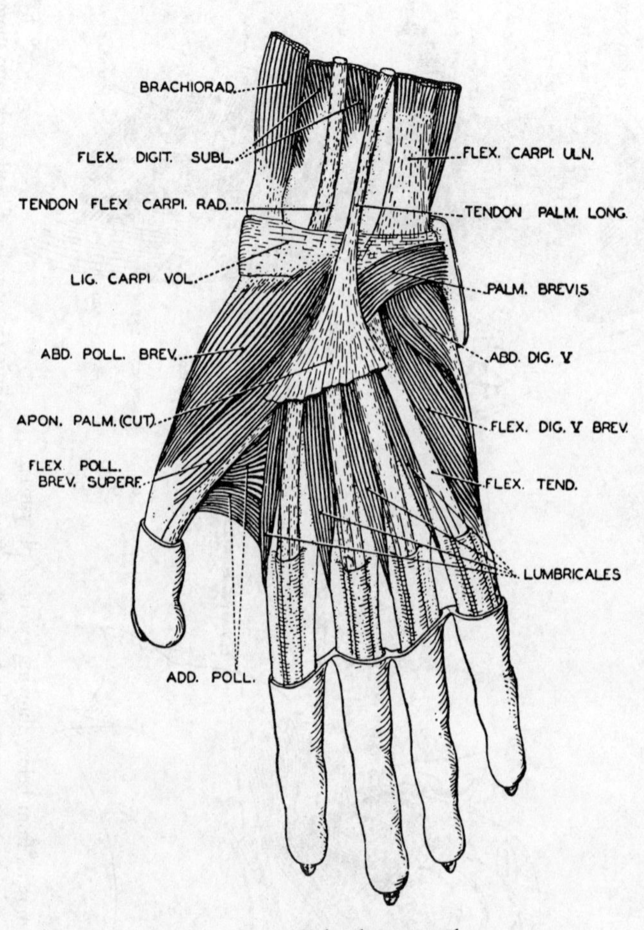

FIG. 14. Superficial palmar muscles.

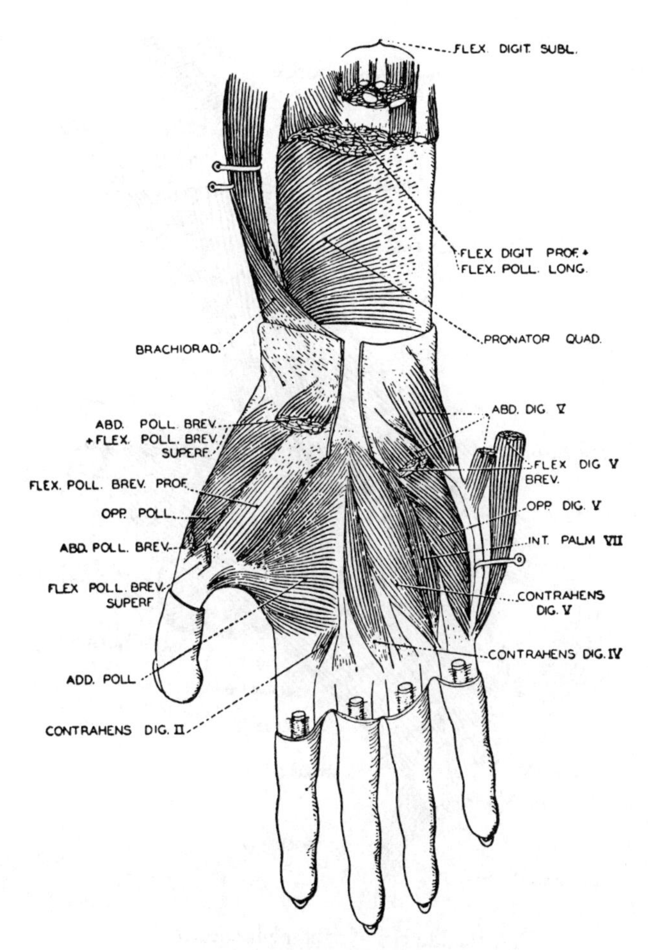
FLEX. DIGIT. SUBL.
FLEX DIGIT PROF. +
FLEX. POLL. LONG.
PRONATOR QUAD.
BRACHIORAD.
ABD. DIG. V
ABD. POLL. BREV.
+ FLEX. POLL. BREV.
SUPERF.
FLEX DIG V
BREV.
FLEX. POLL. BREV. PROF.
OPP. DIG. V
OPP. POLL.
INT. PALM VII
ABD. POLL. BREV.
FLEX POLL. BREV.
SUPERF
CONTRAHENS
DIG. V
CONTRAHENS DIG. IV
ADD. POLL
CONTRAHENS DIG. II

FIG. 15. Deeper palmar muscles.

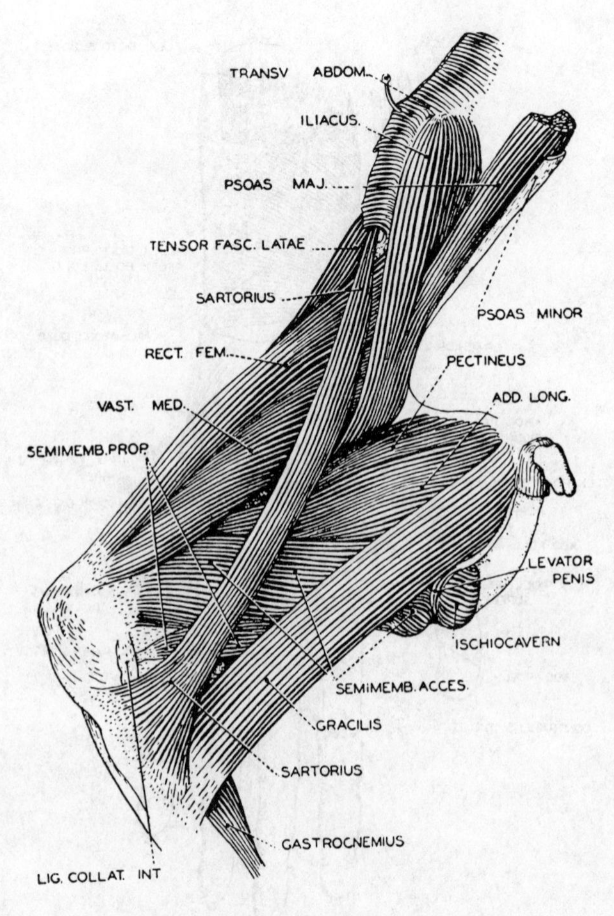

FIG. 16. Muscles of right thigh, medial view.

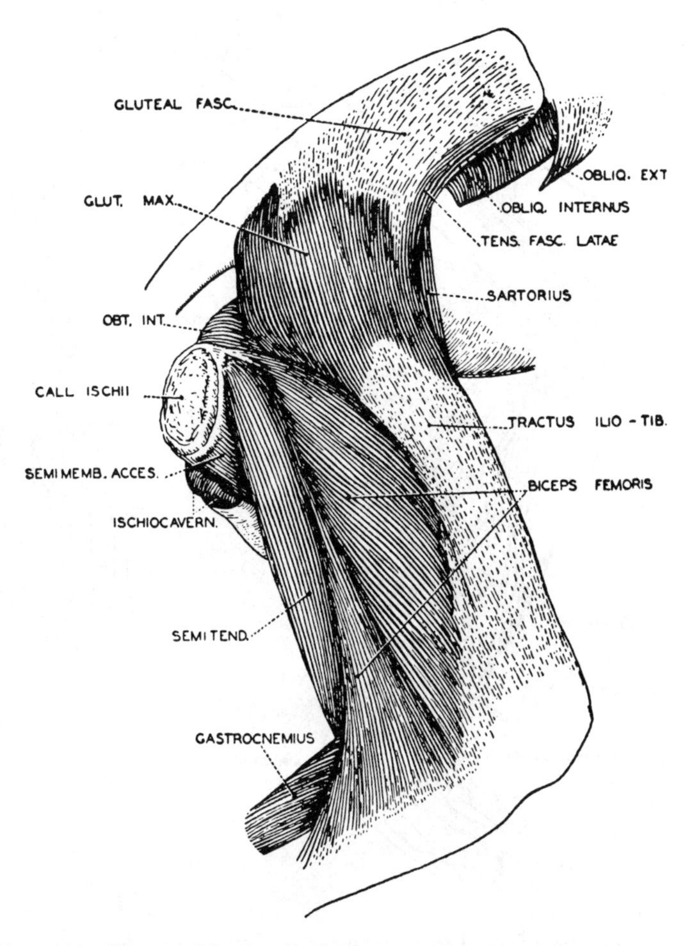

FIG. 17. Muscles of right hip and thigh, lateral view.

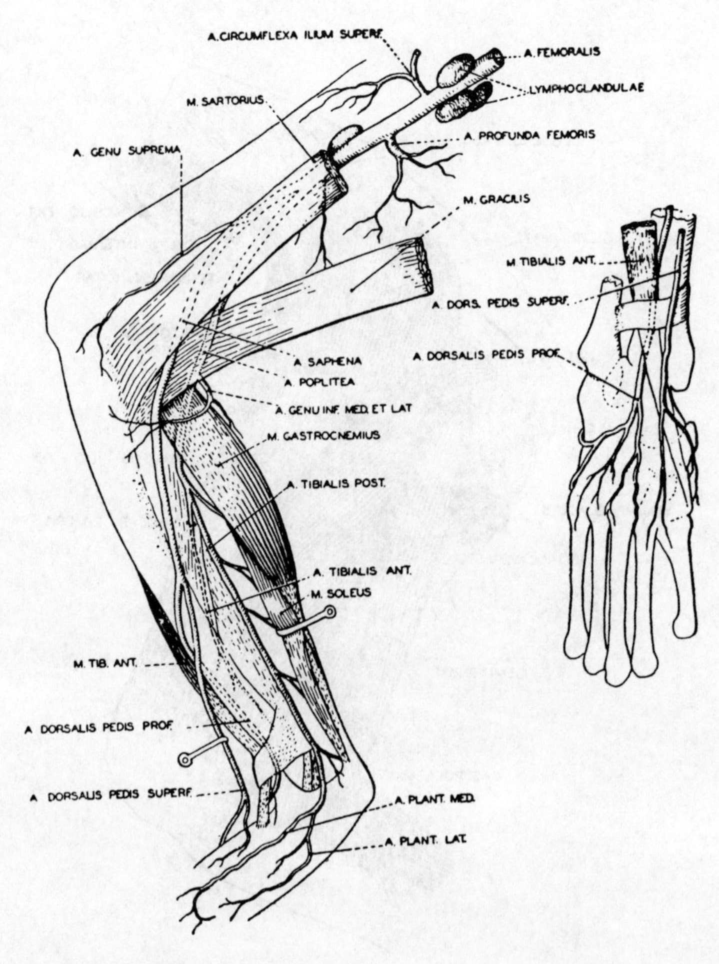

FIG. 18. Right femoral artery and branches. Insert shows arteries of dorsum of foot.

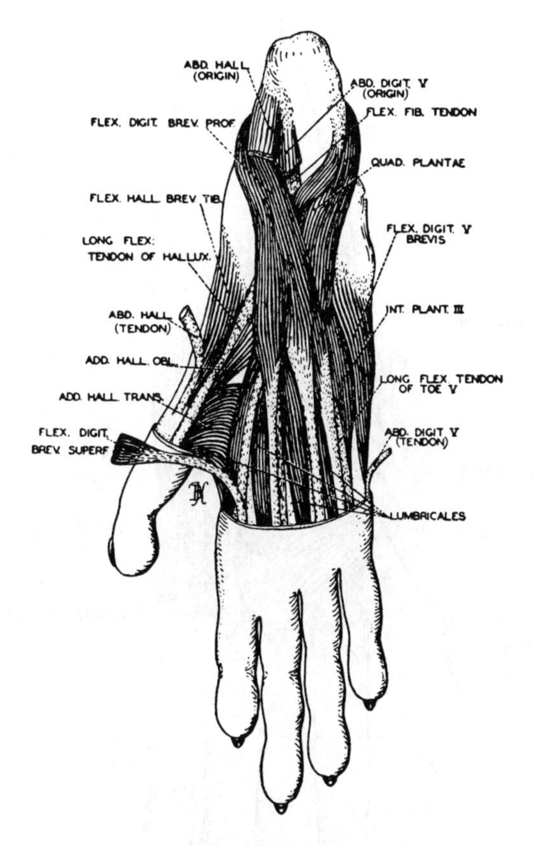

FIG. 19. Superficial plantar muscles.

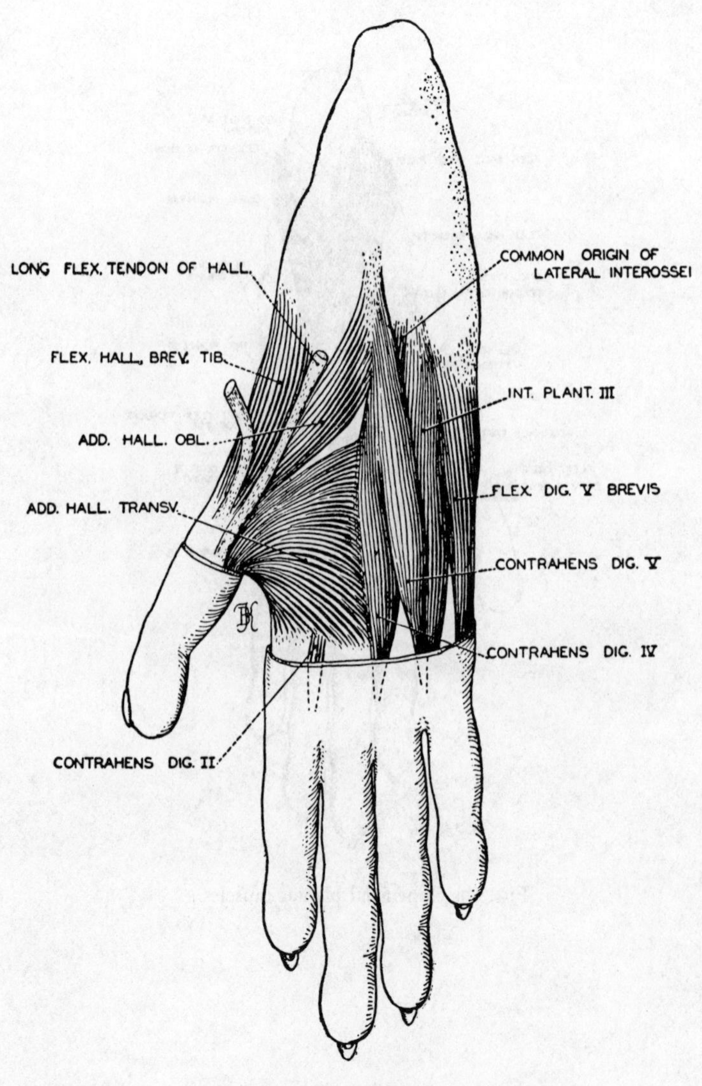

FIG. 20. Deeper plantar muscles.

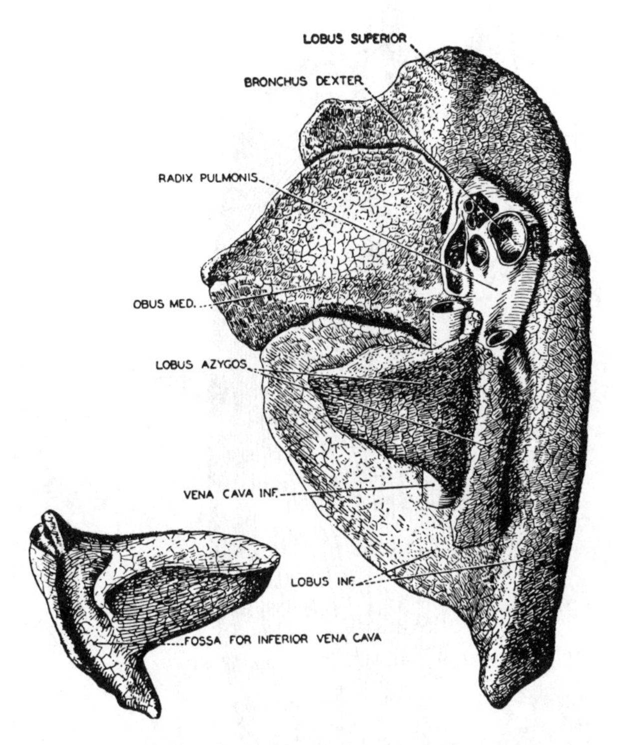

FIG. 21. Right lung together with separated azygos lobe.

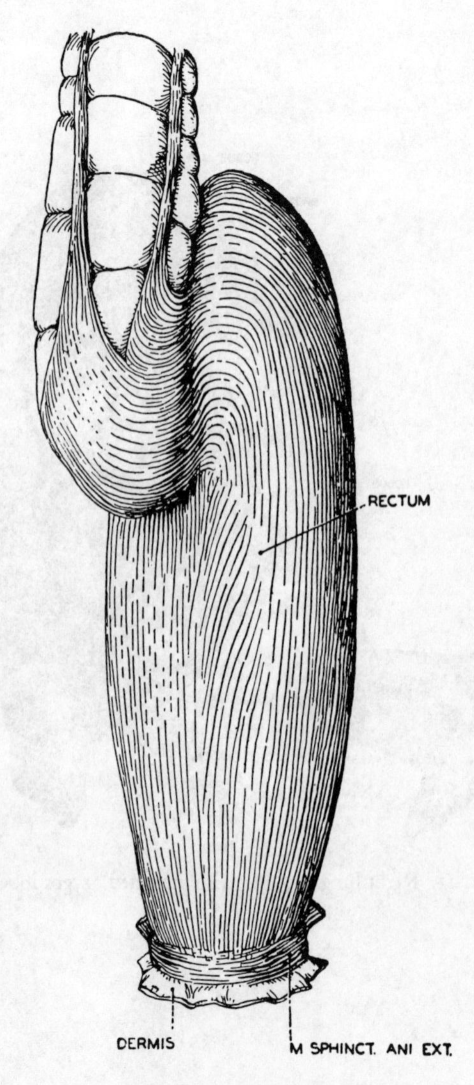

FIG. 22. The rectum.

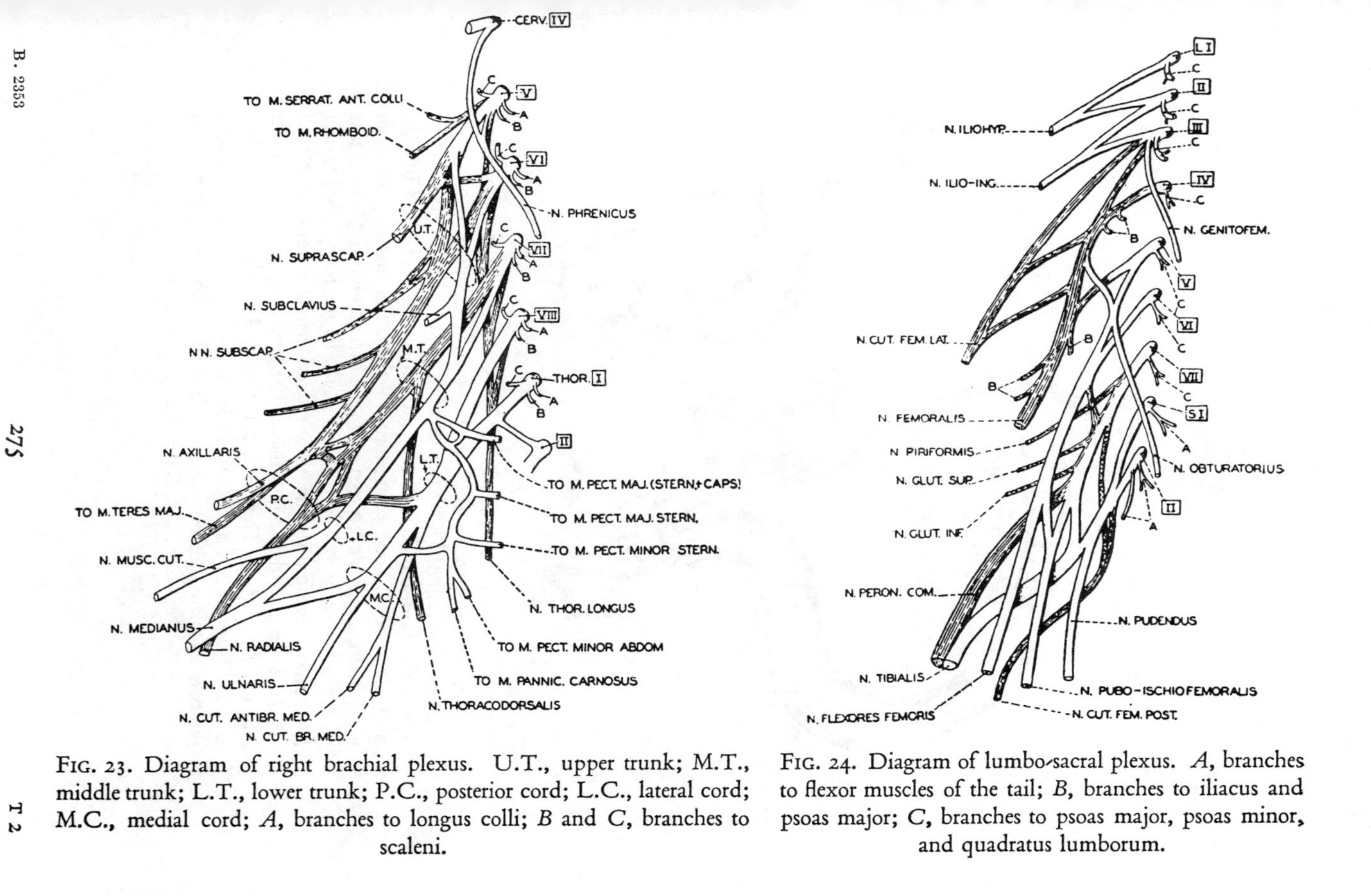

FIG. 23. Diagram of right brachial plexus. U.T., upper trunk; M.T., middle trunk; L.T., lower trunk; P.C., posterior cord; L.C., lateral cord; M.C., medial cord; *A*, branches to longus colli; *B* and *C*, branches to scaleni.

FIG. 24. Diagram of lumbo-sacral plexus. *A*, branches to flexor muscles of the tail; *B*, branches to iliacus and psoas major; *C*, branches to psoas major, psoas minor, and quadratus lumborum.

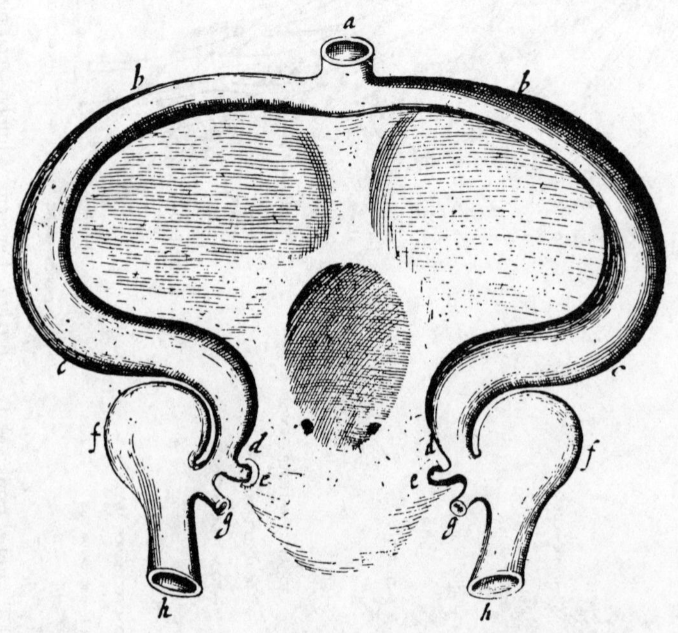

FIG. 25. Diagram of the posterior cerebral sinuses, to illustrate the interior *torcular*, from Richard Lower, *Tractatus de corde*, London, 1669. *a*, part of longitudinal sinus; *b b*, the two lateral sinuses; *f f*, two tortuous sinuses hollowed within the skull bone to prevent backflow of blood into the cerebral sinuses. These enlargements of the lateral sinuses, here much exaggerated, are seldom represented in modern anatomies. Galen speaks of this enlargement as LĒNOS, translated by the Latin word *torcular* (winepress). He distinguishes these 'internal' *torculares* from the external *torcular* formed by the conjunction of the lateral superior longitudinal and straight sinuses. This he calls the external *torcular* (LĒNOS) or *torcular Herophili*. Vesalius wrongly accuses Galen of confusing the two torculares, although he had himself edited the very book in which Galen distinguishes them

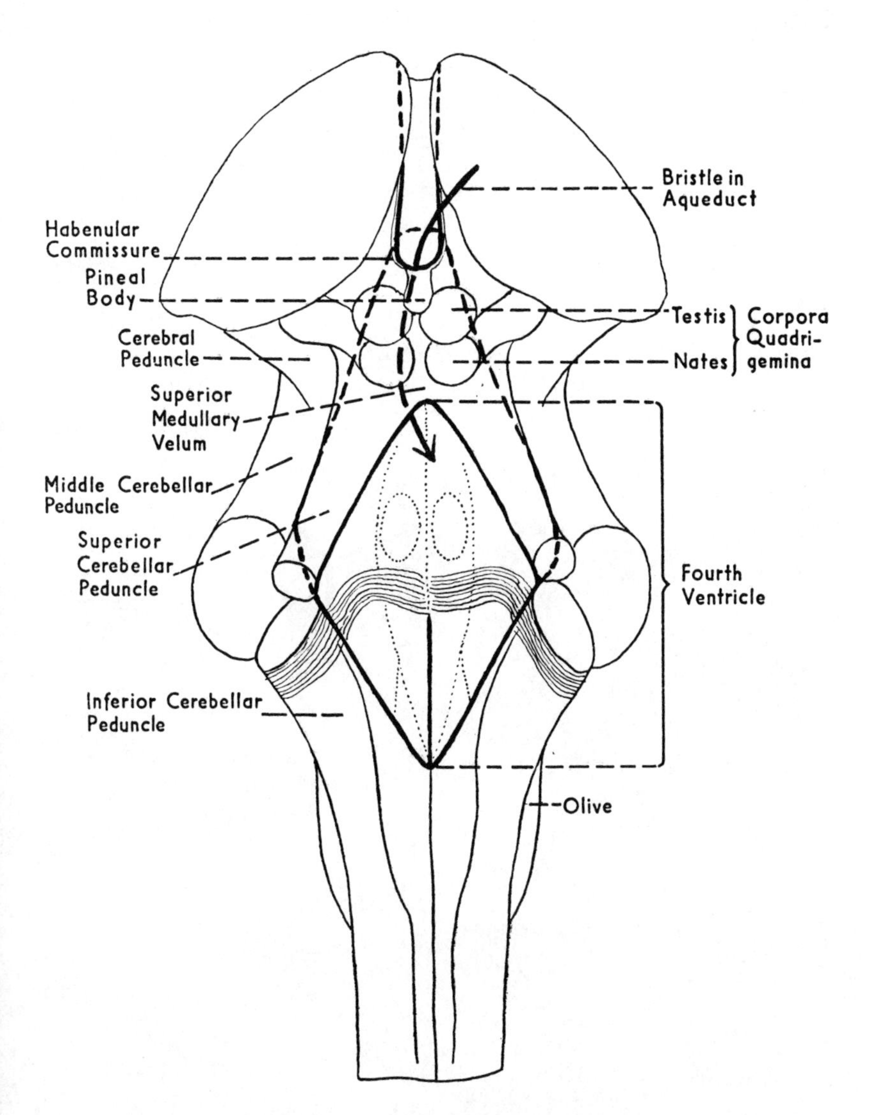

FIG. 26. Diagram of fourth ventricle, aqueduct, and part of third ventricle, to illustrate the *calamus scriptorius* of Herophilus and Galen. The pen is indicated by the heavy line. (Drawing by Professor A. J. E. Cave.)

Index

OTHER TITLES IN THIS HARDBACK REPRINT PROGRAMME FROM SANDPIPER BOOKS LTD (LONDON) AND POWELLS BOOKS (CHICAGO)

ISBN 0–19–	Author	Title
8143567	ALFÖLDI A.	The Conversion of Constantine and Pagan Rome
6286409	ANDERSON George K.	The Literature of the Anglo-Saxons
8228813	BARTLETT & MacKAY	Medieval Frontier Societies
8111010	BETHURUM Dorothy	Homilies of Wulfstan
8142765	BOLLING G. M.	External Evidence for Interpolation in Homer
9240132	BOYLAN Patrick	Thoth, the Hermes of Egypt
8114222	BROOKS Kenneth R.	Andreas and the Fates of the Apostles
8203543	BULL Marcus	Knightly Piety & Lay Response to the First Crusade
8216785	BUTLER Alfred J.	Arab Conquest of Egypt
8148046	CAMERON Alan	Circus Factions
8148054	CAMERON Alan	Porphyrius the Charioteer
8148348	CAMPBELL J.B.	The Emperor and the Roman Army 31 BC to 235 AD
826643X	CHADWICK Henry	Priscillian of Avila
826447X	CHADWICK Henry	Boethius
8219393	COWDREY H.E.J.	The Age of Abbot Desiderius
8148992	DAVIES M.	Sophocles: Trachiniae
825301X	DOWNER L.	Leges Henrici Primi
814346X	DRONKE Peter	Medieval Latin and the Rise of European Love-Lyric
8142749	DUNBABIN T.J.	The Western Greeks
8154372	FAULKNER R.O.	The Ancient Egyptian Pyramid Texts
8221541	FLANAGAN Marie Therese	Irish Society, Anglo-Norman Settlers, Angevin Kingship
8143109	FRAENKEL Edward	Horace
8201540	GOLDBERG P.J.P.	Women, Work and Life Cycle in a Medieval Economy
8140215	GOTTSCHALK H.B.	Heraclides of Pontus
8266162	HANSON R.P.C.	Saint Patrick
8224354	HARRISS G.L.	King, Parliament and Public Finance in Medieval England to 1369
8581114	HEATH Sir Thomas	Aristarchus of Samos
8140444	HOLLIS A.S.	Callimachus: Hecale
8212968	HOLLISTER C. Warren	Anglo-Saxon Military Institutions
8223129	HURNARD Naomi	The King's Pardon for Homicide – before AD 1307
8140401	HUTCHINSON G.O.	Hellenistic Poetry
9240140	JOACHIM H.H.	Aristotle: On Coming-to-be and Passing-away
9240094	JONES A.H.M	Cities of the Eastern Roman Provinces
8142560	JONES A.H.M.	The Greek City
8218354	JONES Michael	Ducal Brittany 1364–1399
8271484	KNOX & PELCZYNSKI	Hegel's Political Writings
8225253	LE PATOUREL John	The Norman Empire
8212720	LENNARD Reginald	Rural England 1086–1135
8212321	LEVISON W.	England and the Continent in the 8th century
8148224	LIEBESCHUETZ J.H.W.G.	Continuity and Change in Roman Religion
8141378	LOBEL Edgar & PAGE Sir Denys	Poetarum Lesbiorum Fragmenta
9240159	LOEW E.A.	The Beneventan Script
8241445	LUKASIEWICZ, Jan	Aristotle's Syllogistic
8152442	MAAS P. & TRYPANIS C.A .	Sancti Romani Melodi Cantica
8142684	MARSDEN E.W.	Greek and Roman Artillery—Historical
8142692	MARSDEN E.W.	Greek and Roman Artillery—Technical
8148178	MATTHEWS John	Western Aristocracies and Imperial Court AD 364–425
8223447	McFARLANE K.B.	Lancastrian Kings and Lollard Knights
8226578	McFARLANE K.B.	The Nobility of Later Medieval England
8148100	MEIGGS Russell	Roman Ostia
8148402	MEIGGS Russell	Trees and Timber in the Ancient Mediterranean World
8142641	MILLER J. Innes	The Spice Trade of the Roman Empire
8147813	MOORHEAD John	Theoderic in Italy
8264259	MOORMAN John	A History of the Franciscan Order
8116020	OWEN A.L.	The Famous Druids
8131445	PALMER, L.R.	The Interpretation of Mycenaean Greek Texts
8143427	PFEIFFER R.	History of Classical Scholarship (vol 1)
8143648	PFEIFFER Rudolf	History of Classical Scholarship 1300–1850
8111649	PHEIFER J.D.	Old English Glosses in the Epinal-Erfurt Glossary
8142277	PICKARD–CAMBRIDGE A.W.	Dithyramb Tragedy and Comedy
8269765	PLATER & WHITE	Grammar of the Vulgate
8213891	PLUMMER Charles	Lives of Irish Saints (2 vols)
820695X	POWICKE Michael	Military Obligation in Medieval England
8269684	POWICKE Sir Maurice	Stephen Langton
821460X	POWICKE Sir Maurice	The Christian Life in the Middle Ages
8225369	PRAWER Joshua	Crusader Institutions

8225571	PRAWER Joshua	The History of The Jews in the Latin Kingdom of Jerusalem
8143249	RABY F.J.E.	A History of Christian Latin Poetry
8143257	RABY F.J.E.	A History of Secular Latin Poetry in the Middle Ages (2 vols)
8214316	RASHDALL & POWICKE	The Universities of Europe in the Middle Ages (3 vols)
8154488	REYMOND E.A.E & BARNS J.W.B.	Four Martyrdoms from the Pierpont Morgan Coptic Codices
8148380	RICKMAN Geoffrey	The Corn Supply of Ancient Rome
8141076	ROSS Sir David	Aristotle: Metaphysics (2 vols)
8141092	ROSS Sir David	Aristotle: Physics
8142307	ROSTOVTZEFF M.	Social and Economic History of the Hellenistic World, 3 vols.
8142315	ROSTOVTZEFF M.	Social and Economic History of the Roman Empire, 2 vols.
8264178	RUNCIMAN Sir Steven	The Eastern Schism
814833X	SALMON J.B.	Wealthy Corinth
8171587	SALZMAN L.F.	Building in England Down to 1540
8218362	SAYERS Jane E.	Papal Judges Delegate in the Province of Canterbury 1198–1254
8221657	SCHEIN Sylvia	Fideles Crucis
8148135	SHERWIN WHITE A.N.	The Roman Citizenship
9240167	SINGER Charles	Galen: On Anatomical Procedures
8113927	SISAM, Kenneth	Studies in the History of Old English Literature
8642040	SOUTER Alexander	A Glossary of Later Latin to 600 AD
8222254	SOUTHERN R.W.	Eadmer: Life of St. Anselm
8251408	SQUIBB G.	The High Court of Chivalry
8212011	STEVENSON & WHITELOCK	Asser's Life of King Alfred
8212011	SWEET Henry	A Second Anglo-Saxon Reader—Archaic and Dialectical
8148259	SYME Sir Ronald	History in Ovid
8143273	SYME Sir Ronald	Tacitus (2 vols)
8200951	THOMPSON Sally	Women Religious
8201745	WALKER Simon	The Lancastrian Affinity 1361–1399
8161115	WELLESZ Egon	A History of Byzantine Music and Hymnography
8140185	WEST M.L.	Greek Metre
8141696	WEST M.L.	Hesiod: Theogony
8148542	WEST M.L.	The Orphic Poems
8140053	WEST M.L.	Hesiod: Works & Days
8152663	WEST M.L.	Iambi et Elegi Graeci
822799X	WHITBY M. & M.	The History of Theophylact Simocatta
8206186	WILLIAMSON, E.W.	Letters of Osbert of Clare
8114877	WOOLF Rosemary	The English Religious Lyric in the Middle Ages
8119224	WRIGHT Joseph	Grammar of the Gothic Language